AMERICAN PRONGHORN ANTELOPE
—articles published in
The *Journal of Wildlife Management*
1937–1977

The Wildlife Society
Washington, D.C.
1979

AMERICAN PRONGHORN ANTELOPE
articles published in
The *Journal of Wildlife Management*
1937–1977

Compiled by:
James D. Yoakum and Donald E. Spalinger

1979
The Wildlife Society
Washington, D.C.

Available from: The Wildlife Society, Suite 611
                 7101 Wisconsin Ave., N.W.
                 Washington, D.C. 20014

Table of Contents

FOREWORD

The Wildlife Society is an international organization oriented to professionals in wildlife management and research. One of its primary missions is to disseminate results of scientific studies and management experiences on wildlife populations and their habitats. To that end, the Society has published *The Journal of Wildlife Management* since 1937. This quarterly publication has become widely recognized for its definitive literature on the biology and management of wildlife.

The profession of wildlife management is relatively young, gaining recognition only a little more than four decades ago. As a result, development of the knowledge that undergirds the art and science of wildlife management is revealed in a chronological perusal of the *Journal*. Those volumes contain critical information accumulated on a number of wildlife species that have received considerable attention from wildlife managers, biologists and other research specialists.

With the *Journal* having been issued for more than 40 years, a complete set of the more than 160 separate quarterlies fills several bookshelves. For most beginning wildlife professionals, the investment required to stock their shelves with a complete set of the *Journal* is prohibitive. Also, the time required to search the thousands of pages for information on a given species, scattered among the myriad of articles on a wide variety of topics, often is difficult for a wildlife biologist or manager.

To help overcome these cost and time problems, Jack Ward Thomas suggested in 1977 that consideration be given to develop a compendium to bring together under one cover all articles on an individual species that had appeared in the first 40 volumes of the *Journal*. This compendium on the pronghorn is the first such volume to be issued by the Society. It is part of the continuing effort to disseminate information essential to help advance the management and well-being of wildlife. Such scientific knowledge is the backbone for any wildlife management activity.

We hope this volume provides interested individuals with easy access to the pronghorn literature that appeared in the first 40 *Journal* volumes and other pertinent literature cited in those articles. Comments from users on the usefulness of this approach are invited. If the compendium is useful, other volumes on selected wildlife species will be considered in the future.

Jack Ward Thomas, President 1977
W. Leslie Pengelly, President 1978
Laurence R. Jahn, President 1979
The Wildlife Society

July 1979

Preface

The constitution of The Wildlife Society was ratified February 28, 1937. Plans were immediately implemented to publish the Society's major periodical entitled, *The Journal of Wildlife Management*. Volume 1, Number 1 and 2 (a combined issue) was printed and dated July, 1937. Each year since, the *Journal* has been published with 4 numbers per year.

The objective of this volume is to print in one book all the papers published from 1937 to December 1977 in the *Journal* on the American pronghorn antelope *(Antilocapra americana)*. This includes major papers, briefer articles, and book reviews. The criterion for inclusion was that the paper pertained 50 percent or more specifically to pronghorns.

The first paper on antelope was published in 1942. Since then, 41 papers have been published for an average of one paper per year for the first 41 years of the *Journal*. However, the number of papers per year has greatly accelerated during the last decade as depicted in Figure 1.

How antelope have fared in the *Journal,* and the emphasis that has been placed on pronghorns since the *Journal's* inception, can possibly be illustrated by analyzing the percent of the pages published on antelope. Using this criterion, it is possible to indicate the increased importance antelope have received in wildlife management during the past decade. Figure 2 shows a significant increase in papers published during the past decade, (1.5 percent) compared to any of the previous three decades which had the highest of .9 percent.

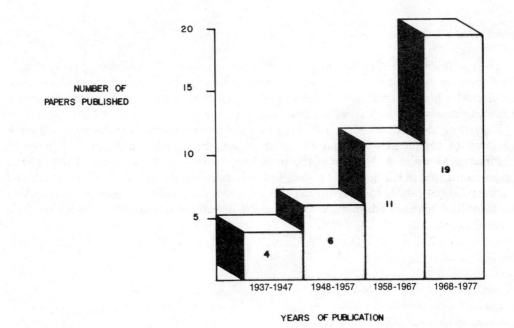

Figure 1. The number of papers published on pronghorns in *The Journal of Wildlife Management* from 1937 through 1977.

iii

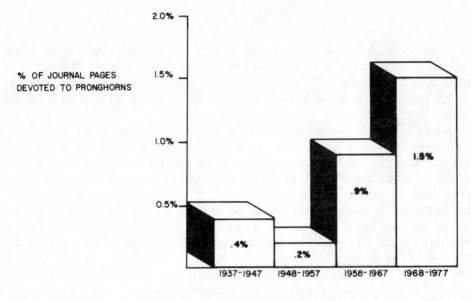

% OF JOURNAL PAGES
DEVOTED TO PRONGHORNS

2.0%

1.5%

1.0%

0.5%

.4%

.2%

.9%

1.5%

1937-1947   1948-1957   1958-1967   1968-1977

YEARS OF PUBLICATION

Figure 2. A comparison of the percent of pages in *The Journal of Wildlife Management* devoted to pronghorns in ten-year intervals from 1937 through 1977.

The compilers classified the major subject material for all published papers (Table 1). Papers on food habits were twice as frequent as any other subject. Suspicions were confirmed when an analysis of Table 1 disclosed that papers on habitat-pronghorn interrelationships were the least abundant.

Regarding an analysis of the different types of papers published, there were 2 book reviews, 11 briefer articles, and 28 major papers. Each paper published is listed in chronological order. At the top of the page is a citation of the Volume, Number, and pages as printed in the *Journal*. A detailed index of authors and subject was developed in order for the reader to more quickly locate items of interest or research value. Also included is a selected bibliography of antelope literature citations assembled by Dale Toweill.

Table 1. Frequency of major subjects on pronghorns published in the *Journal*.

Subject	Number Articles
Animal Characteristics:	
Weight	2
Physiology	4
Aging	4
Behavior	3
Mortality Factors:	
Diseases	2
Winter loss	2
Predation	2
Food Habits:	9
Habitat Factors:	
Range conditions	2
Water	2
Winter use	2
Management techniques:	
Raising fawns	2
Census	3
Capture and marking	2
Trapping and transplanting	3

Work commenced on this volume during July 1977 and terminated in January 1979. The idea for developing readily available technical information on one wildlife species from the *Journal* was initiated by Past President Jack Ward Thomas of The Wildlife Society; consequently, we dedicate this book to his leadership in developing new media for the dissemination of wildlife management information.

Jim Yoakum
Don Spalinger
Bureau of Land Management

January 2, 1979
Reno, Nevada

LIVE TRAPPING TEXAS ANTELOPES

Lee William Fisher

The credit for the first successful live-trapping and transplanting of prong-horned antelopes (*Antilocapra americana*) belongs to Elliot S. Barker, State Game Warden, and Paul Russell, District Deputy Game Warden, New Mexico Department of Game and Fish. The antelope trap and shipping crate now used by the Texas Game Department are modified from those employed by the State of New Mexico. The Texas method of drifting the antelopes into the trap and of removing the animals for shipment differs from the New Mexico live-trapping technique. An airplane replaces horsemen and antelopes removed from the crowding pen in a group.

There are two main purposes of live-trapping and transplanting antelopes. The first is to remove antelopes from sheep to cattle range, the incompatibility of domestic sheep and antelope having been convincingly demonstrated by management and habitat studies. The second objective is to reduce the population on enclosed areas where there is a surplus and to distribute them over former and present suitable ranges from which they are now absent. Antelopes are unable to escape from sheep-wired enclosures but can crawl under or through ordinary barbed wire fences; by transporting them to favorable cattle ranges they may increase in number, spread, and become more firmly established in the fauna of the state.

The first attempt to transplant antelopes in Texas was made in Sterling County during 1939, when 257 head were trapped and liberated in twenty-one new localities. Trapping operations were resumed in the Davis Mountain Range in Brewster and Presidio Counties during October, 1940. Because of the mountainous terrain of this section of western Texas and also the large pastures (10,240 to 22,400 acres) in which the antelopes were to be trapped, it was soon learned that the method of employing horsemen for drifting the animals into a trap was too costly.

While the writer was taking a census of antelopes by airplane near Alpine, Texas, it was observed that the animals tended to flee from the drone of the airplane motor. This tendency was found to increase in proportion to the nearness of the plane. Following up this lead, it was learned that scattered herds of antelope could be assembled into one and drifted in any desired direction, provided the airplane was maneuvered so that the drone of the motor issued from a position behind or to one side of the antelopes and at altitudes of 50 to 500 feet.

Further experiments showed that a modification of the trap would be necessary before this species could be captured by airplane driving. Numerous variations in trap construction were tried before success was achieved. Since the adoption of this method of herding antelope by airplane, 467 animals have been trapped, sexed, aged, weighed, ear-tagged, and released in suitable habitats. The trapping operations covered 43 days. Only three animals died, a mortality of but 0.64 per cent. Releases were made at distances of from 25 to

663 miles. The greatest number of antelopes urged into the trap during one drive was 58. The average number of animals released on an area was 30. Plants were made on approximately 750,000 acres of suitable range.

The cost for trapping and transporting each antelope was approximately $4.30. This cost was computed by allowing five years for the useful life of equip-

ft. for a sliding gate. All nets are of $\frac{3}{16}$-inch long-grade staple cord, with a 3-inch square mesh; line ropes are $\frac{3}{4}$-inch diameter, all completely tarred. The end of each net is fastened to a one-inch galvanized iron pipe, in turn is attached to a cedar post, to form a solid tie and prevent a tear at the terminals. It is important that all nets be tied by ropes to posts that are placed some three to four

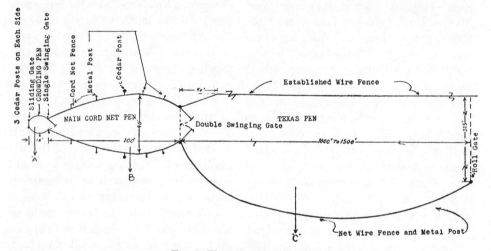

Fig. 1. Plan of antelope trap.

ment such as trap, trucks, tools, and camp outfit. It includes also all current expenditures as rental of airplane, operation of trucks, and salaries of operators.

THE TRAP

A plan of the trop (Fig. 1) shows that it is divided into three sections. Arrows A, B, and C indicate the cord-net crowding pen, the main cord-net pen, and the Texas wire net pen, respectively.

Crowding Pen.—This pen is hexagonal, about 14 ft. in diameter (Fig. 1; Pl. 19, A). It is formed by two 16×8 ft-cord nets (one for each side), one 8×7 ft. for a swinging gate, and one 7×2$\frac{2}{3}$

feet apart, thereby eliminating solid surfaces on which the antelopes may be injured. This also permits adjustment of the nets after they may have stretched or contracted due to wear or weather conditions. The two cord-net gates that open into the crowding pen are covered with a canvas curtain; this serves as a screen to shield from view the trucks and shipping crates, and also the operators before they enter the pen to remove the antelopes. Specifications of the sliding gate and single swinging gate are given in Figure 2, A and B.

Main Cord-Net Pen.—Complete views of this pen including the double swinging gate, are shown in Plate 18 (See also Fig. 1). This pen is formed by four

PLATE 17

A (*upper*).—Antelopes being drifted through open entrance of trap by airplanes.

B (*lower*).—When antelopes are in trap; canvas cloth gate is unrolled temporarily to prevent their escape until replaced by wire-net gate.

PLATE 18

A (*upper*).—The canvas cloth gate is used as a seine to crowd the antelopes into the main cord net pen from the Texas wire net enclosure. One wing of the gate was closed by wind, yet they enter the pen.

B (*lower*).—Double swinging gate is closed behind antelopes by a $\frac{3}{8}$ inch cloth line rope operated from a distance.

A (*upper*).—Antelopes being forced from main cord net pen into crowding pen. The supporting posts and steel cables hold nets taut.

B (*lower*).—Operator pulls rope attached to the single swinging gate to enclose antelopes in crowding pen.

A (*upper*).—Antelopes removed from the crowding pen are sexed, aged, and ear-tagged before crating.

B (*lower*).—Finally the antelopes are crated, weighed and loaded on trucks to take them to new habitats.

50×6 ft. cord nets, two joined for each side, and two 12×5 ft. cord nets fastened to a double swinging gate. The enclosure is about 100 ft. long and 40 ft. wide. The nets are of the same materials as those of the crowding pen. The side nets of the pen are supported by a $\frac{1}{4}$-inch flexible, plow-steel cable (Plate 19) which is suspended above the net from the post of the single swinging gate to that of the double swinging gate. The net is fastened by rope to this cable and is kept taut to prevent antelopes from spilling over and escaping from the pen. In a similar manner a two-strand, barbless wire is placed below the bottom of the net, Further support is added by ropes tied to six posts, about 15 feet apart, on each side of the pen and some three or four feet distant as shown for the crowding pen in (Pl. 19, A). The double swinging gate is detailed in Figure 2, C.

The double and single swinging gates are operated from a distance (Pls. 18, B and 19, B). A $\frac{3}{8}$-inch cotton rope 200 feet long passes through two pulleys attached to stakes driven into the ground at the bottom of the double swinging gate, and another $\frac{3}{8}$-inch rope passes through a pulley fastened to the top of the post of the single swinging-gate.

Texas Wire Net Pen.—The Texas pen is simple to build, since one side is formed by an established line of fence. The other side (Fig. 1) is of galvanized wire net, 52 inches high and of 6-inch mesh, with intermediate and stay wires of 14½ gauge. It is supported by studded iron T-posts, 8 feet long, driven about three feet into the ground. Cedar posts at intervals of about 100 feet give added support. Should the established fence be of barbed wire then a wire net is attached to it so as to form one side of the

TRAP MATERIALS AND ESTIMATED COSTS

Cord Net

1 (7'×3'), sliding gate
2 (16'×8'), sides of crowding pen
1 (8'×7'), single swinging gate
4 (50'×6'), sides of main cord net pen
2 (12'×5'), double swinging gates
Available from the Adams Net and Twine Company, St. Louis, Mo., about 8 cents per sq. ft......... $132.24

Wire Net (galvanized)

120 rods, 52 inches high, line and stay wires 14½ gauge, bottom and top 11 gauge, stays 6 inches apart. (Used tarnished wire preferred); cost, new, about 50 cents per rod...................... 60.00

Posts

70 (7' iron), T-posts, to support wire net; cost about 43¢ each........ 30.10
8 (12'×6") cedar posts, to support gates and net, 12 (8'×5") cedar posts to support wire net....... 4.00

Hardware

100 lbs. spool smooth wire, 9 gauge, for bracing................. 4.25
250 ft. $\frac{1}{4}$" flexible plow-steel cable, to support net................ 12.50
3 pulleys for $\frac{3}{8}$" cotton line rope... .75
12 strap hinges, 6", for 2×4's on wire gate...................... 1.00
Iron spool and frame for canvas roll gate........................ 2.00
5 lbs. 7" staples for net wire....... .35
120 yds. 8-ounce canvas cloth 30" wide for iron and roll gates..... 12.00
500 ft. $\frac{3}{8}$" cotton rope............ 5.00
200 ft. used galvanized pipe to construct gates and attach nets to cedar posts; different sizes at average cost of 7¢ per foot........ 14.00
Welding gates and hinges......... 15.00

Lumber

4 pcs. 2"×4"×8', to support gates
24 pcs. 2"×4"×5', to support wire net gate...................... 3.50
24 shipping crates, completed and painted...................... 240.00
Approximate cost of completed trap, including shipping crates....... $536.69

enclosure. Where there is no established fence, two wire net side nets may be used. The pen is from 1,000 to 1,500 feet long and from 400 to 500 feet wide, depending on the topography of the land. Camouflaged by vegetation and attached to the cedar post at·the entrance

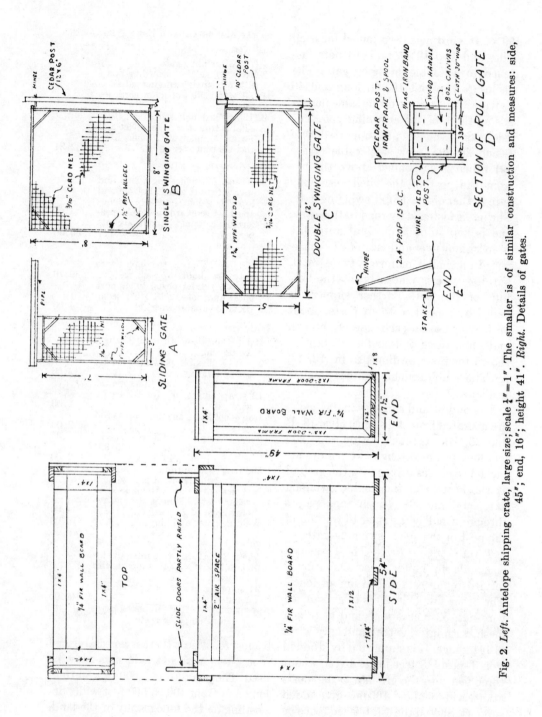

Fig. 2. *Left.* Antelope shipping crate, large size; scale $\frac{1}{4}"=1"$. The smaller is of similar construction and measures: side, 45"; end, 16"; height 41". *Right.* Details of gates.

to the trap is a roll gate. This is made of 325 linear feet of 8-ounce canvas, 30 inches wide, rolled on a spool that is supported by an iron frame (Fig. 2, D). To prevent antelopes escaping from the trap, the canvas-cloth roll gate (Pl. 17, B) is employed temporarily until the wire net-gate is unrolled. The latter is constructed of wire net 325 feet long and 52 inches high and is supported by pieces of 2″×4″ lumber about 20 feet apart that are fastened to the net wire by iron staples. Each wooden support is composed of two pieces of 2″×4″ joined together by a 6-inch galvanized iron strap hinge, thus permitting the gate to be propped up when unrolled (Fig. 2, E). The gate remains in a truck stationed about a quarter of a mile from the trap until the antelopes are driven by the airplane into the open entrance.

Shipping Crates

The dimensions and materials for large and small shipping crates are given in Figure 2 (left), the smaller being for fawns and yearlings. All crates are padded on the ends and bottom with 8-ounce canvas cloth fastened over cotton batting by wooden cleats. A coat of good-quality green paint is applied to the exterior in order to preserve the crates from the weather. Each is stamped with a number and its weight; the large ones weigh about 120 pounds, the small, 90 pounds (Pl. 20).

Trapping Operations

The selection of a proper trap site is of primary importance. Plate 18, A shows a downward slope leading to the cord-net pens. It is necessary to place this part of the trap beyond a mound, knoll, or small hill, that will conceal it from the antelopes passing through the open entrance of the wire-net pen.

An accurate count of the antelopes in a 25-section or 16,000-acre pasture can be obtained within one hour by airplane. Such a survey and the selection of a suitable trap site are made by airplane before proceeding to pen the animals. After completion of the trap, the airplane is maneuvered through a series of shallow, steep, and lazy "eights," and occasional dives to within 50 feet of the ground while drifting the antelopes from five, ten, or more miles toward and into the trap. Once the animals are in the trap, a signal is wig-wagged to the operators, who are seated in a truck located about a quarter of a mile from the open entrance. They immediately speed to the trap and by unrolling the canvas cloth gate (Pl. 17, B), close the open entrance temporarily while the wire-net gate is being erected. The airplane then has completed its function and the five or six operators proceed to remove the antelope from the trap and crate them for transportation.

It is difficult adequately to describe in writing the complete trapping procedure, so that a person unfamiliar with it can clearly visualize each operation; but the illustrations and their legends should make the technique fairly clear.

General Suggestions

Antelopes have been trapped successfully from October to March, but the period between October 1 and January 1 is most desirable, because (1) less inclement weather is encountered; (2) range conditions are generally good in that season; and (3) antelopes are less difficult to handle due to the shedding of their horns, which occurs mostly in October throughout Texas.

One-ton stake-body trucks with beds 7×14 feet and holding 12 crates each were found most serviceable for transport and two were used. The trapping of about 30 head allowed a sufficient margin so that a group balanced as to age and sex ratios, and with possible undesirables eliminated, could be selected for release. The taking of just the number that can be promptly transported does away with holding any antelopes in the pens, which tends to weaken them; some, however, have been retained as long as 48 hours.

In order to avoid injuries to the antelopes while removing them from the trap as well as when loading and transporting them to new habitats, the following procedures should be closely followed. No person should be within 300 yards of the trap when antelopes are being drifted into it; no sounds or sudden movements should be made by any of the personnel when urging the animals from one pen to another; much patience is needed as over-eagerness on the part of operators may cause the antelopes to spill over or through the wire net and injure themselves.

It is best to weigh the animals in the crate just before loading. Crates should be arranged on the trucks so that the head of each animal points in the direction of travel.

The airplane employed in the trapping project was an Aeronca Monocoupe with a 65-horsepower engine (Pl. 17, A). Any of the numerous makes of light airplanes would doubtless have served the purpose. The purchase price, as low as $1,000.00; the economy of operation, 25 miles per gallon of fuel; and the minimum cruising speed of 40 miles per hour, (about the maximum antelopes can attain) make one of these dependable light airplanes an ideal machine for drifting the animals. It is also of inestimable value in the censusing of many game animals and in surveying and mapping game habitats.

Some questions that may arise and their answers follow:

Does the airplane harmfully disturb livestock on the range where the trapping is in progress? No; if properly maneuvered the airplane is ignored by livestock.

How far is it advisable to drift antelopes by airplane? They have been driven 15 miles and into the trap, but on some occasions have tired or become accustomed to the drone of the airplane motor; when this occurs, it is best to stop and return to trap such animals at a later date.

Is it necessary to have a specially trained pilot to operate the airplane? Yes; but two or three hours of flying time spent in becoming familiar with the habits of the antelopes and their reactions to the drone of the airplane motor should be sufficient to train any competent pilot for drifting the animals into the trap.

Summary

Modifications in the live-trapping technique for antelope are reported, including replacement of horsemen by an airplane for drifting the animals into the trap and removal of antelopes from the crowding pen in a group, rather than one at a time through a chute. They have permitted the use of a simplified and less expensive trap, and afforded a safer, more efficient, and more economical method of capturing antelopes.

Lee William Fisher
Wildlife Restoration Division
Game, Fish, and Oyster Commission
Austin, Texas

GATHERING, TRANSPLANTING, AND CARE OF YOUNG ANTELOPES[1]

A. A. Nichol

Big game workers are now well agreed that the most satisfactory results are obtained in restocking projects when adults and younger age classes are introduced together. Sometimes the difficulty or the cost of capturing fully grown animals makes it more feasible to use only the young. Recently in a restocking project in Arizona it was decided to move only the young for still another reason.

The Tucson Mountain Park is a county recreational area of several thousand acres west of Tucson, Arizona, at an elevation of 2,500 to 5,000 feet. The cover is of cacti and desert shrubs lightly interspersed with palatable forage grasses. When the Park was set aside, sufficient nuclei of quail, mule deer, peccaries and bighorn sheep were present to restock under the subsequent program protection and management. Prong-horn antelope (*Antilocapra americana*) had been native to the foothill portions of the area twenty-five years earlier but had disappeared, and the reintroduction of this species was desired. Animals available for restocking were on the grassland plateau in the northern part of the State, so it was decided to transplant only fawns. The young of the game herbivores have a strong tendency to remain in the vicinity where they have been fed, watered, and cared for. It was feared that if

adults accustomed to open grass country were used for restocking, they would drift away from the desert scrub and cactus cover until they again found the grasslands.

This account of the capture, care, and shipping of the fawns used in this project provides some information on pronghorn behavior, and may be of help to those attempting similar projects.

GATHERING

The fawns were gathered on Anderson Mesa, a high grassland plateau some 25 miles southeast of Flagstaff, Arizona, at elevations of 6,500 and 7,500 feet. As a result of overgrazing, the palatable grasses had largely been replaced by the valueless matchweed (*Gutierrezia sarothrae*) and the poisonous pingque (*Actinea richardsoni*). These two plants are so abundant as to give large portions of the Mesa a striking yellow cast in summer and fall. Other undesirable changes in the plant cover have also taken place on the Mesa. These may be in part the reason that each year antelope females work farther and farther into the juniper and yellow pine parks fringing the Mesa on the south and west. There they drop their fawns in small glades in the forest, instead of on the open treeless plateau as formerly. Possibly the does are finding in the less heavily grazed forest areas species of forage that more nearly meet their needs in pregnancy. Just before fawning, antelopes and deer make important changes in their diets.

[1] The restocking here described was done while the writer was in the employ of the National Park Service, which supplied the photographs.

The fawn drop is definitely under way by May 10, and apparently at its peak by the third week in May. At this time of year sheep bands are returning to their allotments, and antelopes in the protective fringe of timber are least disturbed. The movement from the open land to the forest is a relatively recent phenomenon, and today with reduced grazing permits and more tolerance by stockmen there is less disturbance of the animals than occurred years ago.

Four CCC boys from the N.P.S. Camp at Flagstaff were used in collecting the fawns; three of them had never seen an antelope until they went into the field, but in a remarkably short time they learned to distinguish bucks, does, and yearlings, and to recognize does which showed by their behavior or condition that they were nursing young.

Two methods were employed to locate the fawns. The first was to watch while a doe nursed her fawns and then when she had bedded them down, the observer, by keeping a close eye on the spot where the fawns dropped, could walk over and pick them up (Pl. 23). This was particularly effective in early morning and again in the evenir ;, when antelopes, unless much disturbed, nurse their young. Very young fawns are also fed additionally during the day, but if this occurred at regular intervals the fact was not determined.

The second method was dependent for success on the observer's alertness and quickness of eye. An antelope that has fawns down and hidden will at the first unexplained disturbance or threat of danger look immediately and directly to the spot where her young are hidden, after which she concerns herself with the nature of the menace. This glance is so short and quick that the observer must in a single second determine the angle and direction, and mark the spot for seeking the fawns. By keeping his eye on the place where he judged them to be and immediately proceeding to it, he will often be successful in finding them. In any case proof that fawns are in the immediate neighborhood will shortly be provided by the doe; if her fear of man permits, she will circle the hunter, beat him to the locality, rouse her young, and be away with them at a speed of 20 to 30 miles per hour.

Two accurately measured records of the running speed of antelopes were made. The first concerns a young fawn, judged to be less than 36 hours old, that escaped one collector by the side of a road. No attempt was made to recapture the fawn since the crew was instructed not to chase fawns. The writer and another worker were sitting in a car nearby and when the fawn took off parallel to the road the car was put in motion and quickly drew opposite it. For four-tenths of a mile the fawn ran at a uniform speed of slightly more than 25 miles per hour (the speedometer was divided in only five-mile units). When the fawn first broke cover it spent a few seconds in awkward zig-zag efforts, giving every appearance of being ready to fall over before straightening out on its course. It ran considerably farther than the four-tenths mile but began to veer away from the road where it could not be accurately timed. The surface over which it ran was a mass of malpais rock, of a size often described as niggerheads.

A day or two later an old buck essayed to race the car, and for a few rods little attention was paid to him. Then the writer noticed the characteristic sinking of the animal's back which indicated that he was about to extend himself. The car was speeded up, and for one and two-tenths miles the animal ran at the rate of 45 miles an hour. The constancy of his speed was as remarkable as the pace. At no time could an appreciable variation either way from 45 miles be detected on the speedometer, until a final spurt when the buck crossed the road in front of the car. The speed of the car was not changed, and it is presumed the animal had to add something to his speed in order to cross. For fully two-thirds of this distance the race was on an upgrade steep enough to cause a car to roll back freely if not braked. The surface over which the antelope ran was densely covered with rocks to the size of a milk-bucket or larger. At no time during the race was the antelope more than 30 yeards from the car and the play of its shoulder and flank muscles was remindful of smoothly and swiftly moving shuttles. A few days later the speedometer of the car was checked and found to be accurate.

Getting the fawns safely in hand after they have been located was the greatest test of the field work. Success was dependent upon close adherence to the following instructions:

"When the location of the fawn has been spotted, go to it at a slow walk without stopping or change of pace. When the fawn itself is seen, change direction if need be *very gradually*, so as to appear to deliberately pass by. When within arm's reach, bend over with a smooth *unhurried* movement, holding one hand in readiness over the animal's shoulders to block the leap that in many cases will occur. As quickly as possible, blindfold the fawn by placing a soft bandage or large handkerchief over the eyes, crossing it under the throat and knotting it loosely behind the ears. Carry to the holding pen with the legs tucked up in a natural manner under the body. (Pl. 23, D.) Throughout every step in the procedure avoid quick or sudden movements. Also prevent struggling as it can cause internal hemorrhages."

Ten animals were wanted for the project. On the first day three fawns escaped because over-anxiety on the part of the inexperienced crew made them reach for the fawns too quickly. In the following ten days eleven fawns were collected without any further escapes.

Many of the does had gone into the edge of the timber for fawning, but they still retained the racial habit of placing their young in an open area. With few exceptions the fawns lie from sun-up to sun-down without moving, as they likewise spend the night after they have been fed, except when moved by the mother. At that time of year the sun by midday is uncomfortably warm for a person on the ground, and frosts are common at night. No shade or shelter is over the fawns, so they are subjected to great changes in temperature.

Many of the fawns are placed just below the crest of a gently sloping bank or land swell, among lichen-covered rocks or malpais niggerheads. To hunt and find antelope fawns without first having their whereabouts disclosed by the actions of the mother is a remote possibility. They can be located by using a large crew of men, dragnet fashion, but only a small percentage of the young flushed will be caught; the disturbances and losses certain to accompany this method are contrary to good management.

TRANSPORTING

The fawns were held in camp until the youngest were at least a week old. Then they were moved in a pickup truck altered for the purpose. Individual crates are preferable for transporting wild animals, particularly antelopes, but when very young, they can be moved together successfully if proper safeguards are taken.

A wooden frame with an adjustable canvas cover was built on the truck bed, and burlap sacks, partly filled with straw, lined the interior of the frame. The sacks were fastened only along the top edge, so that if an animal was thrown against them the sacks would slip and not the animal. Clean deep straw was used for a bottom bed. A vertical extension was added to the exhaust pipe to prevent any possibility of monoxide fumes being sucked into the crate.

The haul was only 350 miles, but in that distance there was a drop of more than 5,000 feet in altitude and a rise of more than 60 °F. in temperature. The fawns were loaded in the morning at a temperature of 42° F. and unloaded in Tucson at 2:30 that afternoon at 105° F. When first put on the truck they were nervous and tramped about, but a fast swaying drive for a half-mile put

them down quickly, and they rode quietly thereafter.

Dehydration is one of the "bugbears" attendant on raising and handling young wild mammals, particularly when they are being moved. Therefore, because of the heat and an extremely strong wind, three stops were made. At two of these the fawns were unloaded and fed a ration to which extra water had been added. At the third, time was taken merely to give them water since they were beginning to show signs of distress from the effects of heat and wind. In the early part of the trip a few stops were made to note signs, if any, of travel sickness.

FEEDING AND CARE

The fawns were fed at four-hour intervals until ten days of age. Then the midnight feeding was omitted and the amount of food used in it distributed among the other five feedings. This program was maintained for about another week, when the time intervals were gradually shifted until feedings were on a schedule that started at 6 A.M. and ended with a fifth and last feeding for day at 8 P.M. The beginning formula was:

Evaporated milk (Carnation or Pet preferred): 6 parts

Lime water (sat. sol.): 10 parts

Karo syrup, light: 1 part

At birth the fawns weighed from 4 to $5\frac{1}{4}$ pounds. They were given $2\frac{1}{2}$ to 3 ounces apiece at each feeding. The lime water was made by simply throwing a handful of ordinary lime in a container and filling with water. As long as any lime was visible at the bottom of the container the solution remained saturated. If the stools of the fawns became too soft the quantity of Karo was reduced. It was also decreased when the fawns became old enough to take a little solid food, and was discontinued at the end of four weeks. The fawns then averaged 7 pounds in weight. The amount per feeding was increased to 4 ounces with tap water replacing Karo syrup in the formula.

No further increase was made in the liquid ration, as the additional sustenance needed for growth and increased activity was obtained from forage and grain. The milk ration was stopped at the end of nine weeks.

Ordinary wide-mouthed nursing bottles were used for feeding. Bottles, nipples, and containers were kept sterilized. Feeding was started for each animal with the milk as near a temperature of 100° F. as possible. The muzzles of the fawns were washed after each feeding to remove waste milk.

These three factors of clean utensils, proper temperature, and clean muzzles are very important in assuring the health of the fawns.

Two colitic attacks beset the herd shortly after a change in caretakers. The first believed to have resulted because the animals had not been properly cleaned after feeding. Considerable experience with raising young mammals has shown that milk remaining around the muzzle often is a source of alimentary infections. This first attack was short-lived, oat-water with egg white helped bring the affected individuals quickly to their feet.

The second attack was more serious, and was brought on by a new caretaker believing that the fawns would enjoy their rations better cold, since the weather was hot. They were in a precarious condition, an intestinal infection was well established, and only two of the herd were able to get up. The alimentary tract of young antelopes and deer is so delicate and sensitive that no intestinal antiseptic was believed to be mild enough for them to tolerate. Purely as an experimental measure, each was given 1 tablespoon of sauerkraut juice diluted with 3 parts of water. This was followed in an hour by $\frac{1}{2}$ ounce of milk and 2 ounces of lime water. Through the day each received altogether 5 tablespoonsful of the juice, and by the end of the second day all appeared in normal health. Subsequently, the sickest one of the lot had return "flare-ups," but a dose of sauerkraut juice always brought him back and ready for his next feed.

The fawns began to chew on things when they were a week old. No. 1 dairy or rabbit grade alfalfa hay was then provided for roughage, with one part of calf meal to seven parts of rolled oats for a concentrate. Salt and bone meal also were provided. All of these elements were utilized in small quantities by the time the animals were four weeks old. At six weeks of age they averaged 15 pounds in weight, and most of their diet then was of grain and hay.

Losses and Results

Two of the eleven fawns were malformed, and could not eliminate, and shortly died. A third was lost by a screw-worm infection, and a fourth died from an impaction resulting from having eaten sand and gravel.

The remaining seven were liberated in late summer. At sixteen months of age they were thriving and vigorous and had accommodated themselves to the desert range. Despite their hand rearing and close contact with man, enough of their wild nature had reasserted itself by the time they were ten months old to make them unapproachable.

A. A. Nichol
510 E. 4th St.
Tucson, Arizona

A. Typical antelope range, Anderson Mesa. Most does with fawns, were in the far fringe of forest where the fawns were collected. B. Typical terrain of slight curvature with malpais rock between grass and weeds where does leave fawns between feedings. C. Fawn as found on the ground. The low camera angle makes the animal more prominent than when usually seen. Some fawns are spotted, like those of deer, but the spots soon disappear. D. Proper way to carry a fawn in the field with its legs folded under the body and a bandana over its eyes.

JWM 10(4): 367

ANTELOPE FOODS IN SOUTHEASTERN MONTANA

Stomach samples from 24 prong-horned antelope (*Antilocapra americana*) in Carter County, Montana, were collected during the hunting seasons of 1944 and 1945, mainly during September and October; a few were obtained in November and December. Information is needed to determine the food habits of antelope, about which there is considerable controversy.

Each sample consisted of a pint of stomach contents; this was partly washed in a piece of burlap to get rid of the stomach juices, and then dried in paper envelopes. The foods were classified and visual estimates made as to volume on a percentage basis (Table 1).

TABLE 1.—AUTUMN FOODS OF PRONG-HORNED ANTELOPE IN MONTANA.

Species	Fre-quency	Percent-age
Sage (*Artemisia*)	22	*51.0*
Snakeweed (*Guterriezia*)	7	*14.3*
Snowberry (*Symphoricarpos*)	14	*10.3*
Salt sage (*Atriplex*)	5	*1.0*
Greasewood (*Sarcobatus*)	1	*0.8*
Cactus (*Opuntia*)	7	*4.2*
Miscellaneous browse	6	*5.7*
Total browse, percentage		*87.4*
Vetch (*Astragalus*)	3	*0.4*
Miscellaneous weeds	17	*5.3*
Total weeds, percentage		*5.7*
Grass	21	*6.7*
Grass, percentage		*6.9*

The principal food of these animals during the autumn obviously consisted of browse plants, based both on the volume and the incidence of occurrence in the diet. The most preferred plant was sage (*Artemisia triden-tata* and *A. cana*) of which leaves and twigs were eaten; several samples were almost entirely of sage. Snowberry or buckbrush (*Symphoricarpos*) was next, twigs, leaves, and berries having been used. Snakeweed or matchweed (*Guterriezia*) was third in importance, and several samples consisted almost entirely of this plant. There was a question as to whether considerable rabbit brush (*Chrysothamnus*) was included here, as this food has been reported from antelope in Colorado and South Dakota. These two plants are quite similar in appearance, and positive identification is difficult in masticated samples. A checkup on the occurrence of these plants in southern Carter County showed snakeweed to be far the more common of the two; and it was identified positively in several of the samples.

Grass was fourth in volume of food taken, but second in occurrence. No sample contained much grass and several included only traces. The material was mostly of wheat grass (*Agropyron*), grama grass (*Bouteloua*), and some cheat grass (*Bromus tectorum*).

Weeds were identified mostly by their seeds and included thistle, knotweed, mallow, pigweed, ragweed, wild buckwheat, and dock.

Of interest was the use of cactus, found in 7 samples. The presence of seeds together with the fleshy, spined leaves leads to the belief that antelope seek the seed pods at this time of year rather than the entire plant.

Samples from other parts of the state and during other seasons of the year are needed to provide more general knowledge as to the food of Montana antelope.—FAYE M. COUEY, *Wildlife Restoration Division, State Fish and Game Department, Helena, Montana.*

THE GOLDEN EAGLE ATTACKING ANTELOPE

On February 21, 1947, while observing antelope on their normal range, I was attracted by five golden eagles grouped on a carcass. Upon approaching closer it was evidenced as a freshly killed doe antelope. The carcass was still warm, and upon opening the abdominal cavity to determine pregnancy, there was yet enough body warmth to result in the steaming of the contents. Evidently I had interrupted the eagles as they were about to divide their kill. The birds had just begun to penetrate the rib case and stomach on the left side of the animal. Upon rolling the antelope over, scattered spots of blood were found covering the side and back of the animal from the middle of the back up to the nape of the neck. I plucked the hair from a large patch on the back and found many talon holes and scratches all over this area. The carcass looked, at first glance, as though it had received a few rounds of 00 buckshot, but close examination proved these to be talon holes.

There was at this time about two inches of snow on the ground, and the flight of the antelope was backtracked about a half mile. Along this route were many blood spots on the snow. Beyond the half mile point no blood was found. Considering that the animal had been able to run about a half mile before any blood fell to the ground after the initial attack, and placing the speed of the antelope at 40 miles per hour, it would mean that it took the eagles about 1½ minutes to kill the animal, death resulting from the repeated attacks upon the neck and back. It is probable that death was caused by either a talon penetrating the spinal nerve column or from shock. There did not appear to be enough blood loss, nor was the stride shortened up to dropping point, to indicate death from bleeding through the numerous talon wounds. There were no death-struggle marks in the snow at the carcass, indicating instant death while in running stride.

A blood sample was taken to the Colorado A & M College, Veterinary Department, for culturing for disease. The report showed no significant organisms present.

The victim was about 33 months old, measured 35″ girth, with corresponding weight about 80 pounds.—Robert W. Lehti, *Game and Fish Commission, Denver, Colorado.*

REVIEW

The Pronghorn Antelope. By Arthur S. Einarsen. The Wildlife Management Institute, Washington, D. C. xvi+238 pp. Illustr. 1948. $4.00.

For those who have never been in antelope country but have a penchant for luxuriating through the winter evenings in an easy chair, for those who delight in recollections of antelope on some promontory, silhouetted against a blue sky which is synonymous with the West, for those who have seen the rich gold and white of antelope through the steel-blue sights of a high-powered rifle, and for those who are interested in prying into the intimate matters of daily and yearly life of this most unique of North American mammals, this book will be a desired possession. Mr. Einarsen has done us all a service in bringing together in a readable fashion a great deal of information on this species, much of it not previously generally available.

Following his introduction, the author has divided his material under the following headings: 1. History, Distribution, and Abundance; 2. Characteristics and Life History; 3. Pronghorn Antelope in Relation to Civilization; 4. Management of Antelope Resources; 5. How to Hunt Antelope; 6. Epilogue; and 7. Appendix.

Many of the book's inclusions will attract those interested in wildlife. For example, the life span in nature is quite short; the visual mechanism is so well developed that small moving objects can be detected at distances of from three to four miles; the unpredictable psychology of antelope is described; the factors making for good or poor range are outlined; reactions of populations to hunting pressure are discussed; and a comparative analysis of antelope and raw and evaporated cow's milk is given.

Through all that is excellent in this book, there are some things which do not measure up to the general standard. The author's occasional editorializing will meet with some resistance among wildlife workers, but as his own statements of opinion he is certainly within his rights to give them. There are several typographical errors so obvious that they should have been deleted early in the proof reading. There is little defense for spelling the generic name (*Astragalus*) for loco weed as *Astorlagus* on p. 62, and *Astralagus* twice on p. 69 and once on p. 70. Numerous such errors occur in the tables in the food habits section. Choice of words or phrases is sometimes not the best if not actually misleading, as on p. 86 where we find " . . . pronghorn deaths may often be classified as due to predation or disease, when actually they are due to natural causes." This reviewer wonders at this point what "natural causes" are. Again on p. 168 is the statement that " . . . accuracy (of shooting) was in direct relationship to distance," where "inverse relationship" is certainly the meaning intended. There are places, as in the last three sentences of the central paragraph on p. 159 where cause and effect are associated with too great facility on the basis of evidence given. As the great amount of the information was collected in and refers to Oregon, a subtitle indicating this geographical limitation would have been desirable.

These criticisms are made, not with the idea of detracting from the value of the book, rather to indicate a greater value had they been corrected.

Mr. Einarsen's thesis, as it unfolds through the pages, that values must be considered in antelope harvest other than the edible flesh furnished by a carcass, seems to be excellent. On p. 200 he states it as follows: "Gone forever are the often mentioned 'good old pioneering days!' It is a simple deduction that there is little comparison between the past and the present. In the past, a handful of hunters faced millions of pronghorns if early reports are correct. Now the existing pronghorns if exposed to unrestricted hunting would not survive one day's efforts by the well equipped and numerous license holders. It is time to substitute other values in hunting, emphasizing improvement in skill and wider appreciation of those attributes of aesthetic worth."

The illustrations are good and to the point. The makeup is excellent. We have again to thank the Wildlife Management Institute for this fine addition to our literature.—HARLOW B. MILLS.

JWM 13(3): 313–314

PREDATION ON ANTELOPE

Several observations of predator activities on pronghorn antelope were made in 1947 and 1948 during the trapping and censusing activities of the Wildlife Restoration Division of the Montana State Fish and Game Department.

On January 28, 1948, while counting antelope in Carter County, Pilot-Biologist Don Brown and I noted a band of 64 antelope running toward the airplane and apparently not frightened by it. At the rear of the herd an adult golden eagle was flying, just behind the last antelope. The eagle suddenly seized the last antelope, a mature male, on either side of the backbone and rode with outspread wings for about 100 yards. It then released its hold and flew behind for a short distance and again grasped the buck. This was repeated three times. The last time we flew down to attempt a picture and the eagle left its prey. Upon regaining altitude we noticed another eagle pursuing a band of nine antelope and the first eagle circled to resume chasing the larger band.

This observation substantiated, in part, the reports of actual observations of golden eagles killing antelope by grasping them along the back and riding with out-spread wings until the antelope collapsed.

We tracked an antelope for over three miles and large flecks of blood marked the trail in the snow. The marks of a large bird, apparently an eagle, were observed in the snow from which we concluded that the bird had landed several times during the chase. The path taken by this animal was meandering in a general northerly direction. There were no indications of the animal seeking protection of coulees, fences or shrubbery. Apparently flight is over the open rolling plains were the greatest speed can be made.

During the aerial census eagles were seen feeding on two antelope carcasses; a fresh snow may have covered additional evidence. Forty-seven golden eagles and three bald eagles were observed during 31 hours of census strip flying.

In August, 1947, Deputy Raleigh Shields on aerial patrol in Musselshell County, watched a golden eagle kill an immature antelope. The eagle first attacked the young animal by grasping it near the small of the back and spreading its wings, making it difficult for the fawn to run. Upon circling a second time with the airplane, he observed that the eagle had the antelope grasped by the throat and ribs, but both were on the ground and the antelope appeared to be on top. At the time of a third circle, the eagle was eating from the hams of the antelope. All efforts to frighten the eagle by diving with the plane were unsuccessful.

Trapping Foreman Bill Koch and Pilot Cliff McBratney reported observations of coyote predation upon antelope during trapping operations. On January 2, 1947, these men and the Restoration Division trapping crew were operating south of Shawmut, Montana. A band of 40 pronghorns was being driven into the trapping area when two coyotes cut into the herd at 11:30 a.m. One of the coyotes grabbed a mature doe by the throat and the other one grasped her high on a hind leg. They pulled the antelope to the ground and were feeding upon her before the plane could circle to drive them off. Of interest was the fact that the antelope had been herded through this area before. It was open with little shrubbery and the coyotes completely disregarded the airplane.

On January 4 in the same area a single coyote broke into another band of antelope being herded by the airplane and pulled another female antelope to the ground. The men succeeded in driving the coyote away by firing revolvers from the airplane. The doe resumed flight with the herd and was trapped. No evidence of injury by the coyote was found on the captured antelope. These observations were reported to a coyote hunter in the area and he shot six coyotes within one-quarter mile of the antelope trap.—W. K. THOMPSON, *Montana Fish and Game Dept., Helena, Mont.*

AERIAL CENSUS OF INTERSTATE ANTELOPE HERDS OF CALIFORNIA, IDAHO, NEVADA, AND OREGON

Leonard M. Springer

U. S. Fish and Wildlife Service, Portland, Oregon

INTRODUCTION

California, Oregon, and Idaho have been making separate aerial censuses for several years to determine the status of their antelope herds and to serve as a basis for recommending open or closed seasons.

For some time these and other western states have known that interstate migration occurs annually among herds ranging in the vicinity of State boundaries. In addition, the U. S. Fish and Wildlife Service in the course of pub- lishing annual big game census figures for the United States, has questioned the degree of duplication that has oc- curred in estimating these interstate herds. To answer this mutual problem the States of California, Nevada, Oregon and Idaho agreed to an aerial census of all antelope herds simultaneously. This initial cooperative inventory was ac- complished in March 1949. The map on the following page shows antelope winter range and numbers observed.

CENSUS

Antelope were most conspicuous in the early morning and late afternoon hours on the desert plains when the light was striking them at an acute angle. By flying low between the ante-

strips varied with the topography, ground cover, and lighting conditions, so that all of the area between strips could be observed.

The best results were obtained by establishing census area boundaries

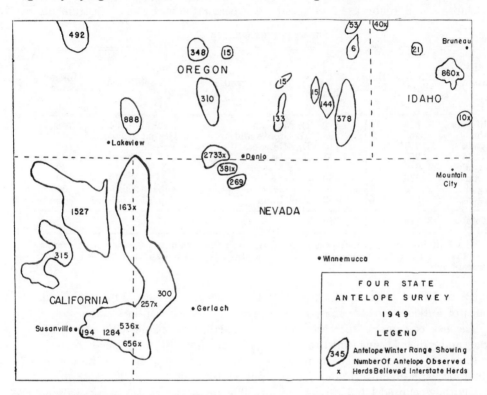

lope and the sun they were sighted at considerably greater distances during these periods. In mountainous terrain it was found most satisfactory to count antelope after the sun was higher, but before the air became rough toward midday. In some areas inclement weather necessitated censusing whenever flight conditions permitted.

Wherever possible, greatest accuracy was achieved by making parallel flights and progressively covering the area or drainage. The distance between flight

using roads, streams, and other landmarks for this purpose and then progressively flying these sections. The flight strips, antelope, and terrain were most easily and accurately checked when the flight lines were kept within five-mile lengths.

The course flown on the census strip was outlined on Civil Aeronautics maps by most of the States and the number of animals seen were then likewise recorded on the maps along the route traveled. Observations were usually best when made from about 200 feet above the ground, in level country with smooth air, but in mountainous regions, or rough air the census had to be flown up to 500 feet to maintain a reasonable safety margin.

California and Idaho used an aerial

and prints were made on high contrast paper. Photographs of extensive groups of animals were enlarged as much as possible and counting was done with the aid of a reading glass. As each animal was counted the white rump patch was perforated with a sharp instrument.

SUMMATION OF CENSUS

State	Antelope Seen	Hours Flown	Average Cruising Speed	Observers	Type Plane	Horse-power
California	4,675	15½	110	D. McLean	Fairchild M-24	165
Idaho	960	23½	105	M. Crooks and W. Shaw	Cessna 170	145
Nevada	257*	3½	110	D. McLean	Fairchild	165
Nevada	950	22½	85	N. Nilsson & R. Hanson	Cub Cruiser	100
Oregon	4,016	37½	80	Ellis Mason	J-5	80
Oregon	1,076	21	80	C. Langdon	J-5	80
Oregon	1,432	7½	90	Bill Lightfoot	Super Cruiser	100
Oregon	513	6¾	90	Paul Bonn	Super Cruiser	100
Total	13,879	137¾	89			

* The Buffalo Mountain herd was counted by both California and Nevada. California's count was larger and this figure was used. This adds 57 to Nevada's total making 1,207 for Interstate herd.

camera to record photographically all groups of antelope greater than 10 or 12. The use of cameras increased accuracy and reduced flying time to about one-third of that necessary to make counts of large bands. Idaho found visually they counted 1,146 antelope in Owyhee County, while the photographic enumeration revealed only 960. The State of California used a K-20 hand camera and attempted to take pictures of the larger groups of animals from about 700 feet. All photographs were taken away from the sun with an oblique shot at an angle greater than 45 degrees. The pictures were taken only when the animals were moving away from the plane.

Most satisfactory results were achieved when fine grain film was used

This procedure avoided duplication and permitted rechecking the count.

A small, slow plane with a cruising speed of about 85 miles per hour and having an engine of at least 85 horsepower has been found the most practicable for aerial census work. Observation is much better from a high-winged plane, and all States used this type.

The most severe winter in recent history delayed the survey by two or three weeks. Most of the antelope observed were below 5,000 feet elevation which coincided with the lower limits of the snow in most areas. Antelope were observed on the valley floors or on protected slopes where snow was absent or occurred only in scattered patches. The greatest concentration was 2,733 animals tallied on approximately 150 square miles of habitat situated west of Denio, Oregon. The antelope estimates for 1948 and the revised estimates after the interstate census are found in the following table.

ESTIMATED STATE TOTAL ANTELOPE
POPULATION AND CORRECTION FROM
THE INTERSTATE ANTELOPE CENSUS

State	Population		Revised Population Est. from Interstate Census
	1948 Est.	1949 Est.	
California	4,500	4,700	+ 200
Idaho	7,600	7,739*	+ 139
Nevada	7,000	3,500	−3,500
Oregon	12,000	14,000	+2,000
Total	31,100	29,939	−1,161

* Actual Count.
Oregon's increase in population is due to natural increase with a good fawn survival.

Nevada for the last several years has estimated 5,000 antelope in the northwestern part of the state for the annual big game inventory. After the interstate census they were of the opinion that part of the 1,192 animals wintering in California east of Wendel summer in Nevada in the mountains north of the Smoke Creek Desert.

A summer antelope census on the Charles Sheldon Refuge in Nevada during 1948 counted 1,120 animals and a similar census on the Hart Mountain Refuge in Oregon in 1949 counted approximately 1,500 animals. The total of these two figures is nearly the exact number found wintering west of Denio during the interstate census.

This would indicate that even a summer estimate of 5,000 for the northwestern part of Nevada would be too high. Annual big game estimates are made on the number of animals on their winter range so that even if this number summered in Nevada and wintered in other states, it would be necessary to reduce the state's total population estimates to the number counted on their winter ranges.

SUMMARY

The first four-state antelope census was flown in March 1949. A total of $137\frac{3}{4}$ hours or 12,350 miles were flown and 13,879 animals were observed. It is believed about 5,000 of these animals migrate back and forth across state lines.

The census was the first complete aerial coverage for northwestern Nevada and only 1,207 animals were found. The state had previously estimated 5,000 head wintering in this area.

Antelope were not found in the Owyhee Desert, High Rock Canyon and High Rock Lake areas. It was formerly believed that antelope wintered in these areas. Additional censuses are needed at different seasons of the year to determine seasonal population in northwestern Nevada and to decide if abnormal concentrations were found this year due to severe winter weather.

REFERENCES

McLEAN, DONALD D. 1944. The Pronghorn Antelope of California. California Fish and Game, **30**(4): 221–241.

NILSSON, NILS N. 1949. Let's Talk Antelope. Nevada Fish and Game, **1**(3): 8–9.

SCHWARTZ, JOHN E. 1948. Sheldon Refuge Narrative Report: May to August, 1948, pp. 4.

SHAW, W. M. 1949. Idaho Antelope Survey for Spring 1949. Federal Aid Quarterly Report, April-June, Project 85–R, pp. 1–15.

Accepted for Publication September 26, 1949.

JWM 14(4): 472–473

USE OF THE HELICOPTER IN WILDLIFE WORK

A helicopter census of pronghorn antelope was made on the Wichita Mountains Wildlife Refuge in southwestern Oklahoma on July 6, 1949 through cooperation of personnel at Fort Sill. James K. Knox, civilian instructor in the Air Training Department piloted the R13B (or 47–D) Bell helicopter. The pronghorn population consisted of 10 bucks, 17 does, and 22 fawns. Only 5 of the males were seen from the helicopter; 5 others were established from the ground. At this season some of the bucks were scattered in mountainous, oak-savanna areas where they were difficult to observe, especially when they did not move about. It was interesting to note that the isolated bucks were not frightened appreciably by the helicopter, although pronghorns in herds ran at top speed to escape the noisy aircraft. The herds attempted to follow established escape patterns even over rough, rocky ground or up boulder-strewn slopes of about 45 degrees. One herd of 18 resorted to oak-savanna cover for protection after running about 1.5 miles in open grassland. Observations from the ground indicated a population of 9 bucks, 17 does, and 19 fawns, but with no assurance that some of the does and fawns had not been counted more than once. From the air one yearling buck was seen; no yearling males were seen from the ground.

The Bell Aircraft model 47-D2 helicopter is probably the most suitable for wildlife work, since its higher horsepower (205 hp. compared with 178 hp for the 47-D) permits greater maneuverability in mountainous terrain where downdrafts, air pockets, and high altitude handicap flying. It also has the advantages of being 3-place, rather than 2-place, and having a greater gasoline capacity. Purchase price of the Bell helicopter is $27,000.00; that of the Sikorsky $50,000.00. Operating costs given by Bell Aircraft are $36.00 per hour when operating at a minimum of 300 hours per year, or less when operating more hours. This cost includes purchase of the machine, insurance, pilot's salary, maintenance, and operating costs. Pilot training courses are given at factories and by several flying services in various parts of the country at a cost of approximately $1,500.00. Since helicopters may be hired for about $50.00 per hour, it is probably more economical at present for State game departments and other agencies to hire helicopters rather than purchase them unless they are used frequently and effectively.

The helicopter obviously has many advantages over the airplane for wildlife censusing in that it may be flown at any speed from 0 to about 90 mph and has much greater maneuverability. It may be safely flown near the ground or in canyons, providing the pilot is skilled in flying, takes advantage of winds, and avoids downdrafts. There are definite limitations imposed by timber and to some extent by downdrafts in mountainous terrain. Only 25 elk (5 bulls, 13 cows, and 7 calves) were seen while on the 1-hour (0840–0940) flight during which pronghorns were counted, yet ground observations indicate that at least 143 elk used the area covered. Elk were not seen readily in oak woods where they retired after their early morning feeding period. Movements were conspicuous only when the helicopter approached directly over the elk. Counts made immediately after daybreak would give an index to the elk population but would probably be subject to considerable error. Only four whitetail deer were seen during the flight, indicating that dense foliage makes deer censusing impractical even from a helicopter.

Helicopters have been employed to facilitate wildlife work in other parts of the country. In the southeastern States they have been useful in convicting violators of waterfowl regulations. The State of Washington Department of Game found the helicopter the only instrument that could drive elk out of orchards in the Yakima area during the severe winter of 1948–1949. Helicopters have been used occasionally in Washington for patrolling streams, investigating timber resources, inventorying big game on Forest Service lands, and transporting sportsmen to high mountain lakes. Doubtlessly helicopters will be utilized in many States to aid in wildlife protection, censusing, mapping, photography, and many other phases of wildlife research and management. At the present time high costs limit their use; when they become more economical, helicopters will probably be one of the most useful instruments available for wildlife work.—HELMUT K. BUECHNER, *State College of Washington, Pullman, Wash.*

Accepted for Publication August 10, 1949.

AN AERIAL COYOTE-ANTELOPE OBSERVATION

The extent of coyote predation upon antelope kids has long been a controversial subject and, consequently, one of interest. Two on-the-spot observations, of coyotes diligently searching areas likely to harbor antelope kids, have been recorded in northwestern South Dakota. The bones of young antelope have been found near coyote dens. However, the following observation is the first known record of the behavior of antelope does and kids when pursued by a coyote.

A coyote in pursuit of its breakfast was observed by personnel of the South Dakota Department of Game, Fish and Parks during the 1950 West River aerial antelope census. The incident occurred ten miles west of Buffalo, near highway 8, shortly after dawn on the morning of June 4.

What first appeared to be a lone antelope and a bouncing jackrabbit was soon recognized as a doe and a kid antelope being chased by a coyote. The time was noted at 4:45 A.M., and the plane's altitude was estimated at 150 feet. The animals below paid no heed to the airplane. The plane's altitude was increased to about 700 feet, and circling above the contestants, the scene below was observed in its entirety.

At the beginning of the race the doe was leading, followed by the kid; and trailing about 300 yards in the rear was the coyote. After about a mile's chase, the coyote slowly gained until it was within fifty yards of the kid. At this time the doe dropped back behind the coyote, and then with a sudden burst of speed, boldly ran into the side of the coyote, rolling him end over end. Back on his feet, the coyote, constantly worried by the doe, continued in pursuit of the kid. During the next two miles the doe twice upset the coyote in the same manner—running ahead and then behind, criss-crossing the path between the kid and the coyote. After the third upset the coyote veered from side to side to avoid body contact with the doe. During this latter period, the kid slowly out-distanced the coyote and was soon joined by a second doe from the area. The second doe had a kid hidden near by.

The second doe ran with the pursued kid, seemingly to be leading it. The first doe continued to harass the coyote and the race continued. As the contestants passed over the crest of hills, the leading doe and kid would veer off at right angles in an attempt to lose the coyote. After the third such attempt the doe and kid separated, each going off in opposite directions. The coyote, duped by such a maneuver, followed the leading doe; and the kid was left free to slow its pace and seek refuge in a near-by depression.

The coyote, discovering that he had lost sight of the kid, stopped and rested near the crest of a hill, and scanned the area for some sign of the kid. The two does remained in the area and leisurely trotted about keeping within sight of the coyote.

The observers concluded that the race was over; the time was noted to be 5:00 A.M.; and the total course of the chase was estimated to have been five miles.

The coyote was buzzed by the airplane in an effort to drive him out of the area; but he refused to leave and was little frightened by the plane.

The coyote was small and appeared to be in rather poor condition. It may have been a bitch coyote with a litter of pups. The airplane and observers left the scene, leaving the contestants as before—free to continue the race for survival.—WAYNE DAVIS and DONALD PUTNAM, *South Dakota Dept. of Game, Fish, and Parks, Rapid City, S. D.*

Accepted for publication September 5, 1950.

REVIEW

Life history, ecology, and range use of the pronghorn antelope in Trans-Pecos Texas, by Helmut K. Buechner. American Midland Naturalist, 43(2): 257–354. March, 1950.

Volumes have been written about the pronghorn antelope; however, this modest report from Texas seems to present more new information about the animal, and in fewer words, than anything published previously. The period of field work was short (June, 1946, to September, 1947) but obviously it was well spent. Financial backing came from the Texas Cooperative Wildlife Unit at Texas A and M College. The report itself ultimately was presented as a Ph.D. thesis at Oklahoma A and M College.

Nearly all aspects of antelope life history and ecology are touched upon, but particular stress is laid on food habits and evaluation of food competition with domestic livestock. The author establishes the fact that antelope are primarily forb-feeders, consuming only moderate amounts of browse and very little grass. Food habits were studied by "time-observation" methods (results expressable in "antelope-minutes of use" of various forage plants) and also by stomach analyses. On the basis of 3,044 antelope-minutes representing 4,956 observations the author concludes that the year-long diet of west-Texas antelope is comprised of about 66 per cent forbs, 30 per cent browse and 4 per cent grass. Most of the forbs eaten are unimportant cattle foods and some of them are actually poisonous to cattle. Hence there is little overlap (estimated 19 per cent) in cattle and antelope diets and negligible competition. Conversely, antelope and domestic sheep share many food preferences, the overlap in diets being at least 33 per cent. Most of the range-land in the Trans-Pecos is heavily grazed and in fact 80 to 90 per cent of it is overgrazed according to the author. Yet antelope do well on many cattle ranges because of the lack of direct competition. They do not do well on sheep ranges and were actually observed to die of malnutrition when confined in heavily grazed sheep pastures. These observations are of real importance in antelope management throughout the west since one of the most widespread complaints among ranchers is that antelope compete with domestic stock. The sheepmen have something of a case but cattlemen apparently do not, for Buechner computes that it requires 47 antelope on the range to consume the food of one cow.

A guarded and objective discussion of predator relations is presented. Coyote and golden eagles are both known to catch some antelope in Texas and the steady increase of antelope over the past two decades is popularly assumed to be a direct result of coyote and eagle control. Buechner grants that control doubtless speeded the increase but points out that better game law enforcement and in more recent years increased rainfall may have been equally important or more so. At several points in the report he states flatly that range conditions, as determined in part by livestock grazing and in part by current rainfall, are paramount in determining average density and productivity of antelope populations, the implication being that predators are of less importance than range. This point of view corresponds with most of the recent findings on deer populations.

The whole report is well written and easy to read, possibly excepting the unnecessarily detailed description of the physical and biotic environment of the Trans-Pecos. All in all, it will stand as a classic piece of work on the pronghorn.—A. STARKER LEOPOLD, *Museum of Vertebrate Zoology, Berkeley, California.*

FOOD HABITS AND MEASUREMENTS OF HART MOUNTAIN ANTELOPE

Ellis Mason

Oregon State Game Commission, Burns, Oregon

In January, 1950, representatives attending the Four-State Antelope Meeting at Lakeview expressed interest in conducting a comprehensive food habits study. The available literature revealed that stomach analyses had been largely confined to samples collected during the hunting season and information at other periods of the year was inadequate or lacking.

The Oregon Game Commission agreed to collect two to three antelope per month. Analyses of stomach contents were to be made by the Food Habits Laboratory of the California Division of Fish and Game.

The Hart Mountain Herd was selected for study since it contained the largest number of animals found in any single herd in the state and resides in habitat representative of typical antelope range. Cooperation was extended by the U. S. Fish and Wildlife Service in permitting the collection of animals on the Hart Mountain and Sheldon refuges when necessary. The Nevada Fish and Game Commission also extended authorization for collections south of the Oregon Line.

Collections were commenced on May 4, 1950, and terminated on April 19, 1951. A total of 26 stomach samples was analyzed. As far as practical, collections were made at monthly intervals unless weather or other factors interfered. Severe weather prevented access to the winter concentration area in January, 1951 and no animals were collected from December 11, 1950 to February 8, 1951. With the exception of two females taken in December, 1950, all collections were limited to bucks.

The Hart Mountain herd summers on or adjacent to the Hart Mountain Antelope Refuge and winters in the vicinity of Sagehen Flat and Big Spring Table southeast of the refuge along the Oregon-Nevada state line.

In addition to food habits analyses, field measurements of all specimens were taken.

Antelope Food Habits:

Table 1 summarizes food habits at monthly intervals. This breakdown is presented for rough comparative purposes only since collections were so few and were not all at the same time of the month.

Plant species are listed in the order of their occurrence by total volume. Those species representing traces are not tabulated. Sagebrush, particularly *Artemisia tridentata*, variety *arbuscula*, represents the most important yearlong food item on the Hart Mountain range. Sagebrush species make up approximately 61 per cent of the total diet and are represented each month. Ninety-six per cent of the stomachs collected contained some species of sagebrush. Eleven of the 26 stomachs examined contained over ninety per cent sage with three of the 11 containing 100 per cent sage.

Various species of *Phlox* comprised approximately 14 per cent of the total stomach contents and were found in 46 per cent of the samples. Varying percentages of Phlox were utilized during the spring and early summer months of April, May, June and July, followed by utilization again in November and December.

Forbs made up approximately six per cent of the total diet and were found in 19 percent of the stomachs. Use of forbs was confined to the spring and summer months of April, May, June and July.

The next most important item in the diet was bitterbrush (*Purshia tridentata*) which was utilized very heavily in July and lightly in August.

In descending order, those species representing over one per cent of the total diet included poverty weed (*Iva axillaris*), English plantain (*Plantago lanceolata*), Austin's Erigeron (*Erigeron Austinae*), sticky-flowered rabbit brush (*Chrysothamnus viscidiflorus*, clover (*Trifolium sp.*), and various species of green grasses. The majority of these species were utilized most heavily during July and August with the exception of green grasses, which were taken readily when available during the late fall and early spring months.

JWM 16(3): 388

TABLE 1.—ANTELOPE FOOD HABITS AT MONTHLY INTERVALS

Plant Species and Groups	May, 1950 4 Samples Per cent of Total Volume	June, 1950 1 Sample Per cent of Total Volume	July, 1950 3 Samples Per cent of Total Volume	Aug., 1950 5 Samples Per cent of Total Volume	Sept., 1950 2 Samples Per cent of Total Volume	Nov., 1950 2 Samples Per cent of Total Volume	Dec., 1950 2 Samples Per cent of Total Volume	Feb., 1951 2 Samples Per cent of Total Volume	March, 1951 2 Samples Per cent of Total Volume	April, 1951 3 Samples Per cent of Total Volume	Year-Long Averages % of Tot. Vol.	Year-Long Averages Fre %
Sagebrush, including Artemisia tridentata, A. t. var. arbuscula, A. cana, A. spinescens	67.5	18.0	11.4	66.4	100.0	42.5	91.0	84.0	97.5	31.7	60.73	96.2
Phlox sp.	8.2	5.0	16.3			26.5	6.5			67.7	13.69	46.2
Forbs, including Collinsia sp., Lupinus sp., Mertensia longiflora, Viola sp., Balsamorrhiza sp., Compositae	10.0	75.0	14.7							0.6	6.19	19.2
Bitterbrush (Purshia tridentata)			36.3	1.0							4.38	11.5
Poverty weed (Iva axillaris)				16.0							3.08	7.7
English plantain (Plantago lanceolata)			15.0	4.0							2.50	7.7
Austin's Erigeron (Erigeron Austinae)						31.0					2.38	3.8
Sticky-flowered rabbitbrush (Chrysothamnus viscidiflorus)				11.0							2.12	3.8
Clover (Trifolium sp.)	7.3								2.5		1.12	7.7
Grasses (green)	0.7						0.5	9.0			1.04	23.1
Desert parsley (Lomatium sp.)	5.0										0.77	3.8
Milk vetch (Astragalus sp.)	1.3		4.3								0.69	11.5
Grasses (dry)								6.5			0.50	7.7
Rabbitbrush (C. nauseosus)				0.8							0.31	11.5
Orthocarpus sp.			2.0				2.0				0.23	3.8
Fiddleneck (Amsinckia sp.)				0.8							0.15	3.8
Groundsel (Senecio sp.)		2.0									0.08	3.8
Shadscale (Atriplex confertifolia)								0.5			0.04	3.8

TABLE 2.—ANTELOPE WEIGHTS AND MEASUREMENTS

No.	Date	Area Collected	Sex	Live Weight	Age	Length	Height	Tail	Ear	Hind Foot	Spread	Left Horn	Right Horn
1	5/4/50	Antelope Buttes	M	100	2	53	33½	4	6	16½	11	10½	11
2	5/4/50	Antelope Buttes	M	65	1	49	33½	3	6	16	6	6	6
3	5/4/50	Sagehen Flat	M	110	Mat.	54	36	4½	6	17	13	11½	11½
4	5/25/50	Wire Corral Flat	M	115	Mat.	52	38	4½	6½	17	9½	11½	12
5	6/7/50	Spanish Flat	M	140	Mat.	52	38½	4	6½	17½	12	14	14
6	7/3/50	Upper Rock Creek	M	140	Mat.	53	38	4	6½	17½	12½	13	13
7	7/3/50	Upper Rock Creek	M	125	2	54½	39	4	6	17½	10	11	11
8	7/3/50	Wire Corral Flat	M	135	Mat.	53	37	4	6½	17	11	13	13
9	8/1/50	Hart Mountain	M	130	Mat.	58	37	4	6	17	12	13	13
10	8/1/50	Hart Mountain	M	135	Mat.	57	36	3½	6	16½	15	13	12
11	8/2/50	Hart Mountain	M	125	Mat.	56	35	4	6	17	11	12	11
12	8/22/50	Hart Mountain	M	130	Mat.	50	38	4½	5½	16½	12½	13½	13½
13	8/22/50	Hart Mountain	M	140	Mat.	52	41	5	6	17	12½	14½	15
14	9/22/50	Hart Mountain	M	...	Mat.	53	37	..	6	..	..	12	12
15	9/22/50	Hart Mountain	M	...	Mat.	50	37½	..	6½	..	..	15	15
16	11/3/50	Sagehen Flat	M	125	Mat.	54	37	4	6	17	13	13	14
17	11/3/50	Sagehen Flat	M	130	Mat.	53	37	4	6	17	12	12	11
18	12/11/50	Sagehen Flat	F	105	Mat.	50½	36	4	6	16½	..	2	2
19	12/11/50	Sagehen Flat	F	95	1½	51	36	4	6½	16½	..	1	1½
20	2/8/51	Knot Creek	M	105	2	53	37	4	6	16	11	9	10½
21	2/8/51	Knot Creek	M	100	Mat.	52	38	4	6	16½	12	9	10½
22	3/25/51	Big Spring Table	M	130	Mat.	51	39	4	6	17½	11	10	10
23	3/25/51	Big Spring Table	M	140	Mat.	47	36	4	6	16½	14	15½	15½
24	4/19/51	Antelope Buttes	M	110	Mat.	54	37	4	6	17	10	10	11
25	4/19/51	Antelope Buttes	M	65	1	44	36	3½	6	16	6	4	4
26	4/19/51	Antelope Buttes	M	70	1	46	35	3	6	16	6½	4½	5

Green grass represented slightly over one per cent of the total diet while dry grass made up but one-half of one per cent. The total consumption of grass and forb species that are preferred by domestic livestock is extremely limited. Direct competition with domestic livestock for individual plant species is slight and evidence indicated that substantial increases of antelope numbers can be maintained on this range without conflict.

Measurements:

Measurements of physical characteristics are summarized in Table 2.

All measurements were taped according to standard procedure and recorded in inches. Total weights were recorded and are fairly accurate, subject only to variable losses of blood.

Of the 26 animals collected, 24 were males and two females. The collection included three males and one female from one to two years of age, two males from two to three years of age, and the remaining animals were considered mature, that is three years or older.

The live weight of mature bucks varied from 100 pounds to 140 pounds. Although the 100-pound male was collected in February, it is significant that one of the four bucks which weighed 140 pounds was taken in March.

The total length of mature bucks averaged 52.9 inches with a variation from 47 inches to 58 inches. Shoulder height averaged 37.4 inches with a variation from 35 to 41 inches. Since lengths of tail, ear, and hind foot were recorded in inches and appear uniform, maximum and minimum measurements are not significant. An inadequate number of samples for immature males and for all females does not justify comparisons.

Accepted for publication Aug. 27, 1951.

JWM 26(1): 1

CHANGES IN MANDIBULAR DENTITION ASSOCIATED WITH AGE IN PRONGHORN ANTELOPE

Sumner A. Dow, Jr. and Philip L. Wright

Tennessee Game and Fish Commission, Nashville, Tennessee;
and Department of Zoology, Montana State University, Missoula, Montana

The pronghorn (*Antilocapra americana*) has increased over much of its former range and is now a game animal of considerable importance in several Western states. A reliable method of age determination would enable game biologists to evaluate productivity and mortality by examining hunter-killed animals. The project was conducted because no published accounts of age determination studies based on known-age antelope specimens could be found. Since the present study was completed, a number of known-age antelope jaws have been briefly described from Colorado by Hoover, *et al.* (1959).

This study is a project of the Montana Cooperative Wildlife Research Unit, the U. S. Fish and Wildlife Service, the Montana Fish and Game Department, Montana State University, and the Wildlife Management Institute cooperating. The study was initiated in 1950 by the staff of the unit, and the first stage was chosen and designed by the senior author as a master's thesis topic. He carried out the field and laboratory work during 1951–52, collected jawbones by mail (Dow, 1954), made the initial study of the hunter-killed sample of jawbones, and made most of the photographs and all of the radiograms (Dow, 1952). The junior author supervised the project during 1951–52, collected the 8 known-age specimens from 1953 through 1957, and restudied the hunter-killed jawbones after known-age specimens were available for comparison.

The authors are indebted to John Schwartz and Victor B. May of the National Bison Range, the former for permitting and making arrangements for the use of the fenced range as a field laboratory and the latter for extensive help in collecting the specimens. Assistance from personnel of the Montana Fish and Game Department in trapping and transporting the antelope to the Bison Range is gratefully acknowledged. E. L. Cheatum and John J. Craighead contributed in many ways while administratively supervising the project for the Montana Cooperative Wildlife Research Unit. Howard Reinhardt, Director of the Montana State University Statistical Laboratory, constructed the hypothetical life table and made the statistical analyses of the age classification. His contribution is especially appreciated. Wildlife students assisted in many parts of the study during the first two years' work.

METHODS AND MATERIALS

The study herd was maintained on the National Bison Range, Moiese, Montana. Two releases of wild-trapped animals were made; one in 1951 and the other in 1952. After release the antelope were free to roam over the 19,000-acre range. Antelope were not native to this part of Montana, and none occurred on the Bison Range at the time of the first release in 1951. The introduced animals have thrived, and only one of the released animals was found to be retarded in body growth and development when shot later. It had broken a front foot at the time of release. All other antelope have been in excellent condition when collected and no evidence of disease has been found.

Two types of animals were used to obtain the series of aged specimens. The term "aged animals" refers to either "established-age animals" or "known-age animals." When antelope are trapped during the winter months for relocation in Montana, the fawns born the preceding spring are easily recognized. At this time fawns are not fully grown, they possess the entire set of deciduous incisor and canine teeth, and the horns of the males are markedly smaller than those of older bucks. Such animals, in which the year but not the specific birth date is known, are referred to as "established-age animals." Antelope caught near Gardiner, Montana on February 14, 1951, provided the nucleus herd. Eight fawns were included in this group. Another release of 10 fawns was made on March 20, 1952. There were then 18 established-age animals. The other source of classified animals came from marked fawns born to adult does on the range. Fawns captured after careful observation of the does at the time of parturition constituted "known-age animals." Six fawns born during the spring of 1951 were marked within a day or so of birth.

There was a total of 24 aged animals on the Bison Range available for use in the study. Twenty of these were collected by shooting at designated intervals to obtain the specimens described in this paper. Their ages ranged from 44 days to 6⅓ years. No additional animals of known age were believed to be alive on the range after the 6⅓-year-old animal was killed in September 1957. Four aged animals disappeared from the range during the winter of 1955–56. It was planned that they be collected at 7, 8, 9, and 10 years of age. The lack of these specimens represented a major loss in terms of the objectives of the study.

Six newborn fawns and each of the released animals were eartagged with a numbered metal stock tag to which a colored plastic disc was attached. Those animals collected within the first year after tagging all had the metal tag and generally had the colored discs attached. Some of the animals killed later had lost both the discs and the tags. Conspicuous scars on the appropriate region of the ears served to permanently identify the older animals. Three of the known-age antelope lost their ear tags prior to being shot and were, therefore, classified as established-age animals when they were recorded. All 8 of the established-age fawns that were released in 1951 were killed within a year of the time of release.

The animals used to establish the older age classes were all born the same year, 1951. Included in these were the 10 fawns released on March 10, 1952 and those known-age fawns marked in the spring of 1951 and left alive to be used for that purpose because they appeared to be well marked. All of the marked animals over 3½ years old were males. To prevent possible confusion in the field of unmarked antelope, which might have been born to some of the does still on the range, with known-age antelope that had lost their tags, an effort was made each fall to kill all of the unmarked yearling bucks. It was possible to distinguish these yearling males from the adults by the smaller size, coloration of the face, and appearance of the horns (Dow, 1952). We were successful in this effort during each year except 1953 when 2 yearling bucks survived. They were killed in 1957 when 5⅓ years old and are discussed with the 5⅓-year age class.

Five fawns born in the spring of 1951 were not marked. One of these (K-7) was the twin to K-2 and could not be located when the latter was tagged. However, it was shot on August 13, 1951 after it, along with its marked twin, was seen nursing its color-marked mother. Because of the extremely clear circumstances surrounding its history, it was regarded as a known-age fawn.

The other 4 unmarked fawns were later collected; 1 was killed in February 1952 at the age of 8 months, 2 were killed in Sep-

TABLE 1.—COLLECTION DATES AND STATUS OF MANDIBULAR DENTITION OF KNOWN-AGE AND ESTABLISHED-AGE ANTELOPE

Known-age (K) Estab-lished-age (E)	No.	Date Examined or Killed	Age	Sex	Incisors			Canine	Premolars			Molars		
					1	2	3	1	2	3	4	1	2	3
K	1[1]	May 30, '51	Birth	M	¼[3]						¼			
K	2[1]	June 7, '51	Birth	M	¼						¼			
K	3[1]	June 6, '51	Birth	F	¼						¼			
K	4[1]	June 6, '51	Birth	M	¼						¼			
K	5[1]	May 31, '51	Birth	M	¼						¼			
K	6[1]	May 31, '51	Birth	F	¼						¼			
K	1	July 14, '51	44 days	M	D	D	D	D	D	D	D	½		
K	7[2]	Aug. 13, '51	67 days	M	D	D	D	D	D	D	D	½		
K	3	Sept. 27, '51	110 days	F	D	D	D	D	D	D	D	P		
K	4	Dec. 2, '51	180 days	M	D	D	D	D	D	D	D	P	¼	
E	8	Feb. 10, '52	8 mo	F	D	D	D	D	D	D	D	P	P	
E	9	June 12, '52	12 mo	M	D	D	D	D	D	D	D	P	P	⅓
E	10	Aug. 16, '51	14 mo	F	P½	D	D	D	D	D	D	P	P	¾
E	11	Sept. 20, '51	1⅓ yr	F	P	D	D	D	D	D	D	P	P	¾
E	12	Sept. 26, '51	1⅓ yr	M	P	D	D	D	D	D	D	P	P	¾
E	13	Nov. 27, '51	1⅓ yr	F	P	D	D	D	D	D	D	P	P	¾
E	14	Feb. 10, '52	1⅔ yr	M	P	D	D	D	D	D	D	P	P	P
E	15	Feb. 10, '52	1⅔ yr	F	P	D	D	D	D	D	D	P	P	P
E	16	Sept. 26, '53	2⅓ yr	M	P	D	D	D	D	DP¼	DP¼	P	P	P
E	17	Oct. 27, '53	2⅓ yr	M	P	P¾	D	D	DP½	DP¾	DP½	P	P	P
E	18	Oct. 8, '54	3⅓ yr	M	P	P	P	D	P	P	P	P	P	P
E	19	Dec. 20, '54	3½ yr	F	P	P	P	P¾	P	P	P	P	P	P
E	20	Sept. 21, '55	4⅓ yr	M	P	P	P	P	P	P	P	P	P	P
E	21	Sept. 27, '55	4⅓ yr	M	P	P	P	P½	P	P	P	P	P	P
E	22	Sept. 7, '56	5⅓ yr	M	P	P	P	P	P	P	P	P	P	P
E	23	Sept. 18, '57	6⅓ yr	M	P	P	P	P	P	P	P	P	P	P

[1] Data recorded from living animals.
[2] See text for source of this animal.
[3] Where fractions are used it indicates that the teeth are not erupted enough to occupy their normal position in contact with the corresponding upper teeth. D and P are used to indicate deciduous and permanent teeth. The conventional abbreviations for the lower incisors, canine, premolars, and molars (i, c, p, and m, respectively) are used throughout the paper. Thus Di3, deciduous incisor three; Pp4, permanent premolar four; m1, molar one (the P is omitted since molars by definition exist only as permanent teeth).

tember 1953 at the age of 2⅓ years, and the last was killed in September 1956, recognizable as a 5⅓-year-old animal at that time by the level of wear of its teeth.

The herd was kept at less than 30 animals throughout the study, and a fairly accurate appraisal of the sex and age composition of the herd could be made during late summer and fall when the herd often banded together.

After the animals were killed on the Bison Range, they were weighed and measured. All skulls and left metacarpal bones were saved, and a number of the pelvic girdles were also preserved. This material is permanently catalogued in the Montana State University Zoological Museum. Only the data from the mandibular dentition will be discussed in this paper.

The eruption of the maxillary teeth occurred at about the same time as the corresponding mandibular teeth, but for application in managing the species the lower jaw is much more readily obtained. Table 1 indicates the pattern of tooth eruption in the aged series.

Since the number of aged animals was small, we obtained a sample of hunter-killed antelope jawbones to compare with the known-age specimens by sending prepaid postal envelopes to 3,000 randomly selected antelope hunters prior to the 1951 season (Dow 1952, 1954). Approximately 1,500 envelopes were returned and lower jaws were obtained from over 1,300 animals.

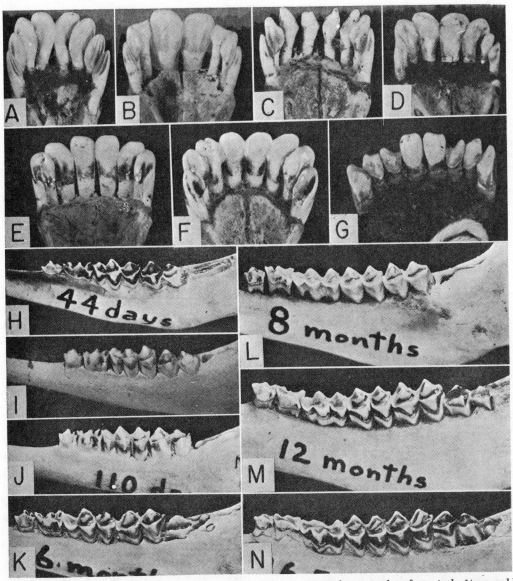

FIG. 1. A–G, natural size; H–N, ⅝ natural size. A. Incisiform teeth of typical ⅓-year-old hunter-killed fawn showing all slightly worn deciduous teeth. B. Incisiform teeth of typical 1⅓-year-old hunter-killed animal. The tips of Di2 have become broken in handling. C. Incisiform teeth of 1⅓-year-old hunter-killed animal in which all of the deciduous incisiform teeth are still present but extensively worn and widely spaced. About 15 per cent of yearling antelope as killed during the hunting season are in this state. D. Incisiform teeth of 2⅓-year-old hunter-killed animal. About two-thirds of the hunter-killed animals are in this condition with the incisiform teeth, Pi1, Pi2, and Di3, and Dc1. E. Incisiform teeth of hunter-killed animal estimated to be 3⅓ years old showing only Dc1 not yet replaced. The tips of Pi1 and Pi2 show considerable wear. F. Incisiform teeth of animal estimated to be 4⅓ years old. Almost 80 per cent of animals classified in this class have the full set of permanent incisiform teeth. G. Incisiform teeth of animal classified in the 6-plus age class. All teeth show heavy wear at this stage. H. Jaw of 44-day-old animal (K-1). I. Jaw of 67-day-old animal (K-7). J. Jaw of 110-day-old animal (K-3). K. Jaw of 180-day-old animal (K-4). L. Jaw of established-age 8-month-old animal (E-8). M. Jaw of established-age 12-month-old animal (E-9). N. Jaw of established-age 1⅓-year-old animal (E-11).

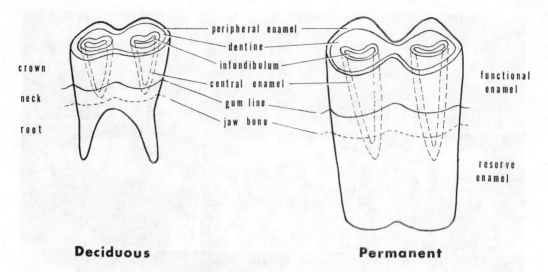

Deciduous   Permanent

MOLARIFORM TEETH

FIG. 2.   Diagrams of typical deciduous premolar and a typical molar of pronghorn antelope.

TOOTH DEVELOPMENT

The terminology to be used for designating the teeth is that of Riney (1951) and Sisson and Grossman (1953). The dental formula follows: I_3^0, C_1^0, P_3^3, M_3^3. The incisors are simple spade-like teeth without cusps or infundibula (Fig. 1, A–G). The permanent incisors (Pi) and canines (Pc) are much larger than their deciduous predecessors (Di and Dc). They are arranged in fan-like manner and imbedded so as to allow a slight movement. The size decreases progressively so that the first incisor is the largest and the canine is smallest. The molariform teeth, premolars (Dp and Pp), and molars (m), of the pronghorn are selenodont like those of other Pecorans, but the permanent teeth differ markedly from the short-crowned long-rooted brachyodont teeth of the Cervidae as described by numerous workers in that they are hypsodont, that is, with long crowns and either entirely without roots or with roots developing months or years after the teeth have first erupted (Fig. 2). Sisson and Grossman (1953:397) have an excellent description of the terminology used to describe the hypsodont teeth of the horse. In order to show the entire form of the molariform teeth of the antelope without destroying

the jaws, it was necessary to X-ray the jaws (Fig. 3, A–J). The hypsodont tooth continues to erupt throughout the life of the individual animal. Measurements of the height of the tooth above the gum line (functional crown), used so effectively by Severinghaus (1949) in his work on white-tailed deer, are of little value in this species since the extent of exposure remains more or less constant throughout life. Excellent radiograms of the teeth of the chamois (*Rupicapra rupicapra*), diagrammed by Couturier (1938), show much more highly developed roots than are found in the pronghorn.

The parts of the molariform teeth referred to in this study are illustrated in Figure 2. That part that contacts its opposing tooth in the maxilla is called the occlusal surface. The contact surface is that part of the crown that touches the adjacent tooth in the same row. The infundibulum is the funnel-shaped cavity extending from the occlusal surface downward through the body and is surrounded by the central enamel. As can be seen in the radiograms, the central enamel often extends down below the jaw line (Fig. 3, D). The peripheral enamel surrounds the outside of the tooth. The reserve enamel lies below the

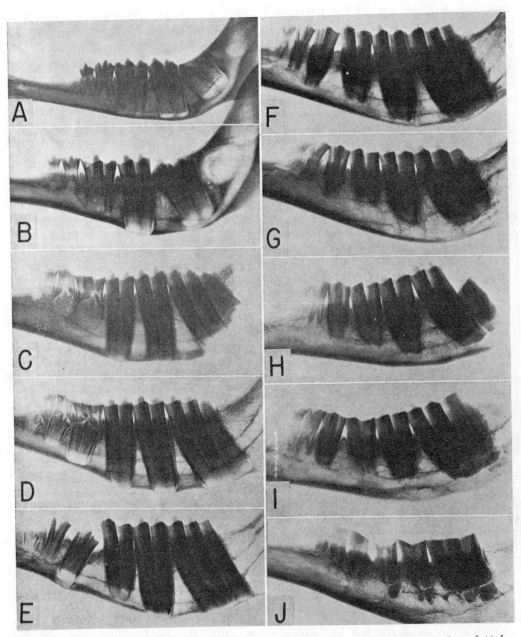

Fig. 3. Radiograms of typical stages of antelope jaws. All about ⅗ × natural size. A. Jaw of 44-day-old animal (K-1). The rooted deciduous premolars show distinctly. m1 is well formed although additional ossification is occurring at the base of the tooth. The central enamel in the rear cusp is visible extending downward through about two-thirds of the crown. m2 is partially formed within the jaw. B. Jaw of 180-day-old animal. The deciduous premolars are continuing to erupt. m1 has been further lengthened by additional ossification. m2 is now partially erupted and m3 is just beginning to form. C. Jaw of 1⅓-year-old animal (E-13). The permanent premolars are beginning to form in the jaw and result in some dissolution of the roots of the deciduous premolars. m1, m2, and m3 continue to increase in length and now extend almost completely through the jaw. D. Jaw of 1⅔-year-old animal (E-14) to show further developing permanent premolars encroaching on the roots of the deciduous premolars. E. Jaw of 2⅓-year-old animal (E-16) showing eruption of the permanent premolars.

gum line, and this part of the crown will progress upward during subsequent wear and eruption. The neck of the tooth is the part between the crown and the root, but this is seen clearly only in the deciduous premolars since they are the only ones that regularly develop distinct roots. The permanent premolars may not develop roots for several years and then the degree of development is highly variable and the roots are often not clearly discernible.

Molars 1 and 2 are typical with 2 cusps on the medial or lingual side and 2 cusps on the lateral or buccal side with 2 infundibula between. These lingual cusps probably represent the paraconid and the metaconid and the buccal cusps the protoconid and the hypoconulid. Molar 3 is the largest tooth in the jaw and contains 3 lingual and 3 buccal cusps and 3 infundibula. The cusps of premolars 2 and 3 in both the deciduous and permanent forms are represented by an irregular ridge, and the homologies of the cusps in these teeth and in m3 are not clear. Deciduous premolar 4 possesses 3 lingual (medial) and 3 buccal (lateral) cusps and 3 infundibula.

There are 12 infundibula normally present on each side of the jaw in an unworn set of fully erupted mandibular premolars and molars distributed as follows: Pp2, 1; Pp3, 1; Pp4, 3; m1, 2; m2, 2; m3, 3. The gradual disappearance of these cavities in older animals provided the main criteria used in distinguishing the older age classes.

Tooth succession proceeds in the same order as described for various cervids. However, it is considerably more delayed than in the deer as described by Severinghaus (1949). The last permanent tooth to erupt in the pronghorn, the canine, may appear in about 50 per cent of animals classed as 3½-year-olds but has still not erupted in 16 of 148 (10.8 per cent) animals classed as 4⅓-year-olds; and in 1 animal classed as a 5⅓-year-old, it has not erupted.

Description of Mandibular Dentition of Known-Age Animals

Birth (6 animals)

Deciduous incisor 1 and Dp4 had pierced the gum in all 6 animals examined. The crown of Di1 was from 1 to 3 mm wide along the gum line and was covered by a thin translucent vascularized membrane which broke during examination in one case. Deciduous premolar 4 extended about 1 mm above the gum line in all 6 fawns examined.

Forty-four Days (Figs. 1, H; 3, A)

The deciduous incisors and canines have reached full height above the gum but show no wear. The buccal cusps of the fully erupted Dp4 display slight wear that exposes the dentine. No dentine is exposed on Dp2 or 3. Molar 1 has erupted completely through the jaw but has not reached the full height in the gum line.

Figure 3, A shows that roots have already formed on the premolars while m1 is still developing reserve enamel. Molar 2, although present in the jaw, has not emerged through the gum and m3 is not visible.

Sixty-seven Days (Fig. 1, I)

Deciduous incisors 1 and 2 have begun to show slight wear, and all of the premolars now show wear but the dentine is exposed only in Dp3 and Dp4. The premolars are now fully erupted, but m1 is still not in apposition with the corresponding maxillary tooth. Molar 2, although erupting through the jawbone, has still not emerged through the gum.

F. Jaw of 3⅓-year-old animal (E-18). All teeth are now almost fully formed yet distinct roots are visible only on Pp3. In only Pp4 and m1 have the bases of the teeth begun to move away from the lower edge of the jaw. G. Jaw of 4⅓-year-old animal (E-20). All of the teeth are erupting further but especially m1, as the occlusal surfaces become worn. H. Jaw of 5⅓-year-old animal (E-22). I. Jaw of 6⅓-year-old animal (E-23). Note small area of central enamel surrounding central infundibulum on m3. J. Jaw of 6-plus animal in which no infundibula remain. This animal is probably 9 or more years old.

One Hundred and Ten Days (Fig. 1, J)

Deciduous incisors 1 and 2 show only slight wear on the medial side, Di3 and Dc1 show no wear. Further wear is now evidenced on the premolars by widening areas of dentine showing on both the buccal and lingual cusps of Dp3 and 4. Molar 1 is now in apposition and shows dentine on the anterior buccal and lingual crest, but the posterior cusps show no wear. Molar 2 has continued eruption so that the anterior cusps are emerging through the gum.

The radiogram of this stage (not illustrated) shows m3 beginning to take shape within the jaw. The anterior cusps are now clearly outlined.

One Hundred and Eighty Days (Figs. 1, K; 3, B)

The deciduous incisors and canine continue to show progressive wear but the dentine is not yet exposed. The posterior cusp of Dp2 does not yet show dentine but the dentine of Dp3 and Dp4 is more conspicuous. The anterior cusps of m1 show further wear but the posterior ones are still unworn. Molar 2 shows all 4 cusps through the jawbone but still covered by the gum.

The radiogram (not illustrated) shows well-defined roots on all of the premolars. Molars 1 and 2 have both increased in length and the former now extends through to the ventral side of the ramus.

Eight Months (Fig. 1, L)

Deciduous incisors 1, 2, and 3 all show moderate wear on the medial side of each tooth, exposing the dentine slightly in Di1 and 2. Deciduous canine 1 is still unworn.

The premolars show further wear so that dentine is showing on Dp2. The infundibulum is gone from the left side of Dp3, but the infundibula were still present on the right side of Dp3 and 4. Molar 1 is worn to the point where the dentine is now wider than the enamel and m2 is now in apposition but does not show dentine. Molar 3 has produced a slit-like opening in the jaw, but it has not erupted through the bone.

A radiogram (not illustrated) shows m3 to be well formed within the jaw.

Twelve Months (Fig. 1, M)

Deciduous incisors 1, 2, and 3 and Dc1 all show some wear and the occlusal surface shows dentine in all. Deciduous premolars 2, 3, and 4 are now worn so that all 5 infundibula have disappeared. Molar 1 now shows dentine areas on both lingual and buccal cusps that are wider than the enamel. Molar 2 shows dentine for the first time, and the anterior and middle pairs of cusps of m3 have erupted through the jaws. The bone has not been eroded for entry of the rear cusps.

Fourteen Months

Permanent incisor 1 has now erupted through the jaw and is just coming through the gum, and Di1 has been shed. The remaining deciduous front teeth are in place, and additional wear is conspicuous.

The deciduous premolars show further wear beyond the previous stage and show more exposure of the roots as the teeth erupt further. Only a minute portion of central enamel remains between the posterior cusps of Dp4. Molar 1 now shows 3 times as much dentine as enamel in the buccal cusps, and almost as much dentine shows on m2. The rear cusps of m3 are just emerging through the jawbone but the anterior cusps show no wear. The deepest portion of m2 now extends all the way through the jawbone and has caused decalcification of portions of the jaw resulting in a hole on the ventral side at that point.

One and One-third Years (3 animals, Figs. 1, N; 3, C)

This stage corresponds to that of yearling animals taken by hunters. In 2 of the 3 animals, Pi1 is fully erupted, but in the 1 taken September 20, Di1 is still in place on both sides but the right Pi1 is breaking through the jaw. The deciduous premolars do not show any appreciable difference from the previous stage. Molars 1 and 2 show moderate wear but the infundibula are deep and clearly demarked. The anterior cusps of m3 are beginning to show slight wear, the dentine is becoming visible, the middle pair of cusps are without wear, and the posterior pair are just emerging through the jawbone.

Figure 3, C shows that the permanent premolars are beginning to ossify within the jaw, and the oldest specimens show some dissolution of the roots of the deciduous premolars. The slight wear on the anterior cusps of m3 together with the posterior cusps just emerging through the jaw are most characteristic of this stage.

One and Two-third Years (2 animals, Fig. 3, D)

The jaws of the 2 animals are in the same state of wear. Of the permanent incisors, only Pi1 is present. Deciduous incisors 2 and 3 and Dc1 are showing more wear with dentine exposed in the former 2. The molariform teeth look very much like those taken in the fall at 1⅓ years. The deciduous premolars are worn further than at 1⅓ years, and Dp2 and 3 have the crowns largely worn away and are attached to the jaw only by the tips of the roots. The jaw has lengthened considerably behind m3, and this tooth has now reached a position of full apposition. Both the forward and middle pairs of cusps show exposed brown dentine. The rear cusps of m3 are unworn.

Figure 3, D shows the crowns of all 3 permanent premolars well formed, but there is no sign of the deciduous premolars being lost at this stage.

Two and One-third Years (2 animals, Figs. 4, A; 3, E)

The September specimen shows only Pi1 in functional position with Di2, 3 and Dc1 still in place. The October specimen has Pi2 almost fully erupted. In both specimens Dp3 and 4 were in place in the living animals as thin shells covering the partially erupted Pp3 and Pp4. These caps were lost before the photograph (Fig. 4, A) was taken; therefore, Pp3 and 4 are visible as partially erupted teeth. The radiogram of this jaw (Fig. 3, E) shows Pp2 still not erupted through the jawbone. Molar 1 shows more wear than m2, and m3 shows

TABLE 2.—STATUS OF INFUNDIBULA ON MOLARIFORM TEETH OF ESTABLISHED-AGE ANTELOPE FOR 3⅓ YEARS TO 6⅓ YEARS

Number	Age	Side	Pp2[1]	Pp3	Pp4	m1	m2	m3
E-18	3⅓	Left	P	P	PPP	PP	PP	PPP
		Right	P	P	PPP	PP	PP	PPP
E-19	3½	Left	P	P	PPP	PP	PP	PPP
		Right	P	P	PPP	PP	PP	PPP
E-20	4⅓	Left	P	P	PAP	AA	XX	PPP
		Right	P	P	PPP	AA	PP	PPP
E-21	4⅓	Left	P	P	PPP	PP	PP	PPA
		Right	P	P	PPP	AA	PP	PPA
E-22	5⅓	Left	P	P	PPA	AA	AP	PPX
		Right	X	X	XXX	XX	XP	PPP
56-101[2]	5⅓	Left	P	P	PPP	AA	AP	PPA
		Right	P	A	PPP	AA	AP	PPA
57-1[2]	5⅓	Left	P	P	PPA	AA	AP	PPA
		Right	P	P	PPA	AA	AP	PPA
57-2[2]	5⅓	Left	P	A	PPP	AA	AP	PPA
		Right	P	A	PPP	AA	AP	PPA
E-23	6⅓	Left	P	P	PAA	AA	AA	PPA
		Right	P	P	PAA	AA	AA	PPA

[1] In this system of abbreviations for the status of the infundibula, P means the infundibulum is present, A means the tooth is worn to the point where the infundibulum is no longer present, and X means the tooth is broken or missing from the jaw.

[2] These animals taken on the Bison Range in September 1956 and 1957 were unmarked but, because of records of the composition of the experimental herd, were known to be 5⅓ years old when shot.

less wear than m2. The 7 infundibula of the molars are still distinct but are becoming reduced on m1.

Figure 3, E shows that m2 and m3 extend almost completely through the jaw. Only m1 has begun to draw away from the ventral surface of the jaw, but deposition of reserve enamel and dentine is still occurring.

Three and One-third Years (1 animal, Figs. 4, B; 3, F) and Three and One-half Years (1 animal)

The October specimen shows Pi3 fully erupted. Deciduous canine 1 is still in place, but Pc1 is erupting through the jaw. The December specimen has Pc1 almost fully in place. The permanent premolars of both now show some wear, but all of the infundibula are still present (Table 2). On m1 the infundibula are still distinct on the September specimen, but on the December one they are present only as tiny pits surrounded by a small amount of central

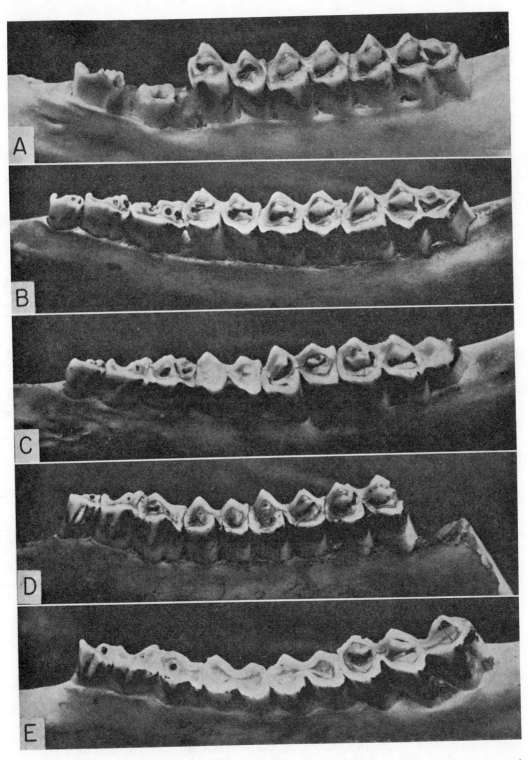

FIGURE 4.

enamel. The lingual crests are sharply pointed in both specimens.

Figure 3, F shows indistinct roots on Pp3 and m1. Molar 2 and m3 are clearly still developing at the bases and both teeth extend almost entirely through the jaw.

Four and One-third years (2 animals, Figs. 4, C; 3, G)

Each of the 4⅓-year-old animals has a dental abnormality. In one (E-20) the left m2 has been broken off near the gum line; in the other (E-21) the left jaw has Pp4 tilted to the left so there is no contact between it and m2, and the space had become packed with food material.

The right jaws of both animals (Table 2) are normal, however, and the left tooth row shows slightly less wear than the right ones. In each animal m1 is worn so that both infundibula have disappeared, and in one the rear infundibulum on m3 is also gone. One (E-20) has all of the permanent incisiform teeth in place, but the other (E-21) has the right Pc1 only half erupted.

Figure 3, G shows all of the molariform teeth moving away from the ventral surface of the jaw and apparently all of these teeth are fully formed.

Five and One-third Years (Figs. 4, D; 3, H)

The marked animal of this age was unfortunately shot in the right jaw, and on the left side the rear cusp of m3 was also destroyed by the bullet. The corresponding cusp on the right side was recovered and it is possible to visualize a composite of the entire dentition. Three other animals taken on the range in Septembers of 1956 and 1957, although unmarked, are known through indirect evidence to represent this age class.

The 5⅓-year-old animals in Table 2 all show approximately the same level of tooth wear with 4 or 5 infundibula gone from the teeth. The anterior infundibulum on m2 is gone on all the complete jaws, and the posterior one on m3 is gone on 2 of the 4. The incisiform teeth of all 4 are essentially similar. Permanent incisors 1 and 2 are worn so that the dentine is showing over extensive area; Pi3 has some dentine exposed, but Pc1 still shows no visible wear.

Figure 3, H is not markedly different from that of the 4⅓-year-old animal (Fig. 3, G).

Six and One-third Years (Figs. 4, E; 3, I)

The molariform teeth show considerable further wear beyond the 5⅓-year class. The infundibular pattern is as indicated in Table 2. Molars 1 and 2 are clearly the most heavily worn teeth followed by Pp4 that has only 1 infundibulum remaining. Permanent incisor 1 is now worn so that the anterior edge is straight across and is now narrower transversely than in younger animals.

Figure 3, I shows all of the teeth are now continuing eruption so that even the base of m3 has moved some distance away from the ventral edge of the jaw. Only Pp2 and Pp3 show distinct roots.

Comparison between Maxillary Dentition and Mandibular Dentition as Aid to Age Determination

The eruption of the maxillary molariform teeth occurs at about the same time as the corresponding mandibular teeth. Thus a fawn or ⅓-year-class animal could be recognized because it would have only 4 functional maxillary teeth, DP^2, DP^3, DP^4, and M^1. The 1⅓-year class would have these same teeth plus M^2, and M^3 would be erupting. The 2⅓-year class would have

Fig. 4. Molariform teeth of established-age animals ranging from 2⅓ years to 6⅓ years old. All about 1½ × natural size. A. Jaw of 2⅓-year-old animal (E-16) showing permanent premolars in process of eruption and molars with all infundibula present. B. Jaw of 3⅓-year-old animal (E-18) showing full set of permanent teeth with all 12 infundibula clearly visible. C. Jaw of 4⅓-year-old animal (E-20) showing m1 with wear such that both infundibula are gone as well as the rear one from m3. D. Jaw of 5⅓-year-old animal (E-22). The rear cusp of m3 has been shot away but in the corresponding tooth on the right jaw the infundibulum is gone. The rear infundibulum on Pp4, both on m1, and the anterior one on m2 have all disappeared. E. Jaw of 6⅓-year-old animal (E-23) showing only 5 of the original 12 infundibula still remaining.

PP^2, PP^3, PP^4 just erupting or newly erupted and without wear. The complete set of permanent maxillary molariform teeth has only 9 infundibula in contrast to 12 in the mandibular set. They are distributed as follows: PP^2, 1; PP^3, 1; PP^4, 1; M^1, 2; M^2, 2; M^3, 2. These infundibula do not disappear as rapidly as they do in the mandibular teeth and study of the rate of their loss would not be as useful. For example, animal E-22, the 5⅓-year-old, has lost only one maxillary infundibulum and that one on M^1; and E-23, the 6⅓-year-old animal, has lost only 3, the one on PP^2 and both on M^1.

CONDITION OF MANDIBULAR DENTITION OF HUNTER-KILLED ANIMALS

The antelope hunting seasons for 1951, the year the hunter-killed sample was obtained, included two 10-day seasons; the first from September 7–16, and the second from October 26–November 4. Thirty of the 32 open areas had only one 10-day season; the other 2 had both an early and a late season.

One-third Year Class (fawns)

The jaws of fawn antelope were separated according to the season in which they were killed because those killed during the second season were about 7 weeks older than those taken in the early season. Generally the jaws of the early killed animals were smaller and had less advanced stages of tooth succession and wear than the older jaws. There were only 2 known-age jaws with which these jaws could be compared: the 110- and 180-day stages.

Mason (1947) states that in Oregon "antelope differ from most big game animals in that the season during which the young are born extends over a short period of time. The first and last fawns of the season are seldom dropped over 2 weeks apart." If we assume that the average date of birth of wild fawns was June 1 and that most births occurred within 5 days either side of this date, then fawns killed by hunters during the September 7–16 season would be from about 98 to 108 days old. Comparison of the 77 early-season fawn jaws with the 110-day stage indicated that 50 fawns appeared to be about the same age, 26 appeared older, and only 1 seemed younger. This suggests that two-thirds of the hunter-killed fawns were about 110 days of age, but one-third were older, possibly born before June 1, or had worn their teeth more rapidly than the 110-day Bison Range animal.

Following the above line of thought, the late-season fawns would be about 147 days old when the season opened October 26. Comparison of their jaws with the 180-day stage indicates that 95 fawns appear younger, 31 about the same, and 4 older. Again the evidence suggests that quite a number of wild fawns were born prior to June 1 or that the rate of tooth wear was somewhat greater than on the Bison Range animal. Although it is not possible with the data at hand to estimate accurately the span of the fawning season, it is not unreasonable to assume that the majority of fawns were born in late May and early June. Thus, established-age and hunter-shot animals killed in September and October are classed as being ⅓, 1⅓, 2⅓, etc. years of age because of the uncertainty of the precise time of birth.

The appearance of the incisiform teeth of the fawn stage as seen in a hunter-killed animal is shown in Figure 1, A.

One and One-Third Year Class (yearlings)

The status of the 402 jaws of hunter-killed animals belonging in the 1⅓-year class is summarized in Table 3.

About 85 per cent of this yearling class have Pi1 either in place (Fig. 1, B) or partially erupted, and in the remaining 15 per cent the deciduous incisiform teeth are all still in place but are well worn and have become widely spaced (Fig. 1, C). These widely spaced deciduous incisiform teeth that occur in a minority of yearlings provide an excellent criterion to separate these from the fawn class. The partly erupted m3 and the well-worn deciduous premolars are the 2 characters that most readily identify this stage. The ages of all animals in this class can be recognized with certainty.

TABLE 3.—STATUS OF DENTITION OF 402 HUNTER-KILLED ANTELOPE ASSIGNED TO THE 1⅓-YEAR-OLD CLASS

Incisiform Teeth[1]	Number of Animals	Molariform Teeth[1]	Number of Animals
Pi1, Di2, Di3, Dc1	190	m3 partly but not fully erupted, infundibula worn out of Dp3 and 4	345
Pi1 partially erupted, Di2, Di3, Dc1	145		
Di1, Di2, Di3, Dc1	65	Same as above but with infundibula still present on Dp4	54
No front teeth on specimen	2		
		No rear teeth on specimen	2
	402	With m3 growing anteriorly against m2	1
			402

[1] Symbols or abbreviations used are the same as those in Table 1.

Two and One-third Year Class

The status of the 244 jaws of hunter-killed antelope judged to be of this age is summarized in Table 4.

In two-thirds (161) of the animals of this class the incisiform teeth appeared as in Figure 1, D and most of the remainder show some sign of eruption of Pi2. In over half of the animals (154) of this class the deciduous premolars had dropped out and the permanent premolars were in apposition. In 83 others the permanent premolars were still not in apposition. The almost unworn freshly erupted premolars or the thin caps remaining of the deciduous premolars on top of the partially erupted permanent premolars are most characteristic of this age class.

Twenty-six animals clearly of this age class because of the eruption pattern of their dentition show wear so that either the anterior or the posterior infundibulum on m1 have disappeared, and in one both infundibula are gone. Our established-age animals suggest that these infundibula are not usually lost until the fourth year of life.

Three and One-third Year Class

The status of the 136 hunter-killed animals assigned to this age class is summarized in Table 5.

In the period between 2⅓ and 3⅓ years of age, m1 receives less wear than at any other time during the life of this tooth, but the premolars and m3 become conspicuously worn during this period (Fig. 4, A and B).

Over half of the animals judged to be 3⅓ years old have all of the permanent incisiform teeth. Most of the rest have either the deciduous canine present (Fig.

TABLE 4.—STATUS OF DENTITION OF 244 HUNTER-KILLED ANTELOPE ASSIGNED TO THE 2⅓-YEAR-OLD CLASS

Incisiform Teeth	Number of Animals	Molariform Teeth	Premolars m1 m2 m3	Number of animals
Pi1, 2, Di3, Dc1	161	Pp2[1], 3, 4, in place with slight wear	PP PP PPP	131
Pi1, 2, Pi3 erupting, Dc1	35	Same except	AP PP PPP	22
Pi1, Pi2 erupting, Di3, Dc1	24	Same except	AA PP PPP	1
Pi1, 2, 3, Dc1	13	Pp2, 3, 4 erupting	PP PP PPP	79
Pi1, Di2, 3, and Dc1	6	Pp2, 3, 4 erupting	PA PP PPP	4
Pi1, 2, Pi3 on one side, Di3 erupting on other side; Pc1 on one side, Dc1 on other side	3	Dp4, Pp2, 3		3
		Pp2 missing		2
Pi1, 2, Pi3 erupting on one side, Di3 on other side, Dc1	1	No rear teeth on specimen		2
No front teeth on specimen	1			
	244			244

[1] Where only one set of symbols is shown the 2 sides of the jaw were alike or only one was available.

TABLE 5.—STATUS OF DENTITION OF 136 HUNTER-KILLED ANTELOPE ASSIGNED TO THE 3⅓-YEAR-OLD CLASS

Incisiform Teeth	Number of Animals	Pp2	Pp3	Pp4	m1	m2	m3	Number of Animals
Pil, 2, 3, Pc1	75							
Pil, 2, 3, Dc1	44	P	P	PPP	PP	PP	PPP	73
		P	P	PPP	PP	PP	PPP	
		P	P	PPP	AP	PP	PPP	46
		P	P	PPP	AP	PP	PPP	
Pil, 2, 3, Pc1 erupting	11	P	P	PPP	AA	PP	PPP	7
		P	P	PPP	AP	PP	PPP	
		P	P	PPP	AP	PP	PPP	9
Pil, 2, 3, Dc1 on one side, Pc1 erupting on other side	3	P	P	PPP	PP	PP	PPP	
		P	P	PPP	X	PP	PPP	1
Pil, 2, Pi3 erupting, Dc1	3							136
136								

1, E) or the permanent canine erupting. The molariform teeth must be studied in order to recognize animals in this class. The premolars all show some wear, but Pp3 and 4 are more heavily worn than is Pp2. Over half of the animals in this class still show all 12 of the infundibula but about one-third have worn out the anterior infundibulum of m1. The smaller number of jaws classified as 3⅓-year-olds as compared to the numbers judged to be 2⅓-and 4⅓-year-olds suggests that some may have been misclassified. Probably in some 3⅓-year-olds, both infundibula on m1 are gone and such animals were aged as 4⅓-year-olds. Weather records (U. S. Dept. Commerce, 1948) for 1948 do not suggest that weather conditions, during or after the period when the 3-year-old animals were born, were extreme enough to have caused unusual mortality.

Four and One-third Year Class

The status of the dentition of the hunter-killed animals is summarized in Table 6.

TABLE 6.—STATUS OF DENTITION OF 148 HUNTER-KILLED ANTELOPE ASSIGNED TO THE 4⅓-YEAR-OLD CLASS

Incisiform Teeth	Number of Animals	Pp2	Pp3	Pp4	m1	m2	m3	Number of Animals
Pil, 2, 3, Pc1	121							
		P	P	PPP	AA	PP	PPP	77
		P	P	PPP	AA	PP	PPP	
Pil, 2, 3, Pc1 erupting	5	P	P	PPP	AA	PP	PPA	51
		P	P	PPP	AA	PP	PPA	
Pil, 2, 3, Dc1	16	Other combinations involving loss of 3 infundibula						16
Pil, 2, 3 (One side Dc1, other side Pc1 erupting)	4	Cheek teeth incomplete						4
No front teeth in specimen	2							148
148								

TABLE 7.—STATUS OF DENTITION OF 51 HUNTER-KILLED ANTELOPE ASSIGNED TO THE
5⅓-YEAR-OLD CLASS

Incisiform Teeth	Number of Animals	Molariform Teeth						Number of Animals
		Pp2	Pp3	Pp4	m1	m2	m3	
Pi1, 2, 3, Pc1 _____ 50								
Pi1, 2, 3, Dc1 _____ 1								
	51	P	P	PPP	AA	AP	PPA	9
		P	P	PPA	AA	AP	PPA	4
		P	P	PPP	AA	AA	PPA	4
		P	P	PPA	AA	PP	PPA	4
		P	P	PAA	AA	PP	PPA	2
		P	A	PPA	AA	PP	PPA	2
		P	A	PAA	AA	PP	PPP	2
		X	P	PPP	AA	AP	PPA	2
		22 other combinations each occurring only once in which the infundibula were different on the two sides ____						22
								51

The proposal that in 4⅓-year-old antelope either 2 or 3 infundibula have disappeared from the molariform teeth seems to be reasonable in the light of the findings from the aged animals together with the findings of this sample of 148 hunter-killed animals with this level of wear. Because this sample is larger than the hunter-killed sample of 3⅓-year-olds, it appears that some 3⅓-year-old animals have been classed with the 4⅓-year-olds.

Since the majority of antelope have replaced Dc1 by the time they have reached the 3⅓-year age class, it was felt that perhaps those animals estimated to be 4⅓-year-olds from the cheek teeth that had Dc1 still present were actually 3⅓-year-olds. There were 20 animals with either 1 or both Dc1 still present, and these jaws were separated from the others. Six animals had 3 infundibula missing and 14 had 2 infundibula gone; thus, these animals showed about the same amount of tooth wear as other animals classed as 4⅓-year-olds. It seems more likely to us that a delay of 1 year in the shedding of Dc1 occurred in these 20 animals rather than the molariform teeth of 3⅓-year-olds being worn to the point where the rear infundibula of m3 had been lost. This is substantiated by the fact that one of the established-age 4⅓-year-olds has Pc1 only partially erupted. The incisiform teeth of a hunter-

killed animal judged to be 4⅓ years old is shown in Figure 1, F.

Five and One-third Year Class

Animals placed in this class are ones with molariform teeth that have lost 4 or 5 infundibula. The status of the tooth wear of the 51 animals classed in this group is summarized in Table 7.

The 1 animal assigned to this class with Dc1 still present was carefully checked. It may, of course, represent a 4⅓-year-old with more than usual wear on the molariform teeth.

We see in the 5⅓-year class clear evidence that some older animals tend to wear the premolars more heavily than the molars and some do the reverse; for example, 2 animals have lost 3 infundibula on the premolars and only 2 on the molars, while 4 animals have lost 5 infundibula on the molars and none on the premolars, and yet both groups have about the same total amount of wear on the cheek teeth.

Six and One-third Year Class

Thirty-three hunter-killed animals that had lost 6 or 7 infundibula were placed in this class. The known-age animal had lost 7 infundibula from each jaw. Three animals had lost Pp2. All animals show all of the permanent incisiform teeth, but 26 combinations of infundibula are present in the

33 animals placed in this class. The posterior infundibulum of m3 is gone from all 33 animals and both infundibula on m2 are gone from at least 1 jaw in 18 animals. Only 7 have the infundibulum remaining on Pp3, but the pattern of loss of infundibula on Pp4 is extremely variable.

Six-plus Year Class (animals older than 6⅓ years)

Eighty-three animals show 4 infundibula or less remaining and are classed as over 6⅓ years old. Twenty-seven have all 12 infundibula worn away. These 27 animals are probably over 9 years old. Fourteen animals have lost Pp2; five of them have also lost Pp3, and five have lost Pp4. One animal has only m2 and m3 left in the jaw.

Generally if only 1 infundibulum remains in the jaw it is the middle one on m3; if 2 remain they are usually the anterior and the middle ones on m3; if 3 remain they usually include these latter 2 plus 1 on the premolars. Hoover, *et al.* (1959) describe the jaw of a 9-year-old antelope, their only specimen more than 3 years old. This 9-year-old, as illustrated, shows only the infundibulum on Pp2 remaining.

The appearance of the incisiform teeth of a hunter-killed animal assigned to the 6-plus class is shown in Figure 1, G. A radiogram of a hunter-killed 6-plus-class animal is shown in Figure 3, J. This animal shows no infundibula remaining in the teeth. The total height of each of the teeth is much less than in the 6⅓-year class. Distinct roots do not show on any of the teeth.

HYPOTHETICAL POPULATION STRUCTURE

A tentative life table based on estimated age composition of the hunter-killed sample was constructed by Howard Reinhardt. The assumption was made that the statewide antelope population was increasing at a constant rate prior to the 1951 hunting season, which is confirmed generally by census figures of the Montana Fish and Game Department.

Beyond the selection of adult antelopes over fawns, there was little evidence of

TABLE 8.—PREDICTED AND OBSERVED DISTRIBUTION OF HUNTER-KILLED ANTELOPE FROM 1⅓ TO 6⅓ YEARS OLD

	Age in Years					
	1⅓	2⅓	3⅓	4⅓	5⅓	6⅓
Number predicted	415	253	154	94	57	35
Number observed	402	244	136	148	51	33

selection of either sex or any particular age class. Although hunters were requested to indicate the sex of antelope killed, in many cases this information was not provided, and there was reason to believe that some hunters were reluctant to admit that they had killed does. Since it is impossible to distinguish the sex of antelope from examination of the mandible, both sexes were considered together. It was assumed that all ages beyond the fawn class were equally vulnerable to hunters.

A comparison between the assigned number of antelope in the hunter-killed sample and the predicted distribution is shown in Table 8.

The agreement for classes 1⅓, 2⅓, 5⅓, and 6⅓ is surprisingly good according to the χ^2 test, but the discrepancy for the 3⅓- and 4⅓-year classes is too great to be attributable to chance according to the χ^2 test. Either the population has not been increasing at a constant rate during this period or there are errors in assignment of hunter-killed animals to these age classes. The latter seems to be more probable.

If one assumes that there has been a constant increase and that all animals reported as 3⅓- or 4⅓-year-olds do in fact belong in one or the other of these classes, a "minimum χ^2" prediction of the numbers in these classes, using the regressions of Table 8, an estimate of 177 three and one-third-year-olds and 104 four and one-third-year-olds results, and the agreement as judged by the χ^2 test is satisfactory. This would mean that about 40 animals estimated to have been 4⅓-year-olds are in fact 3⅓-year-olds. It is recognized that the assumptions made in this connection may not be valid and some of the animals aged as 4⅓-year-olds probably are actually 5⅓-year-olds.

If one attempts to extend the regression as summarized in Table 8 to the animals beyond the 6⅓-year-old age class, a prediction of 51 six-plus animals is obtained, whereas 83 hunter-killed animals were classified as belonging in the 6-plus class. The most likely suggestion here seems that a lower rate of mortality prevailed in these older animals prior to 1944. They were born in that year or earlier.

Certainly this deduction is reasonable from the standpoint of legal kill by hunters as judged by the number of hunter permits issued by the Montana Fish and Game Department. The permits increased from 1943 to 1951 with the number issued for the respective years as follows: 750, 650, 1,575, 2,424, 2,854, 2,652, 3,932, 8,345, and 9,272.

In 1943 and 1944, when antelope hunting was first reinstituted in Montana, all hunting was confined to 2 areas in the southeastern portion of the state. In 1945 the hunting areas were extended to cover a fairly large portion of the state's antelope range. From 1946 to 1950, the changes in the hunter kill were largely those of increased quotas in the permit areas rather than opening additional areas.

Since the younger aged animals lost infundibula at about the rate of 2 each year from 3⅓ years to 6⅓ years, an objective way of classifying those 83 specimens of the 6-plus class would be to predict that the rate of wear would continue into old age. When this is done the distribution shown in Table 9 results.

This distribution of animals in each category is not consistent with that seen in the younger age classes and therefore suggests that this measure of rate of wear may not be uniform in the older age classes. This is further indicated by the appearance of the 9-year-old known-age specimen with 1 infundibulum reported by Hoover, *et al.* (1959). It is likely that more than one age group is represented by each of the latter classes; that is, those with 0, 1, or 2 infundibula. Since it is not known whether or not any sizable portion of the population died from malnutrition actually resulting from wearing out the teeth, as occurs in

TABLE 9.—DISTRIBUTION OF HUNTER-KILLED ANIMALS ESTIMATED TO BE 7-, 8-, AND 9-YEAR-OLDS ON THE BASIS THAT ANTELOPE CONTINUE TO LOSE INFUNDIBULA AT THE RATE OF 2 PER YEAR

Estimated 7-year-olds with 3 or 4 infundibula	19
Estimated 8-year-olds with 1 or 2 infundibula	37
Estimated 9-year-olds with no infundibula	27
	83

domestic sheep (Murie, 1944), or from other factors associated with old age, further refinement cannot be made with the data at hand. It seems safe to conclude, however, that the number of 6-plus-class animals harvested by hunters in 1951 was higher than would be expected from a population increasing uniformly for all years prior to 1951. It also appears that a small number of the hunter-killed animals was more than 10 years of age.

While the statistical analysis of the distribution of assigned age classes tends to suggest that age classification of antelope can be fairly accurately undertaken up through the 6⅓-year age-class, it should be remembered that only 5 known-age animals beyond 3½ years of age are available (2, 4⅓; 1, 5⅓; 1, 6⅓; and 1, 9); and we do not know the range of variation that would prevail in a large sample of known-age animals in these older age classes. We do not know that other jaws exist of known-age antelope in the older age classes. Actually, in a well-managed antelope population very few animals would exist in the age classes beyond 6⅓ years.

SUMMARY

A series of known-age and established-age pronghorns was allowed to range freely on the National Bison Range, Moiese, Montana. Periodically, animals were shot to obtain the data that were used to establish criteria for determining age in wild antelope. The mandibular dentition of 20 known- or established-age animals ranging from 44 days to 6⅓ years is described. A series of over 1,300 jaws obtained from Montana hunters during the 1951 season supplemented the known-age series.

The incisor and canine teeth are all deciduous in fawn antelope killed during September or October. In yearling antelope 1 permanent pair of incisors is generally present. In 2-year-olds, 2 pairs of permanent incisors are usually present. Three-year-olds and older animals cannot be aged by their incisiform teeth because of great variation in the time of eruption of the incisiform canine.

The deciduous premolars are not shed until about 2⅓ years. The permanent premolars and the molars are hypsodont with long crowns and either no roots at all or roots that develop after several years. Twelve infundibula are visible in the jaws of 2⅓-year-old animals and over half of 3½-year-olds. The infundibula are gradually lost by wear on the teeth at the rate of about 2 per year. Animals with no infundibula remaining in the teeth are estimated to be 9 or more years of age.

A statistical analysis of the hunter-killed sample was made with the assumption that Montana antelope were increasing at a constant rate prior to the time of sampling in 1951. The distribution of assigned ages fits this assumption well except for 2 year classes. Apparently about one-third of the animals estimated to be 4⅓ years old were only 3⅓ years old. The 6-plus age-class is present in greater numbers than would be expected, and this may reflect the fact that prior to 1943 none of the Montana antelope population was legally hunted. More known-age animals are needed to show the range of variation of middle-age animals and to determine the limit of longevity for the species.

REFERENCES CITED

COUTURIER, M. A. J. 1938. Le Chamois. Grenoble, France. 1–11, 1–857. (2 volumes)

DOW, S. A., JR. 1952a. An evaluation of some criteria for age determination of the pronghorn (*Antilocapra americana* Ord). Unpubl. master's thesis, Montana State University, Missoula. 1–71.

————. 1952b. Antelope ageing studies in Montana. Special Report No. 3, Montana Coop. Wildl. Res. Unit. 1–7. (mimeographed).

————. 1954. Anatomical specimen collection by prepaid postal envelope. Proc. 8th Ann. Conf. Southeast Assn. of Game and Fish Comms. Pp. 120–121.

HOOVER, R. L., C. E. TILL, AND S. OGLIVIE. 1959. The antelope of Colorado. Tech. Bull. No. 4, Department of Game and Fish, State of Colorado. 1–110.

MASON, E. 1947. Oregon antelope. Oregon State Game Comm. Bull., 2(6):1, 4, and 7.

MURIE, A. 1944. The wolves of Mount McKinley. Fauna of the National Parks of the United States, Faunal Series No. 5, 1–19:1–238.

RINEY, T. 1951. Standard terminology for deer teeth. J. Wildl. Mgmt., 15(1):99–101.

SEVERINGHAUS, C. W. 1949. Tooth development and wear as criteria of age in white-tailed deer. J. Wildl. Mgmt., 13(2):195–216.

SISSON, S. AND J. D. GROSSMANN. 1953. The anatomy of domestic animals. 4th ed. W. B. Saunders, Philadelphia. 1–972.

U. S. DEPARTMENT OF COMMERCE, WEATHER BUREAU. Climatological data. Montana Section. 1948. 51(5):40–44; (6): 69–75; (7): 102–106.

Received for publication May 27, 1961.

MINIMUM BREEDING AGE IN PRONGHORN ANTELOPE

Philip L. Wright and Sumner A. Dow, Jr.

Department of Zoology, Montana State University, Missoula, Montana;
and Tennessee Game and Fish Commission, Nashville, Tennessee

Mason (1947), Einarsen (1948), and Hoover, et al. (1959) have indicated that female antelope (*Antilocapra americana*) mate for the first time in September of their second year of life and thus give birth to their first fawns at the age of 2 years. No evidence for the minimum breeding age of males is presented by any of these authors.

During the course of investigations of antelope aging reported elsewhere in this journal (Dow and Wright, 1962), information was obtained on minimum breeding age in both sexes. From a herd of free-ranging antelope on the National Bison Range, Moiese, Montana, a number were shot that gave evidence of the time of first breeding. Pertinent data on these animals are summarized in Table 1.

These animals were either known-age animals or were aged according to criteria presented in the other paper (Dow and Wright, 1962). Seven of these animals apparently did not become pregnant as fawns. One, No. E-8, killed at 8 months of age would have been visibly pregnant if it were to produce fawns at the age of 1 year. Six others, Nos. E-12, E-11, E-13, E-15, 54–101, and 54–107, were not lactating nor did they show udders that had been suckled when they were killed in August, September, October, November, or February of their second year of life. Evidence from the above animals agrees with the evidence presented by previous authors.

Yearling animal No. 55-101, however, was accompanied by two fawns when it was shot, and

TABLE 1.—STATUS OF UTERI AND UDDERS OF FEMALE PRONGHORN KILLED ON NATIONAL BISON RANGE

Animal No.	Age	Date Shot	Condition of Uterus	Condition of Udder
E-8	8 months	Feb. 10, 1952	Not visibly pregnant	Dry
E-12	14 months	Aug. 16, 1951	Not visibly pregnant	Dry
E-11	1⅓ years	Sept. 20, 1951	Not visibly pregnant	Dry
E-13	1⅓ years	Nov. 27, 1951	Pregnant (2 embryos)	Dry
E-15	1⅔ years	Feb. 10, 1952	Pregnant (2 embryos)	Dry
54-100	2⅓ years	Sept. 9, 1954	Not visibly pregnant	Lactating
54-101	1⅓ years	Sept. 9, 1954	Not visibly pregnant	Dry
54-107	1⅓ years	Oct. 28, 1954	Pregnant (2 embryos)	Dry
55-101	1⅓ years	Sept. 21, 1955	Not visibly pregnant	Lactating

the presence of abundant milk in the udder made it clear that this animal was the mother of these fawns. This animal must have been impregnated while still a fawn and given birth to young at the age of about 1 year rather than at the usual age of 2 years. Her fawns were apparently born a month or so later than the usual birth date of fawns, June 1 or earlier, because this doe was seen traveling alone as late as July 11, and fawns of this species usually begin to accompany the mother about 2 weeks after birth.

Since they were pregnant when collected, 3 of the above yearling females, Nos. E-13, 54-107, and E-15, would have produced their first fawns at the age of 2 years had they not been shot. This appears to be the usual situation as described by previous authors. Two others, No. E-11 and No. 54-101, were killed during or within a few days after the breeding season so that visible embryos would not have been found even if the animals had already been impregnated. Thus, the evidence from these animals is simply that they did not produce fawns at the age of 1 year.

The data from No. 54-100 show that this animal produced young at the age of 2 years as evidenced by the presence of an abundant milk supply. We do not know whether or not it might have produced young at the age of 1 year.

We have not had the opportunity to investigate the extent to which breeding in female antelope fawns may occur generally. If the problem were

to be studied by utilizing hunter-killed animals in areas where hunting of either sex of the species is permitted, it could be best approached by determining the status of the udder in yearling females. Antelope hunting seasons are generally too early in the fall for developing embryos to have reached a stage where they can be readily recognized.

During the 1952 breeding season, there were no male antelope on the Bison Range older than 1⅓ years. In the spring of 1953, several does that were present during the breeding season in 1952 produced fawns, clearly showing that yearling male antelope are capable of impregnating females. Only 1 male fawn has been taken during the breeding season, and its testes were infantile in size and clearly not in breeding condition.

REFERENCES CITED

Dow, S. A., Jr. and P. L. Wright. 1962. Changes in mandibular dentition associated with age in Pronghorn Antelope. J. Wildl. Mgmt., 26:1–18.

Einarsen, A. S. 1948. The pronghorn antelope and its management. The Wildlife Management Institute, Washington, D. C. 238pp.

Hoover, R. L., C. E. Till, and S. Ogilvie. 1959. The antelope of Colorado. Tech. Bull. No. 4, Department of Game and Fish, State of Colorado. 1–110.

Mason, E. 1947. Oregon antelope. Oregon State Game Commission Bulletin 2(6):1, 4, and 7.

Received for publication May 27, 1961.

GROWTH OF THE LENS OF THE PRONGHORN ANTELOPE

George Ben Kolenosky[1] *and Richard S. Miller*

University of Saskatchewan, Saskatoon, Saskatchewan, Canada

A structure in mammals that grows continually throughout life but has only recently been studied with respect to its applicability as an indicator of age is the lens of the eye. Lord (1959, 1961) found that the lens serves as a reliable age indicator in cottontail rabbits (*Sylvilagus floridanus*) and gray fox (*Urocyon cinereoargenteus floridanus*). The purpose of the present study is to describe the rate of growth of the lens of the eye in pronghorn antelope (*Antilocapra americana*) and to establish, within the limitations of the data available, an age index for this species based on lens growth and size.

We would like to express our appreciation to P. L. Wright who aged the samples of jaws and advised on the use of dental characters for determining the age of antelope. This research was supported by a bursary from the National Research Council of Canada.

METHODS AND MATERIALS

A total of 92 adult antelope and 13 fetuses were collected in the Province of Saskatchewan from October 1960 to May 1961. The largest sample (69 specimens) was obtained during the hunting season in November 1960 at check stations located at Maple Creek, Shaunavon, Val Marie, Leader, and Mankota. An estimated age was assigned to each specimen on the basis of tooth eruption, development, and wear, as outlined by Dow (1952). Radiograms of the lower jaws were used to supplement the classification that was made on the basis of external dentition. The ages shown are based on an assumed mean birth date of June 1.

Each intact eye was injected with 10 per cent formalin as soon after the death of the animal as possible. The injection was made with a number 18 needle and plastic syringe near the edge of the eye, to avoid striking the lens, and enough formalin was injected to make the eye turgid. During winter months when air temperatures were near –20°F, the formalin solution was liable to freeze and split the lenses. Under these conditions a mixture of 30 per cent alcohol and 10 per cent formalin was used. The alcohol caused a slight but relatively insignificant decrease in the density of the lens.

The lenses were removed after they had become fixed, dried for 72 hours at 60°C, and weighed to the nearest 0.01 mg on a Mettler analytical balance. Lenses taken from fetuses required only about 24 hours for complete drying. The dried lenses were

weighed immediately after they were removed from the drying oven and, as they are hygroscopic, were dried again for 24 hours whenever they were reweighed.

RESULTS

The data for dry weights of the lenses are shown in Table 1. The mean difference in weight between the right and left lens of each specimen was 5.51 mg, or 1.1 per cent of the total mean weight. Although a difference between the 2 lenses almost invariably occurred, the heavier lens was not consistently the left or right. The left lens was the heavier in 54.7 per cent and the right was heavier in 45.3 per cent of 86 specimens.

A growth curve of the lens based on dry weights is shown in Figure 1. This curve suggests a division of lens growth into three phases: a period of extremely rapid growth with a straight line relationship between lens weight and age from 3 months after conception to 5 months after birth; a negative acceleration phase from the age of 5 months to 3½ years; and a steady but slower growth rate from the age of 3½ years to death.

A straight line relationship between lens weight and age (from the age of 5 months to 9½ years) is obtained by applying Huxley's differential growth

TABLE 1.—DRY WEIGHTS OF ANTELOPE LENSES

Age from Conception (months)	Number of Specimens	Mean Weight of Lens (mg)	Range
3	2	15.61	15.22–16.00
4	5	44.78	36.65–54.55
6	2	114.97	111.57–118.37
6.5	4	145.35	137.90–157.60
13	16	361.61	330.35–410.00
15	1	391.22	391.22
17	2	415.48	399.00–431.97
18.5	2	450.53	444.17–456.90
25	19	551.77	509.22–603.02
27	2	550.38	544.65–556.12
28	1	562.65	562.65
29	2	561.61	551.27–571.95
38	14	623.97	601.50–645.22
42.5	1	630.07	630.07
49	8	664.39	632.57–678.77
53	2	665.22	660.20–665.22
54	1	689.90	689.90
61	4	711.96	693.87–738.05
73	2	739.27	736.55–742.00
77	1	730.60	730.60
85	2	766.96	763.77–770.15
97	3	794.78	786.87–804.92
109	1	827.70	827.70
121+	1	857.50	857.50

---

[1] Present address: Department of Forestry and Wildlife Management, University of Wisconsin, Madison, Wisconsin.

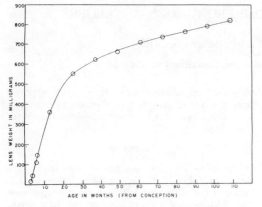

FIG. 1.   Growth curve of the lens of the antelope eye based on mean vales for each age class.

equation of $y = bx^k$ when $b = 237.1$ and $k = 0.275$. This equation may be expressed in the following forms:

$$W = 237.1\,M^{0.275} \qquad \text{or} \qquad M = \frac{W^{3.636}}{237.1}$$

where $M =$ age in months and $W =$ lens weight in milligrams.

The ages of specimens younger than 3½ years are relatively easy to determine, as differences in lens weight between the different age groups are large and the amount of overlap in lens weights between the age groups is small. The critical stage in age estimation is reached after 3½ years when the differences in lens weight between the age classes are considerably less, thus allowing a smaller margin for variability and overlap. The regression of weight on age, or Y on X, from 3½

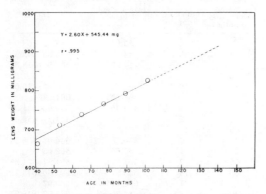

FIG. 2.   Regression of lens weight on age from the age of 3½ years.

years onward approximates a straight line, with a value (b) of 2.60 mg increase per month or 31.20 mg increase per year. The correlation value (r) of 0.995 is highly significant. The derived equation is:

$$Y = 2.60\,X + 545.44 \text{ mg}$$

where $X =$ estimated age in months.

This equation and the regression of lens weight on age are shown in Figure 2. Extension of the curve in Figure 2 allows one to estimate the expected lens weights for animals older than 8½ years.

Four of the specimens showed wide discrepancies between ages as calculated by the jaws and those determined by the lenses. In 3 of the 4 cases, dentition showed the specimens to be older than did the lens weight. It was felt that excessive tooth wear in these 3 older animals led to their ages being overestimated when using dentition as the age index. The single specimen where the reverse situation existed had abnormally long teeth with an uneven wear pattern, which probably accounted for its age being underestimated on the basis of dental criteria.

In the above 4 cases where wide discrepancies existed, radiograms showing the decrease in root length with an increase in age in the lower jaw were used to help verify the assigned ages. One radiogram supported the age as determined by the lens and 3 supported the ages as estimated by external dentition.

DISCUSSION

The data obtained during this study were based upon random samples of a natural population in which none of the ages of the animals was known. Thus, the lens measurements had to be correlated with estimates of age based upon dental characters and are subject to the same sources of error. However, it has been demonstrated that lens growth proceeds at a species-predictable rate in antelope, and the growth curves that have been established in this study can be verified when tagged specimens of known age are available.

REFERENCES CITED

Dow, S. A. 1955. An evaluation of some criteria for age determination of the pronghorn (*Antilocapra americana* Ord.). Unpublished master's thesis, Montana State Univ., Missoula.

Lord, R. D., Jr. 1959. The lens as an indicator of age in cottontail rabbits. J. Wildl. Mgmt., 23(3): 358–360.

————. 1961. The lens as an indicator of age in the gray fox. J. Mammal., 42(1):109–111.

Received for publication August 25, 1961.

SIEVE MESH SIZE RELATED TO ANALYSIS OF ANTELOPE RUMEN CONTENTS

Herman J. Dirschl[1]

Department of Biology, University of Saskatchewan, Saskatoon, Saskatchewan

The first step in quantitative botanical analysis of rumen contents consists of washing the material through a screen in order to separate small unidentifiable plant fragments from the larger identifiable ones. Size of the mesh used in this screening process determines the minimum particle size with which the investigator has to deal. Subsequent manual separation of the particles of various species remaining on the screen is tedious, and the time required for separation increases rapidly with decreasing particle size. The time necessary for quantitative separation of plant material can become an important consideration in the design of a study involving analysis of rumen contents. Therefore, if quantitative analysis could be restricted to relatively large plant fragments without loss of accuracy, more efficient use of rumen contents analysis could be made.

The present tests were attempted to determine whether the percentage composition of food species in antelope rumen contents differs significantly for fractions with different minimum particle sizes.

PROCEDURE

Quart samples of rumen contents were obtained from each of 14 antelope killed during the antelope season in November 1960. Qualitative examination showed the samples to contain representatives of the various types of plants consumed by pronghorns in Saskatchewan (Dirschl, H. J. 1961. Food habits and range of the pronghorn antelope in Saskatchewan. Unpublished master's thesis, University of Sask., Saskatoon, Sask. 72pp.). There also appeared to be a wide range in the proportions of various species in the samples.

In the laboratory, each rumen sample was individually washed through a gang of three screens of the following mesh sizes:

(1) 5.66 mm (U. S. Standard Sieve Series Mesh No. 3½)

(2) 4.00 mm (U. S. Standard No. 5)

(3) 2.83 mm (U. S. Standard No. 7).

Fractions remaining on each screen were placed in pans of water and identified by comparison with a reference plant collection. The various components were then separated by means of forceps and placed into pre-weighed petri dishes. Time required for the separation of identifiable plant material on each screen was recorded. The volume of each species present was determined by water replacement (after excess moisture was removed by rolling in paper towels). After drying for 24–30 hr at 60° C, the weight of each species was determined to 1 mg accuracy.

Volumes below 0.5 ml and weights of less than 1 per cent of the total were recorded as trace quantities. Plants present in trace amounts on a screen were added to the material on the succeeding screen. Weights found to be less than 1 per cent of the total of the oven-dried identified material from a screen were added to the weight of that species on the next smaller screen.

Assumptions underlying this approach are (1) that the time required to separate the plant fragments on all three screens would correspond with the time required when the small screen is used by itself; and (2) that the sum of the times required for large and medium sieves would be equivalent to that required for the medium sieve if it is used alone. This assumption is considered valid, since any worker would tend to remove the largest plant fragments first and gradually work down to the smallest particles present.

RESULTS

The mean composition of foods in the 14 samples was computed according to the aggregate percentage method (Martin, A. C., R. H. Gensch, and C. P. Brown. 1946. Alternative methods in upland gamebird food analysis. J. Wildl. Mgmt., 10[1]:8–12) for each of three mesh sizes tested (Table 1). It is apparent that there is very little difference in the mean compositions found by means of these meshes. Thus the choice of any of

---

[1] Present address: Wildlife Branch, Department of Natural Resources, Saskatoon, Saskatchewan, Canada.

Table 1.—Mean Composition of Foods Found in Samples from Contents of 14 Pronghorn Rumens According to Sieve Mesh Size

| Plant Material | Per Cent Composition | | | | |
| | Weight by Mesh Size | | | Volume by Mesh Size | |
	2.83 mm	4.00 mm	5.66 mm	4.00 mm	5.66 mm
Sagebrush (*Artemisia cana*)	59.3	59.8	59.8	61.3	61.1
Snowberry (*Symphoricarpos occidentalis*)	20.6	21.2	21.8	19.5	20.3
Wheat (*Triticum vulgare*) (heads)	13.7	12.5	11.3	11.1	10.5
Grasses (Gramineae)	2.9	3.0	3.4	4.1	3.7
Rabbitbrush (*Chrysothamnus nauseosus*)	1.5	1.5	1.6	1.9	2.0
Pasture sage (*Artemisia frigida*)	1.4	1.3	1.4	1.4	1.6
Prickly pear (*Opuntia polyacantha*)	0.5	0.5	0.5	0.6	0.7
Flax (*Linum usitatissimum*)	0.1	0.2	0.2	0.1	0.1
Total	100.0	100.0	100.0	100.0	100.0

these three mesh sizes for quantitative analysis of rumen contents does not affect the results to any extent. Aggregate percentages of food species by

Table 2.—Sieve Mesh Size and Time Required for Separation of Identifiable Plant Particles from Screened Quart Samples of 14 Antelope Rumen Contents

| Mesh Size (mm) | Time Required (minutes) | | |
	Mean	Standard Deviation	Range
2.83	54	32	23–110
4.00	38	21	19–70
5.66	25	13	11–50

volume and by weight agree closely, but examination of analyses of individual rumen samples indicated that the volumetric procedure produces slightly more variable results and tends to underestimate those species present in small quantities.

Use of the 5.66 mm mesh size results in considerable saving of time (Table 2). On the average, manual separation of identifiable plant material remaining on the 2.83 mm screen required more than twice as much time as separation of the material on the 5.66 mm mesh. Therefore, since no loss of accuracy occurs, the 5.66 mm mesh size is the most efficient of the three sizes tested in this study.

Received for publication November 30, 1961.

FOOD HABITS OF THE PRONGHORN IN SASKATCHEWAN

HERMAN J. DIRSCHL, Wildlife Branch, Department of Natural Resources, Saskatoon, Saskatchewan[1]

Abstract: Food habits of the pronghorn (*Antilocapra americana*) in the Matador and Cypress Hills regions of Saskatchewan were studied by analysis of the rumen contents of 49 specimens collected at monthly intervals over a full annual cycle, plus 42 rumen samples from animals killed during the 1960 hunting season. Grasses were found to predominate in April; forbs from May to July; deciduous browse, August to October; and evergreen browse, November to March. Cacti and grain crops were minor items. Pronghorns were dispersed throughout the available range during the growing season, while in the winter they were concentrated in areas where sagebrush (*Artemisia cana*) and creeping juniper (*Juniperus horizontalis*) grew, indicating that antelope distribution is correlated with food distribution and that the abundance of these two key food items on the winter range is a prime factor in the carrying capacity of range units. Chemical analyses made of food plants at intervals throughout the year revealed a positive correlation between their protein content and the degree to which they were utilized by pronghorns. Plants having the highest protein levels were the preferred foods in all seasons.

The prairies of western Canada form the northern limit of the distribution of the pronghorn (*Antilocapra americana*). In historical times, antelope ranged as far north as Prince Albert (Rand 1947) and eastward to the plains of southwestern Manitoba (Seton 1953:417). During the early part of this century, following settlement of the western plains, the pronghorn

population declined to a very low level, probably because of indiscriminate shooting, several extremely hard winters, and the destruction of much of the habitat by cultivation. In 1924, the antelope range in Saskatchewan consisted only of a small section in the southwestern part of the province (Nelson 1925).

Severe drought conditions during the late 1920's and the 1930's caused widespread abandonment of farms and a gradual return of large sections of cultivated land to native grass cover. The antelope

---

[1] Present address: Canadian Wildlife Service, University of Saskatchewan, Saskatoon, Saskatchewan.

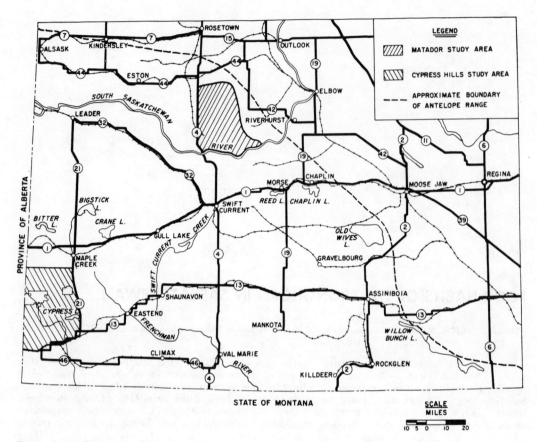

Fig. 1. Geographic location of the two study areas and present pronghorn range in Saskatchewan.

herds responded to the more favorable conditions with a steady increase in numbers. The area of distribution also increased considerably but currently represents less than half of the original range.

Hunting pressure on the pronghorn population has been steadily growing. The number of antelope licenses issued in Saskatchewan in 1940 was 432; by 1960 the number had reached 4,284 (Anon. 1941, 1961). While the antelope population seems to have remained relatively stable during the past 4 years and is estimated at 10,000–12,000 animals, the annual harvest has fluctuated between 2,200 and 3,500 (Nelson 1961). The available data suggest that the pronghorn population in Saskatch-

ewan is now being utilized at or near its maximum and that more intensive harvest management is an imminent requirement. In order to achieve maximum utilization of the antelope resource on a long-term basis, hunting pressure will have to be manipulated to maintain the posthunting season population near the carrying capacity of the winter range. As the carrying capacity of the range is in part governed by food preferences, nutritional requirements, and food availability particularly during the critical winter season, knowledge of the food habits of the pronghorn in Saskatchewan is a prerequisite to effective management.

The objectives of the present study were

Fig. 2. Topography and vegetation of the pronghorn winter habitat in the Matador study area.

(1) to determine the major food plants consumed by pronghorns in Saskatchewan during a full annual cycle and (2) to ascertain the quantitative protein content of important food plants at various times of the year.

Research was carried out under the supervision of Dr. R. S. Miller, Associate Professor, Department of Biology, University of Saskatchewan, to whom I wish to express my sincere gratitude. Appreciation is due T. A. Harper, Assistant Director, Wildlife Branch, Saskatchewan Department of Natural Resources, for his constant encouragement. I am further indebted to Dr. R. T. Coupland, Department of Plant Ecology, and Dr. J. M. Bell, Department of Animal Husbandry, University of Saskatchewan, for their advice and assistance. Finally, I wish to thank W. Davis, graduate student, Department of Biology, Uni-

versity of Saskatchewan, and all others who assisted in the field work.

This study was supported by a Wildlife Management Fellowship from Canadian Industries Limited.

STUDY AREAS

The food habits of the pronghorn in Saskatchewan were studied in two representative parts of the range in order to observe regional differences in the diet and to have a broader basis for generalization. Locations selected were the Matador region and the Cypress Hills region (Fig. 1).

The Matador region was chosen because it is near the northern limit of pronghorn distribution and has distinct summer and winter ranges.

The Cypress Hills region was selected because is has a fairly high pronghorn

Fig. 3. Upland plateau in the Cypress Hills study area. Note the dissected character of the area.

abundance. The highly diversified vegetation of the region offers the pronghorn greater choice in food selection.

The Matador Study Area

Two distinct range types are found in this area. From the banks of the South Saskatchewan River northward, the eroded slopes of the river breaks form a band of rough, strongly rolling terrain, up to several miles wide (Fig. 2). Sagebrush (*Artemisia cana*) is abundant on the lower slopes and coulee bottoms. Rose (*Rosa* sp.) and western snowberry (*Symphoricarpos occidentalis*) appear only in moist locations. Pasture sage (*Artemisia frigida*), moss phlox (*Phlox hoodii*), and broomweed (*Gutierrezia diversifolia*) are common. Prickly pear (*Opuntia polyacantha*) is frequent in arid locations. Steep upper

slopes are often dominated by creeping juniper (*Juniperus horizontalis*).

The land north of the river breaks forms part of the Missouri Coteau and is mainly moderately rolling. Soils of loam texture predominate over sandy soils (Mitchell et al. 1947). The vegetational aspect is mixed prairie (Coupland 1950). Pasture sage, moss phlox, broomweed, and crocus anemone (*Anemone patens* var. *wolfgangiana*) are the principal forbs. Rose is frequent on the exposed upper slopes. Western snowberry is abundant on the sheltered lower slopes and surrounds the many potholes. Sagebrush and creeping juniper are rare. Wheat (*Triticum aestivum*) and flax (*Linum usitatissimum*) are the predominant crops on the few cultivated acreages in the study area.

The climate of the region is characterized by great extremes in temperature be-

Fig. 4. Rolling topography at the lower elevations of the Cypress Hills study area. Note the scattered clumps of sagebrush on the upland and the abundance of western snowberry along the intermittent stream bed.

tween summer and winter seasons and by low precipitation. Mean annual maximum and minimum temperatures are 90 and –30 F, respectively. Total yearly precipitation averages 14 inches; annual snowfall is approximately 40 inches (Anon. 1957). The elevation ranges from 1,800 to 2,500 feet above sea level.

Antelope are dispersed throughout the Matador region in summer but few are found in the eroded breaks. Estimates of population density for July of 1960 and 1961 are 0.34 and 0.54 antelope per square mile, respectively (Dirschl 1961). The winter range in this region is the eroded breaks area, particularly the less steep sections.

The Cypress Hills Study Area

The Cypress Hills are eroded bench-lands, consisting of elevated plateaus dissected by valleys and coulees (Fig. 3). Level to gently rolling plateau areas occur on the higher elevations (Mitchell et al. 1947). Moderately rolling topography occurs on the lower elevations (Fig. 4). Soils have not been studied in detail because of the inaccessibility of the region. Soils of valley slopes usually have eroded profiles. Alluvium covers valley and coulee bottoms.

The vegetative aspect of the upland plateaus is submontane prairie in which rough fescue (*Festuca scabrella*) is the dominant grass. The forb and shrub vegetation is similar to that of the uplands of the Matador study area. Sagebrush is abundant on sandy terrain, steep arid slopes, and alluvial deposits. Creeping juniper is uncommon. On upper north-facing slopes and sheltered plateau areas, greater rainfall has resulted in forest growth. Lodgepole pine (*Pinus contorta* var. *latifolia*) and trembling aspen (*Populus tremuloides*) are the dominant trees. Shrubby cinquefoil (*Potentilla fruticosa*) dominates moderately steep slopes below the forest zone. The most common of the numerous forbs present are crocus anemone, cinquefoils (*Potentilla* spp.), and prairie sage (*Artemisia gnaphalodes*). Only a small acreage of the Cypress Hills region is under cultivation. Wheat is the main agricultural crop. Forage crops, particularly alfalfa (*Medicago sativa*), are grown on a few small irrigated areas adjacent to the lower slopes.

The elevation of the study area is 2,500 to 4,400 feet above sea level. The climate is similar to that of the Matador region. Total annual precipitation ranges from 12 inches in the southern portion of the area to 16 inches on the higher elevations (Anon. 1957).

In summer, antelope are abundant on the open slopes and the rolling areas but less numerous on the high level plateaus. Population densities for July of 1960 and 1961 were estimated as 0.82 and 0.70 antelope per square mile, respectively (Dirschl 1961). Part of the herd winters in sandy terrain north of the Cypress Hills range; other antelope remain on the eroded slopes and alluvial flats of the streams flowing south into the Milk River. The majority, however, are thought to winter along the Milk River drainage system in northern Montana.

METHODS AND PROCEDURE

Analysis of rumen contents was the method used in this investigation. Reasons for choosing this method were:

(1) The open physiography of most of the Saskatchewan pronghorn habitat makes it difficult to approach the animals closely enough to identify the plants consumed, nor is it often possible to pinpoint the exact feeding sites.

(2) The low density of the pronghorn population and the extensive use of the pronghorn range by cattle render plant utilization plots impractical.

Because this study required recognition of only the major food species and of the general pattern of seasonal changes in food habits, it was decided to take a monthly sample of two or three pronghorns from each study area over a full annual cycle. In spite of travel difficulties during the fall and winter of 1960–61, the sampling schedule was adhered to except in the following instances: In the Matador area, only one specimen was taken for each of the months of September, February, and May; and in the Cypress Hills area, no specimens were obtained during January. Twenty-eight pronghorns were collected from the Cypress Hills area and 21 from the Matador area. Additional samples of rumen contents were obtained from 42 pronghorns killed during the hunting season (October 31–November 5, 1960) in various parts of the range exclusive of the two study areas. This group of samples was treated separately and served as a check on the applicability of the data to the Saskatchewan pronghorn range as a whole.

The analytical technique used was similar to that of Cole and Wilkins (1958). Quart samples of rumen contents were preserved, in the field, in a 10 percent solution of formalin. In the laboratory, the samples were washed on a 5.66-millimeter screen (U. S. standard mesh size No. 3½). Material remaining on the screen was placed in a white enamel pan filled with water. Food plants were identified by means of a reference plant collection. Identified particles were separated with

Table 1. Diet of the pronghorn as determined by analysis of rumen contents.

SPECIES	PERCENT OF DIET BY WEIGHT							
	Spring		Summer		Fall		Winter	
	Cypress Hills	Matador	Cypress Hills	Matador	Cypress Hills	Matador	Cypress Hills	Matador
Artemisia cana—Sagebrush	10 (36)*	41 (22)	20 (1)		17 (1)	10 (tr.)†	85 (36)	30 (22)
Juniperus horizontalis—Creeping juniper		25 (51)			1 (0)			45 (51)
Evergreen browse total	10	66	20	0	18	10	85	75
Symphoricarpos occidentalis—Western snowberry	1 (0)		7 (1)	34 (2)	36 (1)	74 (2)		8 (9)
Rosa sp.—Rose			11 (6)	11 (8)	1 (6)	3 (8)		
Prunus virginiana—Chokecherry			2 (0)					
Deciduous browse total	1	0	20	45	37	77	0	8
Antennaria sp.—Everlasting								2 (4)
Artemisia frigida—Pasture sage	11 (76)	13 (56)	3 (86)		7 (86)		7 (76)	4 (56)
Aster spp.—Aster			1 (6)		12 (6)	2 (0)		2 (3)
Vernal forbs (unidentified)		13						
Anemone patens—Crocus anemone			3 (11)	26 (17)	2 (1)	6 (17)		
Cerastium arvense—Field chickweed			3 (0)					
Chenopodiaceae (unclassified)			2 (2)					
Comandra pallida—Bastard toadflax			6 (0)	5 (tr.)				
Erigeron sp.—Fleabane			10 (0)					
Liatris punctata—Purple blazing-star			2 (3)	1 (tr.)				
Medicago sativa—Alfalfa			10 (0)					
Musineon divaricatum—Musineon			1 (0)					
Phlox hoodii—Moss phlox			1 (35)					
Plantago sp.—Plantain				1 (2)				
Polygonum convulvus—Wild buckwheat			3 (0)	2 (0)				
Potentilla sp.—Cinquefoils			1 (1)					
Senecio sp.—Groundsel			3 (0)					
Solidago sp.—Goldenrod			5 (0)	12 (2)	8 (tr.)	1		
Tragopon dubius—Yellow goatsbeard			4 (tr.)					
Zizia sp.—Alexanders			2 (0)					
Astragalus sp.—Milk-vetch						3		
Petalostemon purpureus—Purple prairie clover					13 (0)			
Forbs total	11	26	55	52	42	12	7	8
Grass total	78 (98)	8 (80)	5 (100)	1 (100)	2 (100)	1 (100)	1 (98)	0 (80)
Cacti total	0 (3)	0 (17)	0 (0)	0 (tr.)	0 (0)	0 (tr.)	7 (3)	5 (17)
Wheat				2 (0)	2 (0)			2 (0)
Flax								2 (0)
Cultivated crops total	0	0	0	2	2	0	0	4
Total	100	100	100	100	100	100	100	100

* Figures in parentheses are percentage frequency of occurrence of plants determined with ½-square meter quadrats.
† Less than 1 percent frequency.

forceps, placed in Petri dishes, and dried at 60 C for 30 hours. The composition of dried samples was calculated in terms of percent by weight to 1 percent accuracy. Items of less than 1 percent were recorded as traces.

Choice of mesh size and determination of percent by weight rather than volume resulted from a preliminary investigation of the accuracy and efficiency of the technique employed (Dirschl 1962).

The abundance of antelope food plants was investigated by determining the percentage frequency of occurrence in ½-square meter quadrats. Sampling was carried out in randomly located sites within the range type in which pronghorn specimens were collected during that season.

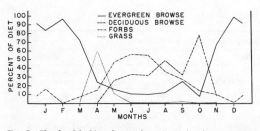

Fig. 5. The food habits of pronghorn in Saskatchewan. The graph shows the average monthly consumption of the four important categories of food plants.

The number of quadrats per range type varied from 140 to 460, depending on the variability of the vegetation (Table 1).

Botanical nomenclature is according to Budd (1957).

RESULTS

Identified food plants in the rumen contents were grouped into six categories: evergreen browse, deciduous browse, forbs, grasses, cacti, and cultivated crops.

The evergreen browse was made up of creeping juniper and sagebrush. Deciduous browse included western snowberry, rose, and chokecherry (*Prunus virginiana*). Rabbitbrush (*Chrysothamnus nauseosus*), found in samples obtained during the hunting season, was also included in this category. The forb category contained all broad-leaved herbaceous plants, including alfalfa and sweet clover (*Melilotus* spp.). It was not thought necessary to distinguish between wild and cultivated forbs because the latter are frequently found along roadsides, and it is likely that pronghorns obtained them there. No attempt was made to distinguish quantitatively between the various grasses present, but spear grass (*Stipa* spp.) and wheat grass (*Agropyron* spp.) appeared to be the most common. The cactus category consisted mostly of prickly pear, with small amounts of brittle prickly pear (*Opuntia fragilis*) and purple cactus (*Mamillaria vivipara*). Wheat and

flax at various stages of growth constituted the sixth category.

The next step was to pool the data from both areas and to determine the mean monthly percentages of each food category in the diet, computed according to the aggregate percentage method (Martin et al. 1946). The values obtained were plotted in Fig. 5. It was apparent that evergreen browse, deciduous browse, grasses, and forbs predominated for a part of the annual cycle, whereas cacti and grain crops were minor items. Thus it was possible to distinguish four distinct periods in each of which a different food type predominated:

1. The spring period (April); grasses
2. The summer period (May–July); forbs
3. The fall period (August–October); deciduous browse
4. The winter period (November–March); evergreen browse

The Spring Period

The short spring period was characterized by the importance of grasses in the diet. In southern Saskatchewan, grasses generally begin to grow during the last week of March or early in April (Coupland 1950) and are soon followed by vernal forbs. In the northern parts of the pronghorn range, growth began 1–2 weeks later than in the southern parts. Probably because grasses were the first succulent growth available, they were attractive to pronghorns in the spring. When forbs and the leaves of rose and snowberry became available, the consumption of grasses practically ceased. Although grasses were found in rumen contents throughout the rest of the year, they made up only a very small percentage of the diet. This fact probably indicated that they were accidentally ingested along with forbs (Hoover et al. 1959:59), except in the spring when grasses were actively sought (Table 1).

The Summer Period

The summer phase of the feeding cycle coincided with the height of the growing season. This period was characterized by the predominance of forbs in a diet containing a large number of plant species. Western snowberry and rose were also important items of the diet. In the Cypress Hills sample, 20 percent of the diet was made up of sagebrush; none was found in the sample from the Matador area. When available, sagebrush was apparently used to some extent during the summer. However, the distribution of antelope on the range was not correlated with sagebrush distribution.

The Fall Period

During the fall period, plant growth gradually decreased due to lack of soil moisture (Clarke et al. 1943), and forbs and grasses dried out. At this time deciduous browse, particularly western snowberry, became the predominant food source for the pronghorns. The proportion of forbs in the diet was lower, and fewer plant species were eaten than during the summer period. Sagebrush was present in small amounts in the rumen samples from both study areas. The consumption of grasses and grain crops was negligible.

The Winter Period

Evergreen browse was the main food source during the winter period. The period began when dry autumn weather and frosts killed the leaves of forbs and western snowberry; it ended with the first growth of grasses and spring forbs.

The pronghorn diet during this period was simple. Data for both study areas indicated that evergreen browse made up approximately 80 percent of the diet, while deciduous browse, forbs, grasses, cacti, and waste grain constituted the remaining 20 percent. In the Matador area, evergreen browse consisted of sagebrush and juniper in varying proportions; in the Cypress Hills area, sagebrush alone was the main winter food (Table 1).

The winter period was the only time when cacti were found in the rumen contents; even then they remained a minor food. Small amounts of flax and wheat in the form of waste grain were found in the November samples from the Matador area. The February sample contained 20 percent wheat straw, which was probably obtained from nearby stubble fields.

During the pronghorn hunting season in early November, 1960, samples of the rumen contents of 42 pronghorns were obtained from hunters in various parts of the range exclusive of the study area. These samples were intermediate in composition between the fall and winter periods but approached the winter diet (Table 2). The presence of rabbitbrush in the sam-

Table 2. Percentage composition of food items in 42 antelope rumen samples, collected during the hunting season, October 30–November 3, 1960.

SPECIES	PERCENT OF DIET BY WEIGHT
Artemisia cana—Sagebrush	48
Juniperus horizontalis—Creeping juniper	11
Evergreen browse total	59
Symphoricarpos occidentalis—Western snowberry	17
Chrysothamnus nauseosus—Rabbitbrush	9
Rosa sp.—Rose	1
Deciduous browse total	27
Artemisia frigida—Pasture sage	1
Forbs total	1
Grass total	1
Cacti total	2
Wheat (heads)	8
Flax	2
Cultivated crops total	10
Total	100

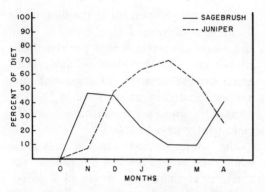

Fig. 6. The pattern of utilization of sagebrush and creeping juniper during the winter period in the Matador study area.

ples is noteworthy. This species is relatively uncommon and has a very localized distribution in the south-central part of the Saskatchewan pronghorn range (Budd 1957). Rabbitbrush found in the rumen contents of 16 pronghorns shot in the Val Marie area composed a significant portion of the samples. It would appear that this species was highly preferred and actively sought by pronghorns, at least during late fall. Couey (1946) and Buck (1947) were unable to distinguish between rabbitbrush and broomweed in their samples. The leaves of the two plants are similar, but in this study the presence of floral parts made positive identification of *Chrysothamnus nauseosus* possible. Apparently, broomweed was not eaten by Saskatchewan antelope, although it was relatively abundant in all parts of the range.

The rate of consumption for sagebrush and creeping juniper from October to April in the Matador study area clearly demonstrated that pronghorns preferred sagebrush in winter. During October, the animals were still on the summer range, where neither species occurred. In the November sample from the winter range, where the initial ratio of relative abundance of creeping juniper foliage to sagebrush foliage was estimated to be 3:1, sagebrush made up almost 50 percent of the diet, creeping juniper 10 percent (Fig. 6). The two species were of equal importance in the December sample. During the following 3 months, juniper was the dominant food plant. Visits to the range during that period revealed that the amount of sagebrush foliage available rapidly decreased and that, by March, sagebrush was severely overbrowsed. As sagebrush became progressively more difficult to obtain, the proportion of juniper in the diet increased while the proportion of sagebrush decreased. About the beginning of April, mild weather resulted in renewed growth of sagebrush, and, in the April sample, 40 percent of the diet consisted of sagebrush while the proportion of juniper dropped to 25 percent.

PROTEIN CONTENT OF FOOD PLANTS

In this study, an attempt was made to correlate protein levels of major food plants with their utilization at various periods of the year. Although the assembled data were not adequate to allow definite conclusions to be drawn, some interesting relationships were apparent.

At intervals throughout the year, samples of sagebrush, creeping juniper, western snowberry, rose, yellow goatsbeard (*Tragopogon dubius*), pasture sage, and native grasses—mixtures of spear grass and wheat grass—were collected on the range, and the crude protein contents were determined in the laboratory of the Animal Husbandry Department, University of Saskatchewan. The Kjeldahl analytical procedure was employed and a conversion factor of 6.25 was used (Table 3).

In general, protein levels were highest in May and then gradually declined; the lowest levels occurred in the winter. Some correlation of protein levels with degree of utilization existed. Plants having the high-

Table 3. Crude protein content of antelope food plants.

| MONTH | PERCENT PROTEIN ON DRY MATTER BASIS | | | | | |
	Sagebrush	Creeping Juniper	Western Snowberry	Rose	Yellow Goatsbeard	Grass*
February	11.5	7.5	7.9†	4.7†		
March	9.7					5.0
April	15.3	5.3				20.3
May	19.2	6.6	25.1	26.4	19.6	16.5
June	17.0	6.3	12.3	16.5	15.3	13.1
July	15.8		10.2	12.2	11.4	12.7
September	12.8	7.1	15.2	11.9	8.8	

* Mixture of spear grass and wheat grass.
† Dry foliage.

est protein levels appeared to be preferred in all seasons:

(1) In April, the early new growth of grasses had a considerably higher protein content than the main winter foods, sagebrush and creeping juniper. Grass was extensively consumed by pronghorns during this period.

(2) During the summer, deciduous browse and forbs such as yellow goatsbeard became available, and were rich in protein. These plants were well utilized at this time.

(3) In the fall, growth of upland vegetation ceased due to lack of soil moisture (Clarke et al. 1943), and the protein levels of the vegetation dropped. However, western snowberry growing in comparatively moist, depressional sites retained a relatively high protein content. It became the predominant food during fall.

(4) During winter, forbs and deciduous browse were low in protein. Sagebrush, however, retained a relatively high protein content and was the main winter food.

If the protein requirements of pronghorns are similar to those of other ruminants, it appears likely that creeping juniper is not a satisfactory winter food. Bubeník (1959:191) reported that for mouflons (*Ovis musimon*), crude protein constituting about 7 percent of the diet

(dry matter basis) met minimum requirements. Einarsen (1956:467) suggested that mule deer require a maintenance ration of 7–8 percent crude protein. It is, of course, possible that the proteins present in creeping juniper are of a high quality or may be more thoroughly utilized by antelope. It should be noted that in this study the rumen contents of a number of pronghorns consisted entirely of sagebrush, but in no instance was creeping juniper the only species present. A more detailed analysis of nutritional properties would be required to evaluate fully the comparative food value of sagebrush and creeping juniper as winter foods.

DISCUSSION

This food habit study showed that during the growing season and early fall a large variety of forbs and browse were consumed by pronghorns in Saskatchewan. Crude protein analysis indicated that many of these species could probably replace each other in the diet during this period. In winter, the foliage of deciduous browse was largely unavailable. Forbs, even when available during snow-free intervals, were low in protein content and probably unpalatable. During this period, the pronghorn depended almost entirely on sagebrush and creeping juniper for food.

The seasonal distribution of pronghorns on the range was correlated with the distribution of their food supply. During the growing season, preferred plants were widely distributed over the grassland, and the pronghorns were also dispersed throughout the range. The staple winter foods, sagebrush and creeping juniper, were limited to eroded soils, alluvium, and sand; during the winter, the pronghorns concentrated in these restricted localities. Thus, sagebrush and creeping juniper were recognized as the essential or key foods of pronghorns in Saskatchewan. Of the two, sagebrush was the preferred species.

The distribution pattern of sagebrush and creeping juniper indicates that suitable pronghorn range in Saskatchewan is much less in winter than in summer. The extent and quality of the winter range within each area of pronghorn occurrence are the limiting factors governing the size of the pronghorn population in Saskatchewan.

The application of the study data to pronghorn management is currently handicapped by lack of detailed knowledge of the distribution of pronghorns in the province. In particular, more information on distribution barriers and migratory patterns is necessary to assess the available winter range in the natural regions of pronghorn distribution. To determine the carrying capacity of these regions, knowledge must be obtained on the comparative value of sagebrush and creeping juniper as winter foods. In addition, a method to measure availability and degree of utilization of these foods must be designed or adapted.

LITERATURE CITED

ANONYMOUS. 1941. Annual Report of the Department of Natural Resources, Province of Saskatchewan, for the fiscal year ended April 30, 1941. 148 pp.

————. 1957. Atlas of Canada. Dept. Mines and Tech. Surveys, Geographical Branch. 110 plates.

————. 1961. Annual Report of the Department of Natural Resources, Province of Saskatchewan, for the fiscal year ended March 31, 1961. 160pp.

BUBENÍK, A. 1959. Grundlagen der Wildernährung. Deutscher Bauernverlag, Berlin. 299pp.

BUCK, P. 1947. The biology of the antelope in Montana. M. S. Thesis. Montana State College, Bozeman. 70pp.

BUDD, A. C. 1957. Wild plants of the Canadian prairies. Canada Dept. Agr. Publ. 983. 348pp.

CLARKE, S. E., E. W. TISDALE, AND N. A. SKOGLAND. 1943. The effects of climate and grazing practices on shortgrass prairie vegetation. Canada Dept. Agr. Tech. Bull. 46. 53pp.

COLE, G. F., AND B. T. WILKINS. 1958. The pronghorn antelope: its range use and food habits in central Montana with special reference to wheat. Montana Fish and Game Dept. Tech. Bull. 2. 39pp.

COUEY, F. M. 1946. Antelope foods in southeastern Montana. J. Wildl. Mgmt. 10(4): 367.

COUPLAND, R. T. 1950. Ecology of mixed prairie in Canada. Ecol. Monographs 20:271–315.

DIRSCHL, H. J. 1961. Antelope population trend survey in Saskatchewan, July 1961. Saskatchewan Dept. Nat. Resources. 9pp. Mimeo.

————. 1962. Sieve mesh size related to analysis of antelope rumen contents. J. Wildl. Mgmt. 26(3):327–328.

EINARSEN, A. S. 1956. Some aspects of mule deer management. Pages 461–470. *In* The deer of North America. Stackpole Co., Harrisburg, Pennsylvania, and Wildlife Management Institute, Washington, D. C. xvi + 668pp.

HOOVER, R. L., C. E. TILL, AND S. OGILVIE. 1959. The antelope of Colorado. Colorado Dept. Game and Fish Game Tech. Bull. 4. 110pp.

MARTIN, A. C., R. H. GENSCH, AND C. P. BROWN. 1946. Alternative methods in upland gamebird food analysis. J. Wildl. Mgmt. 10(1): 8–12.

MITCHELL, J., H. C. MOSS, AND J. S. CLAYTON. 1947. Soil survey of southern Saskatchewan. Univ. of Saskatchewan Soil Survey Rept. 12. 259pp.

NELSON, E. W.   1925.   Status of the pronghorned antelope, 1922–1924.   U. S. Dept. Agr. Bull. 1346.   64pp.

NELSON, J. L.   1961.   Antelope bag check data, 1957–1960.   Saskatchewan Dept. Nat. Resources.   9pp.   Mimeo.

RAND, A. L.   1947.   The 1945 status of the pronghorn antelope, *Antilocapra americana* (Ord), in Canada.   Natl. Museum of Canada Bull. 106.   34pp.

SETON, E. T.   1953.   Lives of game animals. Vol. 3.   Hoofed animals.   Charles T. Branford Co., Boston.   xix + 780pp.

Received for publication March 3, 1962.

A SELF-COLLARING DEVICE FOR PRONGHORN ANTELOPE[1]

DONALD M. BEALE, Utah State Department of Fish and Game, Logan

Abstract: A self-collaring device, which uses rubber collars with plastic streamers attached, was developed for marking pronghorn antelope (*Antilocapra americana*). The collar is held in an extended position in a wooden frame over a water trough. When an animal attempts to drink, it puts its head through the collar and depresses a "trip-pan" suspended in the water. This releases the collar, and it contracts around the antelope's neck.

In an antelope herd-productivity study at the Desert Experimental Range in southern Utah, it was desirable to identify individual does in a herd held in a large enclosure. From previous experience, collars were considered the best means of marking because they are readily visible, a large number of marking combinations are possible, and a minimum of discomfort and interference to the animal results.

Because of the high cost of trapping and the possibility of injury and loss of antelopes, a method of marking which does not require that the animal be captured was

preferred. A number of self-marking devices have been used successfully with large-game animals. For instance, Verme (*J. Wildl. Mgmt.*, 26(4):387–392, 1962) constructed a self-collaring or snare device for white-tailed deer in winter deer yards. These prompted an attempt to use similar means to mark antelope.

No water is available to the antelope in this study except that supplied in troughs used during dry periods. Water could thus be used to entice animals to a marking apparatus.

Basically, the device consists of a wooden frame placed over the trough. Three sides of the frame are screened, leaving one side open through which antelopes drink. A rubber collar is held by four hinged pins at the four corners of this opening. To

[1] A contribution of the Federal Aid in Wildlife Restoration Program, Pittman-Robertson Project, Utah W-105-R. This phase of the project was done in cooperation with Utah State Department of Fish and Game, Intermountain Forest and Range Experiment Station, and Utah State University.

Fig. 1. Antelope being collared at the self-collaring device.

drink, the animal puts its head through the collar and depresses a "trip-pan" suspended just under the surface of the water. This releases the collar at the four corners simultaneously, letting it collapse around the animal's neck (Fig. 1). The collars are available in several colors, and plastic streamers of a variety of colors are attached for additional identification.

A camera was placed about 30 feet from the trough and was coupled by wire to the trigger assembly. This wire was run through a metal tube to prevent it from being tripped prematurely. The camera was triggered by the same action as the collaring device. A photograph was thus taken a fraction of a second after each collar was released. Colored film proved especially useful since it provided a visual record of the animal and its marking.

MATERIALS AND CONSTRUCTION

The antelope collaring device has two operating mechanisms, the four corner mounts with collar-holding pins and the trigger assembly (Fig. 2).

Corner mounts are made from strips of 24-gauge galvanized sheet metal folded over nails which serve as hinge pins. A notch cut at the folded end of each mount provides space for the collar-holding pin to swing (Fig. 2). These pins are ¼-inch steel rods 2½ inches long. A hole drilled through the pin 1 inch from the end accommodates

the hinge pin. Behind the mounts which hold the pins at right angles to the corner mounts, wire stops are attached to facilitate setting and to keep the collar in place until tripped.

The trigger assembly is made from ½-inch conduit and flat steel ³⁄₁₆-inch thick. The conduit is flattened to about ³⁄₁₆ inch and notched on one end to accommodate the trigger and trigger arm. These are assembled with small bolts and adjusted to work freely. The opposite end of the conduit is split and flared to form a base for attaching the trigger assembly to the frame.

The collar-holding pins are held in position against the stops and coupled to the trigger assembly by string or cord of about 30-pound test. The device is set by passing the string around the back of all four collar-holding pins, looping it down through guides or metal rods on the wooden frame (Fig. 2), and over the trigger arm. The string must be tight enough to counter the tension of the rubber collar which is stretched over the front part of the collar-holding pins after the string is in place. The loop of string down through the guides provides the slack required so that the collar-holding pins are fully released when the device is tripped.

The "trip-pan" is a 16- × 16-inch frame of 9-gauge wire woven with nylon filament at ¾-inch spacing. It is suspended in the water by nylon string at three points, two in the back attached to the frame, and one in front attached to the trigger. Screw eyes serve as guides for the trip string. The pressure required to release the collar can be varied by changing the position of the trip string on the trigger.

The rubber collars were 18 inches in circumference and 2 inches wide and were originally intended for deer. They were adapted to the collaring device by splitting them to ⅝ inch in width.

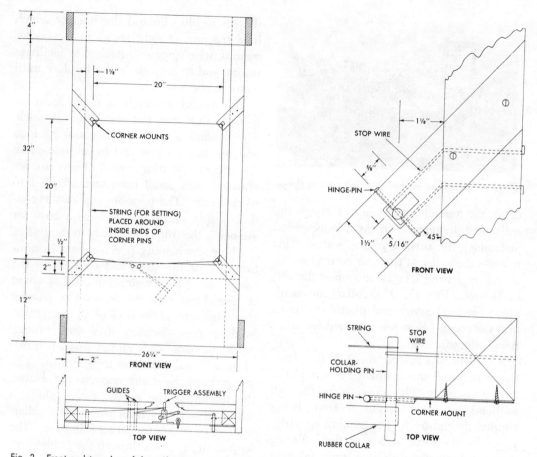

Fig. 2. Front and top view of the self-collaring device with detail of corner mount.

DISCUSSION

After a preliminary period of perfecting the device in the field, 18 collars were placed on adult does in approximately 25 attempts during the fall of 1964. Multiple collaring of an individual was frequent, but at least 10 different does were marked, representing about 50 percent of the adult females in the herd. No fawns or adult bucks were collared. Probably the height of the opening and collar made it difficult for the fawns to drink. Antelopes readily returned to the device and drank after being collared even though water was available at an adjacent trough, so apparently it does not induce fear in the animal collared.

The collars used in this experiment remained on the antelopes for approximately 10 months. None has been seen since and it is presumed that the material deteriorated and broke. However, the Plymouth Rubber Company, Canton, Massachusetts, have indicated that they can supply collars that will last a longer time.

Although this device has been used with antelopes under somewhat specialized conditions, it may prove useful with antelopes on open range and with other animals as well.

Received for publication July 19, 1965.

PRONGHORN DIE-OFF IN TRANS-PECOS TEXAS[1]

T. L. HAILEY, Texas Parks and Wildlife Department, Marfa

JACK WARD THOMAS, Texas Parks and Wildlife Department, Llano

R. M. ROBINSON, Department of Veterinary Pathology, Texas A&M University, College Station

Abstract: Pronghorn antelope (*Antilocapra americana*) numbers on the Marfa Flat, comprising 75,000 acres in Presidio County, Texas, declined from 484 in June, 1964, to 148 in June, 1965. Nearly 60 percent (274) of the original number died from causes other than hunting. Pronghorns were confined on this area by net-wire fences. Three years of below-average rainfall combined with heavy stocking of cattle, horses, and pronghorns caused severe range depletion and forced pronghorns to rely almost entirely on browse species for sustenance. Only tarbush (*Flourensia cernua*), creosotebush (*Larrea divaricata*), and snakeweed (*Amphiachyris dracunculoides*) were readily available. Twelve pronghorns were observed to be utilizing a diet composed almost entirely of tarbush during the winter and spring period. Lesions characteristic of tarbush toxicity were found in 83 percent of the animals examined. Resorbing embryos were found in three of four females that had conceived. Malnutrition coupled with tarbush toxicity was considered to be the cause of the losses. Reproductive rates were reduced from 52 fawns per 100 does in June, 1964, to 17 fawns per 100 does in June, 1965. Pronghorns on ranches with a variety of more desirable browse species suffered only minor losses. Adjustment of stocking rates to forage available, construction of fences allowing pronghorn movement during periods of food shortage, and the possibility of limited, temporary supplemental feeding are management practices that might prevent the recurrence of such losses.

This study was made to determine the extent and causes of a die-off of pronghorn antelope on the Marfa Flat in Presidio County, Texas, June, 1964, to June, 1965.

Approximately 274 antelope (57 percent of those present) perished in the die-off. Examination of 12 animals revealed lesions attributed to tarbush poisoning. While tarbush poisoning was a factor in the die-off it was associated with range depletion and accompanying malnutrition. Toxic amounts of tarbush apparently were taken by antelope as a last resort.

Reports of plant toxicity in pronghorns are rare in the literature. Buechner (1950: 317–318) reported "locoed" pronghorns in Trans-Pecos Texas, attributed to ingestion of *Astragalas* sp., and Ogilvie (1955) reported hydrocyanic poisoning from ingestion of chokecherry (*Prunus melanocarpa*). Buechner (1950:336) and Hoover et al.

[1] A contribution of a cooperative project between the Texas Parks and Wildlife Department and the Department of Veterinary Pathology, Texas A&M University, supported by Pittman–Robertson Projects W-57-R and W-93-R.

(1959:70) stated that pronghorns may, without apparent ill effect, ingest plants that normally have toxic effects on sheep and cattle.

The loss of pronghorns to malnutrition is also little mentioned. Buechner (1950: 339) stated that "Antelope die-offs on sheep ranches have been observed in numerous cases by Texas Game, Fish and Oyster Commission Biologists."

Our gratitude is expressed for the help and encouragement of P. B. Uzzell, Jack Parsons, A. W. Jackson, Frank Hamer, Dr. J. W. Dollahite, and Mrs. Lucille Schultz. Special acknowledgment is given to Hays Mitchell who generously provided the unrestricted use of his ranch for a study area.

STUDY AREA

The Marfa Flat, located immediately southeast of Marfa, Texas, is bordered on the north and west by U. S. Highways 90 and 67 and on the south and east by the Del Norte Mountains. It encompasses approximately 75,000 acres at elevations between 4,750 and 5,200 feet above sea level. The area is an expanse of broad flats interspersed by rolling hills and wide valleys. Primary grass species include blue gramma (*Bouteloua gracilis*)[2], black gramma (*Bouteloua eriopoda*), and tobosagrass (*Hilaria mutica*). Browse plants are soaptree yucca (*Yucca elata*), creosotebush, tarbush, catclaw (*Acacia constricta*), Engelmann's pricklypear (*Opuntia engelmanni*), apacheplume (*Fallugia paradoxa*), and javelinabush (*Microrhamnus ericoldes*). Tarbush, an invader, has increased over the past 20 years and with creosotebush constitutes the primary woody vegetation.

[2] Plant names are according to Kelsey and Dayton (1942), McDougall and Sperry (1951), and Benson and Darrow (1954).

Pronghorns also were observed on ranches surrounding the Marfa Flat, comprised of land of the same type but extending into the foothills of the Del Norte Mountains. These areas were called "Oak–Juniper Life Belt" by Buechner (1950:273) who listed 14 species of browse "important to antelope." Twelve of these browse plants are absent or rare on the Marfa Flat.

Ranges are stocked almost entirely with cattle at approximately 1 animal unit per 32 acres. Rainfall averages approximately 15 inches per year (U. S. Dept. of Commerce 1965:439).

METHODS

Census Counts

Pronghorn numbers were determined by direct observations on ¼-mile strips, made from a Cessna 182 airplane flying at altitudes of 20–100 ft at 80–100 mph. Counts were made by pasture, as the pronghorns were generally confined by 4–4½-ft netwire fences. Censuses were made in June of 1964 and 1965 over the entire pronghorn range of Texas west of the Pecos River and on areas where die-offs were occurring in January, 1965. Personnel who had made these counts over a period of years stated that at least 90 percent of the animals present were observed.

Collection and Examination of Pronghorns

Personnel making aerial counts located sick and dead antelope and directed ground crews to them. Sick antelope were killed by shooting them in the head or neck.

Animals were necropsied using the technique described for deer by Robinson (1964) and representative tissues were preserved in 10-percent formalin for histopathological examination. Blood films and cultures of gross lesions, spleen, and liver were made. Serum samples were taken from fresh specimens. Rumen contents (approximately 1 pint) were taken from nine necropsied animals and preserved in 10-percent formalin for later analysis.

Tissues for routine microscopic examination were imbedded in paraffin, sectioned at 6 micra, and stained with hematoxylin and eosin. Tissues collected for bacteriological examination were cultured on blood agar plates and incubated at 37 C. Cultures were kept for 1 week and were examined daily for evidence of bacterial growth.

Rumen samples were washed with tap water on a fine-meshed screen, air dried, and separated into groups by species. Species were tabulated as a percent of the volume of the total sample.

RESULTS

Aerial Counts and Observations of the Die-Off

In 1957, at the end of a prolonged drouth, pronghorns in the Trans-Pecos region numbered about 7,320. The herd had increased to 12,000 by 1961, over a period when precipitation equaled or exceeded long-term averages, particularly during the critical spring period. Another drouth began in 1961 and pronghorn numbers decreased to about 4,963 by June, 1964 (Hailey et al. 1964).

By December, 1964, vegetation on the Marfa Flat had deteriorated to the extent that stockmen were forced to provide cattle almost all of their nutritive requirements by supplementary feeding. Desirable grasses and forbs were virtually nonexistent. The vegetation which remained was primarily tarbush, creosotebush, and snakeweed.

Although there was some movement of pronghorns between ranches on the Marfa Flat, net-wire fences prevented movement into the foothills of the Del Norte Mountains.

Reports of numerous dead pronghorns were received in December, 1964, from ranch operators. Intensive investigation of the situation was begun in mid-January, 1965.

Initial investigations revealed pronghorns in generally poor condition and 53 carcasses were found in 2 days of searching. Live animals were unthrifty in appearance, loath to run, and noticeably less alert than normal pronghorns. Many were observed eating tarbush.

Pronghorns on ranches surrounding the Marfa Flat and extending into the Del Norte foothills were in good physical condition even though grasses and forbs were almost absent. Although some tarbush was present, no pronghorns were seen feeding on the plant in these areas. The pronounced contrast in physical condition between the pronghorns on the Marfa Flat and those on ranches surrounding the Flat was attributed to the greater variety of browse species outside the Flat.

Results of the aerial censuses on the Marfa Flat compared to those on adjacent ranches in the foothills of the Del Norte Mountains are shown in Table 1.

Some 484 pronghorns were present on the study area (75,000 acres) on the Marfa Flat in June, 1964. Sixty-two males were removed by legal hunting in October, 1964. Of the 422 remaining after the hunting season, 148 survived until June, 1965. Two hundred and seventy-four (65 percent of the population) perished from June, 1964, to June, 1965.

By comparison, census figures available from adjacent ranches containing foothills, with their greater variety and quantity of browse species, revealed 384 pronghorns on 81,400 acres in June, 1964. Thirty-one animals were removed by legal hunting in October, 1964, leaving 353 animals of which 343 survived until the June, 1965, census. Only ten animals (3.5 percent) perished during the year.

Table 1. Pronghorn aerial census data for the Marfa Flat and Del Norte foothills, Texas.

LOCATION	RANCH	JUNE, 1964				OCT. 1965	JANUARY, 1965			JUNE, 1965			
		M	F	Fawns	Total	KILL	M	F	Total	M	F	Fawns	Total
Marfa Flat (75,000 acres)	Nopal	63	64	52	179	24	27	117	144	9	23	3	35
	Loma Vista	22	32	16	70	12	6	4	10	0	11	2	13
	Antelope Springs	23	23	11	57	6	3	7	10	1	6	1	8
	McCabe	21	41	12	74	5	12	44	56	8	17	1	26
	J. Mitchell	10	11	4	25	0				4	22	8	34
	K. Mitchell	30	36	13	79	15				19	28	4	51
Totals		169	207	108	484	62				41	107	19	167
Del Norte foothills (81,400 acres)	C. Mitchell	24	33	16	73	9	21	34	55	27	68	26	121
	101 Ranch	74	114	59	247	16	80	228	308	53	146	62	261
	H. Godbold	20	37	7	64	6				17	32	24	73
Totals		118	184	82	384	31				97	246	112	455

Limited counts made on selected ranches in January, 1965 (Table 1) indicated that the die-off was well under way at that time. Later field observations indicated that some animals were dying in May, 1965.

Condition of Pronghorns

General Symptoms.—Five animals with similar clinical signs were killed and necropsied. They were selected by their slow unsteady gait, arched backs, ruffled appearance of their hair, and general lethargy. Although able to run, they moved stiffly and could not attain the speed for which the species is noted.

Seven pronghorns were found shortly after death. These animals were still warm although some been partially eaten by golden eagles (*Aquila chrysaetos*). Little evidence of struggle by these animals was noted except for one small female apparently killed while in a weakened condition. An eagle was frightened from this carcass and drag marks and other signs of struggle were visible.

Gross Necropsy Findings.—Lesions seen during gross necropsy were predominantly vascular and intestinal. Varying amounts of hemorrhage into the lungs tended to localize into a lobular pattern (Fig. 1). This kind of lesion was found both in freshly killed animals and in carcasses found dead. Hemorrhagic effusions were found on the serosal surface of the omasum, rumen, and abomasum (Fig. 2) and along the mesenteric attachment of the small intestine. Serous fluid had exuded into the pleural cavity and was "frothy" in two cases. A grayish black material adhered to the hair around the tail base and to the hind feet, and had the characteristic aromatic odor of tarbush.

Examination of the gastrointestinal tract of 10 of the 12 animals revealed lesions of varying severity in the abomasum and the small intestine. There was congestive inflammation and necrosis of the gastrointestinal walls. Many petechial hemorrhages in the abomasum of all animals probably were the result of stomach worm (*Haemon-*

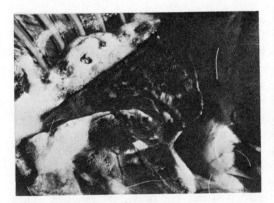

Fig. 1. Hemorrhagic lesions in the lungs of pronghorn antelope. Fresh specimen.

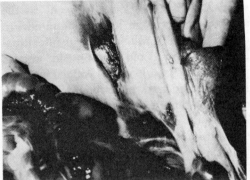

Fig. 2. Hemorrhagic effusions on the serosal surface of the rumen and small intestine of pronghorn antelope.

chus contortus) infestations. The large intestinal worm (*Nematodirus longispiculata antilocoprae*) and the fringed tapeworm (*Thysanosoma actinoides*) were regularly found in the small intestines of all animals examined. Feces in the rectum and colon were well formed and there was no evidence of diarrhea.

Spinose ear ticks (*Otobius megnini*) were present in all specimens. Winter ticks (*Dermacentor albipictus*) were found on three specimens and one doe was heavily infested.

Three of four females that had conceived contained resorbing fetuses in their uteri. No lesions indicating infection were present. The fetal remains were dark, hard, and gritty to the knife. One doe contained two developing fetuses, estimated to be 4 months of age.

Two of the animals necropsied were not diagnosed as tarbush toxicity. One doe was killed because of her poor condition and it was later discovered that no water was available in the small pasture where she was confined. The animal was severely dehydrated, but no gross lesions were found which could be attributed to tarbush toxicity and rumen analysis indicated that this animal had not been consuming large amounts of tarbush as had other pronghorns in the area.

The last animal necropsied was found in the Del Norte foothills. This animal, a large female, died from undetermined causes and was in fair condition. The left hind leg had been eaten to the extent of exposing the femur by a golden eagle which flushed from the carcass as the investigators approached. The left eye was missing and animal had bled freely from the orbit.

The reproductive rate on the Marfa Flat was 52 fawns per 100 does in June, 1964. This rate had decreased to 18 fawns per 100 does by June, 1965. By comparison, census figures (Table 1) from adjacent ranches that contain foothills showed 45 fawns per 100 does in June, 1964, and 46 fawns per 100 does in June, 1965.

Histopathology. — Histopathological lesions were confined to the vascular system and the gastrointestinal tracts. The most marked lesions were in the pulmonary vessels in which degeneration of the vascular endothelium and hemorrhage into the vessel walls and surrounding tissues sometimes were severe. Microscopic vascular lesions were not observed in the animals which lacked gross pulmonary lesions. In the animals that did have pulmonary lesions, the visceral pleura adjacent to the areas of hemorrhage had proliferated. In one case, small proliferations of interstitial tissue suggested old pneumonic lesions, perhaps as a result of parasitic migration. Intestinal lesions were seen to a varying degree in three of the five animals killed. These animals had a necrotic mucosa for two-thirds of the small intestine and the lesions were apparently acute, as there was little bacterial invasion of the villi and no excessive infiltration of the lamina propria by inflammatory cells. In carcasses found dead in the field, intestinal lesions could not be interpreted; autolysis rapidly destroyed the intestinal epithelium. Three females contained dead embryos undergoing resorption. The uterine walls did not contain inflammatory cells and there did not appear to be a maternal reaction to the resorption process. Attempts to culture pathogenic organisms from the lung lesions, spleen, and liver failed. Gram's and Giemsa's stains used on tissue sections in an attempt to demonstrate possible pathogens gave negative results.

Rumen Analysis.—Rumen samples collected from nine of the animals necropsied revealed tarbush to be present in high percentages (six contained 94–99 percent tarbush, one contained 85 percent, one contained 10 percent, and one contained 1 percent). The tarbush portion of the samples was composed of leaves, stems, and buds.

DISCUSSION

Causes of Death

Pronghorn losses on the Marfa Flat were seen in those herds that were confined by net-wire fences and so were unable to move to more favorable foraging areas during the drouth period. During the die-off, little forage was available other than creosote-bush, a totally unpalatable species, and tarbush.

Buechner (1950:278) in speaking of pronghorns on the Marfa Flat said "Antelope retire from this range to the hills . . . during adverse winter weather."

Net-wire fencing added since Buechner's study in the later 1940's has stopped these movements. In effect, the pronghorns that are resident on the Marfa Flat are confined there, and they are confined in many separate pastures on individual ranches. This prevents their movement to areas where browse plants are available. Browse plants are more drouth resistant than forbs that are utilized as the primary sources of food on the Flat.

The drouth, coupled with severe overgrazing by cattle, some few sheep, and pronghorns, reduced available forage to the point that domestic livestock were supplementally fed almost 100 percent of their nutritive requirement. The pronghorn diets were not supplemented. By mid-winter the only available forage was tarbush.

Under ordinary circumstances pronghorns probably would not take enough tarbush to cause losses from tarbush poisoning.

Close observation of grazing pronghorns revealed that tarbush was being taken almost exclusively. Analysis of rumen samples collected during this period supported the observations made of grazing animals.

The toxicity of the fruits of tarbush in sheep and goats has been reported by Mathews (1944:13) who described clinical signs as a listless attitude, arched back, and tucked-in appearance of the abdomen. He stated that a narrow margin existed between slightly toxic and lethal amounts, and that an amount equal to less than 1 percent of the animal's body weight eaten in 1 day would kill sheep and goats. In fatal cases there was usually necrosis of the wall of the abomasum and proximal foot of the small intestine. Congestion of the liver and kidneys was also reported.

Evidence that pronghorns are tolerant of toxic plants has been given by Buechner (1950:336–337), who listed two toxic plants, *Senecio* and *Psilostrophe*, as staple items in the pronghorn diet. He also mentioned that pronghorns used tarbush and listed it as a "fair" food species which was unpalatable to domestic livestock. It appears reasonable that pronghorns may indeed have a superior tolerance to this plant, but that in the situation encountered where the major portion of the diet was tarbush and it was taken while the plants were flowering and fruiting, tolerance was exceeded. The fruits of tarbush are reported to be the most toxic portion of the plant (Mathews 1944:15). The losses reported here as due to tarbush poisoning coincided with the fruiting period of the plant. However, the fruits were not found in the rumen samples. Leaves and stems were easily discernible.

Although the vascular lesions which were the conspicuous gross changes are not reported for sheep and goats, the identical clinical signs and compatible histological findings in the intestines were considered sufficient for the diagnosis of tarbush toxicity. This condition was forced upon the animals and compounded by the severe depletion of the range with resultant malnutrition.

Some of the necropsied animals still retained some mesenteric fat, and the gelatinous change of the bone marrow associated with severe malnutrition had not taken place. Buechner (1950:317) reported similar signs and necropsy lesions which Dr. J. W. Dollahite of Marfa suggested were due to an irritant plant native to the area. Dollahite (now associated with the College of Veterinary Medicine, Texas A&M University) concurred during consultation on

the later cases with the diagnosis of tarbush toxicity.

Heavy parasite loads were also probably a minor contributing factor to the debilitated condition of the pronghorns examined.

It should be recognized that tarbush poisoning was the end result of range depletion and of the restriction of pronghorn movements.

Fetal resorption in three of four females examined was attributed to malnutrition and tarbush toxicity, as little inflammatory reaction was evident in the affected animals. This fetal resorption suggests that lowered reproductive rates during periods of drouth may be a physiological adaptation of these animals for survival. The conservation of protein inherent in fetal resorption may have allowed pronghorns to survive that would have died under drouth conditions if exposed to the continued physiological requirement associated with pregnancy and lactation.

Management Suggestions

Range Management.—It was obvious that the Marfa Flat was overstocked with cattle. However, the long-term drouth was the primary cause of the problem.

Buechner (1950:337) stated that "Most of the plants unsuitable for livestock fall into the fair and good preference ratings for the pronghorn. This inverse relationship indicates the small degree of actual competition between the two animals. Cattle are primarily grass consumers, while antelope are mainly forb feeders." He stated that (pp. 342–343) overgrazing by cattle appears to have little effect upon the pronghorn. The game is able to subsist in healthy and substantial populations upon the wide variety and abundance of forbs that characterize the overgrazed situation.

Buechner (1950:343–344) further suggested that "Detailed observations on ranches stocked with about 10 antelope per section showed that at this concentration antelope forage maintained its annual growth and cattle forage was scarcely influenced by the presence of the pronghorn. It is entirely possible that the carrying capacity of the range is much greater than indicated, but . . . every 10 to 15 years periodic drouths may be expected to greatly decrease the carrying capacity of the range."

The density of pronghorns on the Marfa Flat was approximately four per section before the die-off. Drouth and overgrazing by livestock reduced available grass to a minimum. In our opinion, competition between livestock and pronghorns for the remaining forbs then became intense. When the forbs were exhausted, the livestock was fed supplemental rations while the pronghorns turned to what remained—tarbush. Following the die-off, pronghorn populations were reduced to approximately 1.5 per section.

Obviously, the range was overstocked with a combination of livestock and pronghorns. However, the livestock and pronghorns did not become competitive until most of the grass had been utilized. Livestock numbers could have been reduced when it became apparent that grass supplies were being damaged. This would have benefited the range, the pronghorns, and prevented the added cost for supplemental feed.

At least 25 livestock were found dead on the Marfa Flat during our investigation. The state of the carcasses was such that the causes of death could not be determined.

It would have been impractical to reduce pronghorn numbers; they were already at dangerously low levels. In some pastures all of the pronghorns died and populations in other pastures were reduced to a few animals.

Supplemental Feeding of Pronghorns.— Supplemental feeding of wild ungulate populations is not usually recommended as a game management practice. We feel that this case might be an exception. Grazing pressure by livestock was maintained until the ranges were denuded of palatable vegetation. Then supplemental feeding was done to save the livestock, but no supplements were fed to the pronghorns. Because the pronghorns were already at low population levels, they were minor contributors to the problem. Their numbers were so low (1.5 per section) that the species was in danger in this area, particularly restricted as they were by net-wire fences.

The financial burden to the landowners of feeding the pronghorns would have been canceled by increased pronghorn survival, increased reproduction, and ultimately by increased revenue from hunting. As it was, permits for pronghorn hunting were not issued for the 1965 season and it appeared likely that hunting would be sharply curtailed for several more seasons.

Changes in Fence Construction.—Pronghorns were originally able to move to more desirable areas when food was short. Now no such movement is possible because of the net-wire fencing. Such fences were built to make sheep ranching possible. The economics of cattle ranching proved better in the long run, and most ranches have abandoned sheep ranching entirely. For cattle operations, fences of four strands of barbed wire are suitable, and pronghorns will go under these fences without hesitation.

Replacement of net-wire with barbed wire would allow pronghorn movement. The expense of this operation could be reduced by taking down short strips of net-wire and replacing it with barbed wire at intervals along the fence line. These strips could easily be replaced with net-wire if the occasion called for it.

If pronghorns were able to migrate in response to food shortage, and move to foothills where drouth resistant browse plants were available, the problem might be eliminated. In many cases these shifts might involve relatively short distances.

In Texas, as everywhere in the United States, wild game is public property. However, most of the Texas land is in private ownership and access to game is controlled by landowners through the means of the "trespass law" (Texas Parks and Wildlife Dept., 1965:12–14). Hunters are charged ingress fees for access to game. Income to landowners from this source averages $75 per buck and $55 per doe killed.

These animals represent a valuable resource to landowners who might be reluctant to let resident pronghorns move at will to another ranch. Conversely, pronghorns represent grazing pressure and a landowner with a better forage production might not want pronghorns on his property.

A partial solution might be to alter fences within the large ranches of this area, leaving boundary fences intact. This would permit considerable mobility by pronghorns and still eliminate movement between ranches.

Those charged with management of the pronghorn on areas where the range is not yet criss-crossed with net-wire fences might profitably examine the situation described here.

LITERATURE CITED

BENSON, L., AND R. A. DARROW. 1954. The trees and shrubs of the southwestern deserts. 2nd ed. Univ. of Arizona Press, Tucson, and Univ. of New Mexico Press, Albuquerque. 437pp.

BUECHNER, H. K. 1950. Life history, ecology, and range use of the pronghorn antelope in Trans-Pecos Texas. Am. Midland Naturalist 43(2):257–354.

HAILEY, T. L., D. DEARMENT, AND P. EVANS. 1964. Pronghorn decline. Texas Game and Fish 22(11):22–23.

HOOVER, R. L., C. E. TILL, AND S. OGILVIE. 1959. The antelope of Colorado: a research and management study. Colorado Dept. of Fish and Game Tech. Bull. 4. 110pp.

KELSEY, H. P., AND W. A. DAYTON (Editors). 1942. Standardized plant names. J. Horace McFarland Co. for American Joint Committee on Horticultural Nomenclature. Harrisburg, Pennsylvania. 675pp.

MATHEWS, F. P. 1944. The toxicity of the ripe fruit of blackbrush or tarbrush (*Flourensia cernua*) for sheep and goats. Texas Agr. Expt Sta. Bull. 664. 16pp.

McDOUGALL, W. B., AND O. E. SPERRY. 1951. Plants of Big Bend National Park. National Park Service. 209pp.

OGILVIE, S. 1955. Chokecherry toxic to an antelope. J. Mammal. 36(1):146.

ROBINSON, R. M. 1964. The necropsy of the deer: a field manual. Texas Parks and Wildlife Dept., Austin. 10pp. Multilith.

TEXAS PARKS AND WILDLIFE DEPT. 1965. Parks and wildlife laws: State of Texas. Austin. 577pp.

U. S. DEPT. OF COMMERCE. 1965. U. S. Weather Bureau climatological data: Texas, annual summary 1964. 69(13):430–455.

Received for publication October 29, 1965.

JWM 31(1): 159

MORTALITY OF NORTHERN MONTANA PRONGHORNS IN A SEVERE WINTER[1]

C. J. MARTINKA, Montana Fish and Game Department, Havre

Abstract: Winter mortality of pronghorn antelopes (*Antilocapra americana*) was studied near Glasgow, Montana, in April, 1965. A minimum loss of 500 pronghorns was associated with severe weather and occurred primarily on foothill grassland along the Milk River. Bone marrow examination of 59 carcasses indicated that malnutrition was the principal cause of death. Sex and age composition of 327 carcasses was 28, 33, and 39 percent fawns, adult males, and adult females, respectively. Comparison of carcass age ratios with ratios observed in summer herds suggested a differentially high mortality for fawns but not for yearlings. A low mortality rate was indicated for 2½-year-olds; the rate apparently increased for animals older than 2½. Sex ratio comparisons were inconclusive for fawns but indicated that 1½–3½-year-old females had a higher mortality rate than males of the same age. The mortality rate of males 4½–7½ years and older appeared greater than females of the same age group. Food habits were studied from analysis of 14 carcass rumens and 6,113 instances of plant use recorded at 31 pronghorn feeding sites. Rumen contents were characterized by fringed sagewort (*Artemisia frigida*), creeping juniper (*Juniperus horizontalis*), and a variety of forbs. Comparison of rumen samples with feeding site examinations suggested that starvation occurred while animals were restricted to the grassland vegetative type. Among pronghorns in the Glasgow herd fawn production was 39–55 fawns per 100 does as compared to a normal of 90–110. On the Malta winter range where sagebrush was abundant, available, and heavily utilized, losses were minor and fawn production normal.

During years of heavy snowfall, large numbers of pronghorn antelopes winter on foothill grassland and agricultural areas along the Milk River in northern Montana (Fig. 1). Limited concentrations occur along tributaries south of the Canadian border during milder winters. Summer distribution extends nearly 60 miles northward from the Milk River into Saskatchewan (Martinka 1966a).

[1] A contribution from Montana Federal Aid Project W-76-R-11.

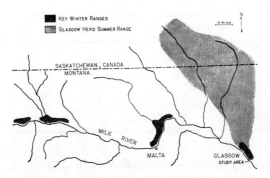

Fig. 1. Key wintering areas of pronghorn antelopes along the Milk River in northern Montana and the summer range of the Glasgow pronghorn herd.

Severe weather from December, 1964, through March, 1965, caused unusually large pronghorn concentrations along the Milk River. Snow depths reached 15 to 40 inches in February and winds of 10–25 mph caused considerable drifting. At Glasgow, Montana, total snowfall was 40 inches as compared to a 36-year mean of 28 inches (U. S. Weather Bureau 1965). The average monthly temperature from December, 1964, through March, 1965, was 7.4 F as compared to a 23-year average of 17.4 F for the same period. Seventy-eight days of zero to –35 F were recorded. Pronghorns damaged ornamental shrubs in several communities and haystack depredations were frequent. This paper presents results from investigations of pronghorn mortality near Glasgow. Results are used to suggest causes for an apparent population decline in the Glasgow pronghorn herd (Fig. 1).

The author is indebted to the following personnel of the Montana Fish and Game Department for their contributions to this study: Kenneth Greer for rumen analysis, Richard Trueblood for field assistance, William Eckerson for information concerning losses, and Thomas Mussehl, Dr. Richard Mackie, and Glen F. Cole (National Park Service) for reviewing the manuscript and providing valuable suggestions.

STUDY AREA

A 5-square-mile area of pronghorn winter range adjacent to Glasgow was selected as a study area. The area was representative of the major portion of the pronghorn winter range habitat along the Milk River. Topography was characterized by numerous finger-like coulees extending from the Milk River flood plain into adjacent benchlands. Two major vegetative types were present.

The coulee bottom type occurred along drainage courses and was characterized by silver sage (*Artemisia cana*) and western wheatgrass (*Agropyron smithii*). Patches of common snowberry (*Symphoricarpos albus*), rose (*Rosa* spp.) and cudweed sagewort (*Artemisia ludoviciana*) occurred on moist sites. Forbs were abundant.

The grassland type occurred on upland sites and was characterized by blue grama (*Bouteloua gracilis*), needle-and-thread (*Stipa comata*), and Junegrass (*Koeleria cristata*) on benches, ridges, and southern exposures. Bluebunch wheatgrass (*Agropyron spicatum*) and creeping juniper (*Juniperus horizontalis*) were common on north and east slopes. Common half-shrubs were fringed sagewort (*Artemisia frigida*) and winterfat (*Eurotia lanata*). Abundant forbs included broom snakeweed (*Gutierrezia sarothrae*), Hood's phlox (*Phlox hoodii*), and vetches (*Astragalus* spp.).

METHODS

Pronghorn carcasses were located by systematically searching the study area on foot or by vehicle during April. Sex was determined for each carcass and age was assigned on the basis of replacement and wear of mandibular dentition (Dow and Wright 1962). When practicable, the marrow of the femur was examined and condition-classed as to white–solid, red–solid, or gelatinous (Cheatum 1949).

Table 1. Sex and age classes of 327 pronghorn antelope carcasses located near Glasgow, Montana, April, 1965. Percentages are in parentheses.

Sex	No.	AGE CLASS							
		½	1½	2½	3½	4½	5½	6½	7½ and Older
Males	157	48 (15)	35 (11)	5 (1)	20 (6)	23 (7)	8 (2)	12 (4)	6 (2)
Females	170	42 (13)	50 (16)	8 (2)	31 (10)	19 (6)	5 (1)	11 (3)	4 (1)
Totals	327	90 (28)	85 (27)	13 (3)	51 (16)	42 (13)	13 (3)	23 (7)	10 (3)

Age and/or sex ratios of the carcasses were compared with ratios obtained from summer aerial classifications of the Glasgow herd in Montana (Trueblood 1964:4) and Saskatchewan (Pepper and Quinn 1965:8). Since data were not available from Montana in 1962 and 1964, classifications in Saskatchewan were considered as representative of the population. The proportion of fawns, 1½-year-old, and 2½-year-old pronghorns expected in the wintering population were each computed by projecting fawn : doe ratios from 1964, 1963, and 1962 summer herds, respectively. If differential hunter harvest and losses from other causes were considered negligible, the expected proportion of each age-class was equal to the fawn : doe ratio for the year of birth. Hunter selection for males, particularly 2½-year-olds (Martinka 1966b), is known to occur in some Montana pronghorn herds but lack of data from northeastern Montana prohibited adjustment of expected ratios. With the exception of fawns, carcass sex ratios were compared only with 1964 summer herd classifications.

Food habits were studied according to rumen analysis and feeding site techniques described by Cole (1956:20). Rumen samples were secured from frozen carcasses during April. The volume of recognizable items in a 1-quart sample was determined and expressed as a percentage of the total volume. Percentages of individual items for all samples were then aggregated and averaged (Martin et al. 1946). Feeding sites were randomly selected, examined, and instances of plant use recorded by species on areas known to be used only by pronghorns during the winter. Use of a rooted stem for single stemmed grasses and forbs, an entire aggregation of stems for bunchgrass, and a single leader for woody plants were each considered as one instance of use. Aggregate percentages were again used in the final analysis.

MORTALITY

Loss of pronghorns was evident on the study area in mid-January and continued until dispersal in April. Direct counts during intensive coverage of the study area indicated a loss of at least 500 pronghorns. In addition, at least 300 pronghorns were killed along railroads and highways. Trueblood (1956:8) estimated a 15 percent herd loss from malnutrition on and immediately adjacent to the study area during the winter of 1955–56.

Extensive survey of other wintering areas along the Milk River indicated relatively few losses when compared to the high carcass density observed on the study area. Losses in these areas occurred primarily in croplands adjacent to river foothills, particularly in the vicinity of haystacks.

Sex and age determination of 327 carcasses on the study area revealed 28, 33, and 39 percent fawns, adult males, and adult females, respectively (Table 1). Examination of 59 femurs showed the marrow of 57 (97 percent) in the gelatinous condition and two in the red–solid condition, suggesting that most animals were suffering from malnutrition when death occurred.

Age-Class Differences

The proportion of fawns among carcasses was 70 per 100 does as compared to a ratio of 53 per 100 does observed on the summer range in 1964. Yearlings occurred in a ratio of 109 per 100 older does, compared to expected ratios of 103 and 110 per 100 older does computed from 1963 summer classifications in Saskatchewan and Montana, respectively. If losses among adult females were proportionate, these data suggest that differential winter mortality occurred for fawns but not for yearlings. Robinette et al. (1957) reported a higher rate of winter mortality for fawn and yearling mule deer than for older age-classes.

The proportion of 2½-year-olds among carcasses (19 per 100 older does) was substantially less than the 95 per 100 older females expected as herd recruitment from the 1962 fawn crop, indicating that this age-class suffered a relatively low rate of mortality. The data may also reflect prior losses from unknown causes among the 2½-year age-class. The 3½- and 4½-year classes each contributed a greater proportion to the total mortality than did the 2½-year class, suggesting that the mortality rate increased after the second year.

Sex Differences

The sex ratio of 90 fawn carcasses was 118 males per 100 females, suggesting a higher winter mortality of male fawns if initial sex ratios and postnatal mortality were equal. The limited data available concerning postnatal sex ratios are inconclusive. Montana Fish and Game Department records of tagged fawns indicate a ratio of 110–120 males per 100 females, while Einarsen (1948:123) reported that

females predominated at birth in Oregon.

Examination of 237 carcasses older than fawns indicated a ratio of 85 males per 100 females, as compared to an expected value of 86 per 100 females from 1964 summer herd classifications. A higher rate of mortality was indicated for females than for males of younger age groups while the trend was reversed among older pronghorns. The ratio of 67 males per 100 females in the 1½–3½ age group was lower than expected from 1964 summer herd classifications. Differential hunter harvest of males would account for a portion of the difference while differential mortality of females may account for the remainder.

In the 4½–7½ and older age group, the occurrence of males in a ratio of 125 per 100 females was higher than expected from 1964 summer herd classifications and the reverse of ratios in the 1½–3½ age group. Taking into account hunter selectivity of males, these data suggest a differential mortality of males in the older age group. Supporting data for a differential winter mortality of adult males was provided by 1965 summer herd classifications in Montana. The ratio of adult males per 100 females decreased from 93 in 1963 to 45 in 1965.

FOOD HABITS

Analyses of 14 rumen samples and 6,113 instances of plant use recorded at 31 pronghorn feeding sites are presented in Table 2.

The relative use of forage-classes was comparable for each food habit category but important differences occurred between categories in the use of individual plant species. Rumen samples which best represented the starvation diet were characterized by fringed sagewort, creeping juniper, and a variety of forbs. Feeding site examinations showed that these plants were common on the grassland vegetative type but

JWM 31(1): 163

Table 2. Winter food habits of pronghorn antelopes as determined from analysis of 14 rumens and 6,113 instances of plant use at 31 feeding sites, April, 1965, near Glasgow, Montana. All figures are expressed in percentages.

| SPECIES* | RUMENS | | FEEDING SITES | | | |
| | | | Grassland Type (22 sites; 4,094 instances of use) | | Coulee Type (9 sites; 2,019 instances of use) | |
	Volume†	Frequency‡	Use§	Frequency‖	Use	Frequency
Artemisia cana	1	14	1	9	40	44
A. dracunculus	—	—	4	14	—	—
A. frigida	13	64	19	86	1	22
Eurotia lanata	Tr	14	23	45	Tr	11
Juniperus horizontalis	43	93	19	27	—	—
Symphoricarpos occidentalis	—	—	1	14	16	44
Unidentified browse	1	43	—	—	—	—
Total Browse	59	100	68	100	58	78
Artemisia ludoviciana	—	—	—	—	17	33
Astragalus spp.	—	—	3	68	—	—
Chenopodiaceae (unidentified)	—	—	Tr	5	15	44
Gutierrezia sarothrae	—	—	12	82	—	—
Lactuca spp.	—	—	Tr	27	2	22
Melitotus officinalis	—	—	—	—	3	11
Phlox hoodii	10	43	1	36	—	—
Phlox spp.	7	43	1	27	—	—
Unidentified forbs	11	100	2	36	1	22
Total Forbs	31	100	22	86	40	77
Agropyron smithii	—	—	Tr	9	2	22
Andropogon scoparius	—	—	2	18	—	—
Bouteloua gracilis	—	—	2	55	—	—
Stipa comata	—	—	3	59	—	—
Unidentified grasses	4	79	—	—	—	—
Total Grasses	6	79	10	95	3	22
Opuntia polycantha	4	58	Tr	14	—	—

* Species comprising less than 2 percent volume or use in each category were excluded but were used in computing totals for each forage class.
† Average of the aggregated percentages of volume per sample.
‡ Percentage of rumens in which item occurred.
§ Average of the aggregated percentages of use per site in that category.
‖ Percentage of sites in which item occurred in relation to all sites in that category.

almost totally absent from the coulee type. These data suggest that the animals may have starved from being restricted to the grassland vegetative type. Excessive snow depths appeared to prohibit use of coulees for most of the winter. Limited observations off the study area during the relatively mild 1965–66 winter showed almost exclusive use of the coulee bottom and sagebrush habitat types.

DISCUSSION

Results of the mortality and food habits studies permit interpretation relative to an apparent population decline in the Glasgow pronghorn herd. Summer range aerial census in July, 1965, revealed a 62-percent population decrease from 1963 in Montana (Unpublished data) and a 38-percent decrease from 1964 in Saskatchewan (Pepper and Quinn 1965:3–4). Direct losses from the 1965 winter mortality appeared to be the major factor involved in the population decline.

The relationship of winter mortality to quantity and quality of winter forage has been well documented for deer and elk. Only limited data are available concerning winter range requirements of pronghorns. Other authors have reported winter diets ranging from a minimum of 30 percent silver sage (Dirschl 1963:87) to, more generally, 70 to 100 percent big sage (*Artemisia tridentata*), silver sage and other shrubby sage species (Einarsen 1948:62, Ferrel and Leach 1952:287, Mason 1952:388, Cole 1956:26–27, Cole and Wilkins 1958:17–18, and others).

In this study, silver sage constituted only 1 percent of the diet in rumens examined. Most rumens examined in the field were full. These data suggest that malnutrition may have been related to a lack of sufficient quantities of shrubby sagebrush in the diet. Only minor losses occurred during this study on winter ranges near Malta where big sage and silver sage were abundant, available, and heavily utilized on southern exposures and windblown ridges.

Aerial surveys also showed low fawn production in the Glasgow herd in 1965. Ratios of 39 and 55 fawns per 100 does were observed in Montana (Unpublished data) and Saskatchewan (Pepper and Quinn 1965:8), respectively, as compared to 90–110 fawns per 100 does observed during most previous years. Low production may have been related to adult females leaving the winter range in poor condition. Pronghorns associated with the Malta winter range exhibited normal production of 90 fawns per 100 does.

LITERATURE CITED

CHEATUM, E. L. 1949. Bone marrow as an index to malnutrition in deer. New York State Conservationist 3(5):19–22.

COLE, G. F. 1956. The pronghorn antelope: its range use and food habits in central Montana with special reference to alfalfa. Montana State Coll. Agr. Expt. Sta. Tech. Bull. 516. 63pp.

————, AND B. T. WILKINS. 1958. The pronghorn antelope: its range use and food habits in central Montana with special reference to wheat. Montana Fish and Game Dept. Tech. Bull. 2. 39pp.

DIRSCHL, H. J. 1963. Food habits of the pronghorn in Saskatchewan. J. Wildl. Mgmt. 27(1): 81–93.

DOW, S. A., JR., AND P. L. WRIGHT. 1962. Changes in mandibular dentition associated with age in pronghorn antelope. J. Wildl. Mgmt. 26(1):1–18.

EINARSEN, A. S. 1948. The pronghorn antelope and its management. Wildlife Management Institute, Washington, D. C. 238pp.

FERREL, CAROL M., AND H. R. LEACH. 1952. The prong-horn antelope of California: with special reference to food habits. California Fish and Game 38(3):285–293.

MARTIN, A. C., C. H. GENSCH, AND C. P. BROWN. 1946. Alternative methods in upland game-bird food analysis. J. Wildl. Mgmt. 10(1): 8–12.

MARTINKA, C. J. 1966a. The international antelope herd. Montana Wildl. July: 28–30.

————. 1966b. A differential hunter harvest of pronghorn antelope in Montana. Proc. Annu. Conf. Western Assoc. State Game and Fish Commissioners. 46: (In press).

MASON, E. 1952. Food habits and measurements of Hart Mountain antelope. J. Wildl. Mgmt. 16(3):387–389.

PEPPER, G. W., AND R. QUINN. 1965. Antelope population trend survey in Saskatchewan 1965. Saskatchewan Dept. Nat. Resources Rept. 11pp. Mimeo.

ROBINETTE, W. L., J. S. GASHWILER, J. B. LOW, AND D. A. JONES. 1957. Differential mortality by sex and age among mule deer. J. Wildl. Mgmt. 21(1):1–16.

TRUEBLOOD, R. 1956. Big game surveys and investigations. Montana Fish and Game Dept. Job Completion Rept. P.-R. Project W-76-R-2. 20pp. Multilith.

————. 1964. Big game surveys and investigations. Montana Fish and Game Dept. Job Completion Rept. P.-R. Project W-76-R-9. 34pp. Multilith.

U. S. WEATHER BUREAU. 1965. Local climatological data with comparative data, Glasgow, Montana. 4pp.

Received for publication May 31, 1966.

INNOVATIONS IN TRAPPING AND HANDLING PRONGHORN ANTELOPES[1]

J. JUAN SPILLETT, Utah State University, Logan[2]

REX S. ZOBELL, U. S. Bureau of Land Management, Cheyenne, Wyoming

Abstract: Pronghorn antelopes (*Antilocapra americana*) were trapped and handled during 11 trapping operations in south-central Wyoming; about 160 animals were handled, some several times. The trap was modified from one developed in Colorado. Men on foot, and in vehicles equipped with two-way radios, moved antelopes into a hook-shaped holding area. Men then moved them down the lane into the trap. Burlap panels reduced injuries and the tendency of animals to jump. A catchpen and chute at the end of the corral helped to single out animals. The human voice and rapid or unusual movements disturbed confined animals.

Studies by Sill (1964) and Spillett (1965) on the effects of livestock fences on movements of pronghorn antelopes afforded unusual opportunity for improving techniques of trapping and handling the animals. This paper describes facilities and procedures employed, with emphasis on useful innovations. The paper is based on experience from 11 trapping operations during which more than 160 animals were trapped and handled. All trapping was the responsibility of the Wyoming Game and Fish Department.

Russell (1937) was the first to report on successful trapping operations for pronghorns. Several other workers subsequently have used his procedure at least with modifications (reviewed by Spillett 1964).

In general, the facilities described in this paper were patterned after those of Hoover et al. (1959), with several alterations suggested by personnel of the Wyoming Game and Fish Commission.

---

[1] Information resulting from cooperative studies conducted by U. S. Bureau of Land Management, U. S. Bureau of Sport Fisheries and Wildlife, Utah State Cooperative Wildlife Research Unit, Wyoming Game and Fish Commission, and University of Wyoming.

[2] Present address: Department of Pathobiology, The Johns Hopkins University, Baltimore, Maryland.

FACILITIES

The trap itself consisted of a corral, catchpen, and chute; dimensions and construction details are shown in Fig. 1.

Wings led into a holding area, which in turn led to the trap lane. The wings were constructed of a short section of 32-inch net-wire fence followed by an 80-rod wing of 47-inch net-wire. The holding area, concealed from the trap by a natural rise, was constructed of a fence 6 ft high, with burlap panels placed at the corners. The holding area was hook-shaped, the "hook" helping to keep animals from escaping to the pasture before the entrance could be closed. The 125-yard lane tapered in width from 40 ft to 25 ft at the corral entrance. It was 8 ft high and made of 5-inch mesh nylon safety netting. Swinging gates led from the lane into the corral, and were closed by a long rope extending down the lane. The 8-ft-high corral, catchpen, and chute were made of ⅜-inch nylon cargo netting with a 2-inch mesh. There was a swinging gate at the entrance to the catchpen, and sliding gates at both ends of the chute. Burlap panels placed on the sides of the corral, catchpen, and chute helped to prevent injuries to animals and to reduce their tendency to jump (Fig. 2). Traps in New Mexico described by Russell

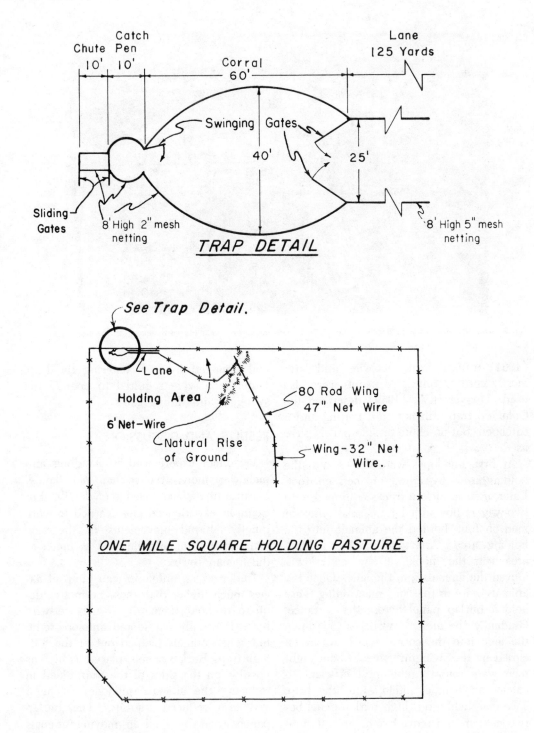

Fig. 1. Sketch of trap, holding areas, and wings.

Fig. 2. Trap in use with burlap panels in place. The burlap panels were later placed at the top of the trap.

(1964) utilized some net-wire, and later mostly cord netting; side panels were also used. Hoover et al. (1959) described the Colorado trap utilizing cord netting and a catchpen, but no chute or side panels were used.

At first, antelopes were driven into the holding area by crews of men on foot. Later, men in pickup trucks equipped with two-way radios, aided by a small crew of men on foot, herded the animals into the holding area. After closing the holding area near the "hook," a few men slowly moved the animals into the lane. Once the animals were in the lane, men hiding there held a burlap panel across the entrance. Gradually the animals were moved down the lane into the corral, which was then closed by the swinging gates. About eight men were found to be most efficient to catch and handle antelopes in the trap. Two men held a 6-ft-high burlap panel between them and moved some animals into the catchpen or chute. The gates were then closed and the animals were caught and removed by men entering the trap. Other men were required to operate the swinging and sliding gates.

RESULTS AND DISCUSSION

Personnel experienced in handling animals were more effective than "new hands" because of their knowledge of details. For example, experienced men learned to work quietly. Rapid movements of the men alarmed the animals, but not as much as did human voices.

Under stress, antelopes can jump obstacles much higher than those normally adequate to hold them. A 47-inch net-wire fence is usually considered antelope-tight, but some animals jumped out of the 8-ft-high trap. Burlap panels, placed as high as possible on the sides of the trap, aided in reducing the animals' tendency to jump and also reduced injuries. The burlap panels used by men in moving animals down the lane and in the corral helped to conceal movements. It proved desirable,

Fig. 3. Antelopes in the lane leading to corral. Note the 5-inch-mesh nylon safety netting in the 8-ft-high lane fence.

when possible, to move only a few animals at a time into the catchpen and chute.

The 1-inch-wide nylon netting with 5-inch mesh, used in the lane, proved effective in retaining antelopes. No animals hit it (Fig. 3). In the trap, a number of animals hit the ⅜-inch nylon rope net with a 2-inch mesh used there.

The 47-inch net-wire wing fence near the holding area was effective in directing antelopes into the trap. However, on two occasions a herd doubled back and jumped the fence wing made of 32-inch net-wire. Any cattleguards in fences along which the antelopes were driven had to be blocked to prevent the animals from crossing them.

Difficulties were encountered when large numbers of animals were in the corral, since they tended to run together in a group. A smaller corral and catchpen (for example, 45 × 30 ft and 8 × 6 ft) would assist in handling animals.

The best results for trapping pronghorns were obtained when there was a light snow on the ground and the animals were more active. Operations in the summer months sometimes required 2 or 3 days; with light snow, less than 1 day's time was needed.

The most useful innovations in procedure and equipment developed in this study were:

1. Use of nylon safety netting, 1-inch wide with 5-inch mesh, in the lane. This material was superior to cotton cord netting or net-wire used in other operations because the animals could see and avoid it.

2. Burlap panels used not only to move the animals (as by earlier workers) but also on the sides of the traps, to quiet animals and reduce injuries.

3. Both catchpen and chute used as adjuncts to the trap instead of only a catchpen or a chute.

4. Use of a hook-shaped side in the holding area to prevent antelopes from escaping before the entrance could be closed and to turn them from running into corners.

5. Trapping when light snow was on the ground instead of during periods when animals were less active.

LITERATURE CITED

HOOVER, R. L., C. E. TILL, AND S. OGILVIE. 1959. The antelope of Colorado. Colorado Dept. Game and Fish Tech. Bull. 4. 110pp.
RUSSELL, T. P. 1937. Antelope transplanting

is success. New Mexico Mag. 15(6):32–33.
———. 1964. Antelope of New Mexico. New Mexico Dept. Game and Fish Bull. 12. 103pp.

SILL, D. 1964. Effects of livestock fencing on pronghorn antelope movements. Spec. Rept. to Cooperators: Wyoming Game and Fish Comm., U. S. Bur. Land Mgmt., Utah Coop. Wildl. Research Unit. 17pp. Typewritten.

SPILLETT, J. J. 1964. A synopsis of the litera-ture and miscellaneous observations on the pronghorn antelope (*Antilocapra americana*). Utah Coop. Wildl. Research Unit Spec. Rept. 13. 38pp. Mimeo.

———. 1965. The effects of livestock fences on pronghorn antelope movements. M.S. Thesis. Utah State Univ. 138pp.

Received for publication May 11, 1966.

ORPHANED PRONGHORNS SURVIVE[1]

PETER T. BROMLEY, Department of Zoology, University of Montana, Missoula
BART W. O'GARA, Department of Zoology, University of Montana, Missoula

Abstract: Two marked sibling pronghorn (*Antilocapra americana*) kids orphaned in July at age 7 weeks survived at least until the following February. Seven kids were observed grazing actively at 3 to 7 weeks of age. These and other supporting observations indicate that kids may survive their mother's death during a September hunting season.

This paper reports observations bearing on survival abilities of pronghorn kids orphaned at an early age. The observations were made during a pronghorn behavior study conducted on the 18,541-acre National Bison Range, Moiese, Montana in 1966. Conditions were comparable to the normal habitat of pronghorns, although the species is not native to the Bison Range. Natural predators, including coyotes (*Canis latrans*), golden eagles (*Aquila chrysaëtos*), and bobcats (*Lynx rufus*) are present. The climate of the Bison Range is milder than that of the eastern Montana plains and the winter of 1966–67 was unusually warm.

Approximately 2 days after their birth on June 1, two male siblings were marked with colored ear tags. Individual kids could be identified from at least ¼ mile with the aid of a 20× spotting scope. These and five other kids, whose approximate ages were known, were observed to mouth vegetation between ages 7 and 18 days. Kids 3 to 7 weeks old grazed actively. On July 19 the mother of the 7-week-old male twins was killed. The kids probably were prematurely and completely weaned at that time. Although the orphaned pronghorns were observed regularly throughout the remainder of the summer and early fall, only two attempts to nurse other does were observed

and the does rejected the approaches. On the Bison Range, weaning normally occurs before or during the rut (September 15 to October 1). September 15 was the latest date we recorded kids nursing their mother, although observation was continued until October 12.

By the age of 6 weeks a group of six tagged kids, which included the two orphans, had established a social hierarchy. Regular observation during the 2 months following the death of the doe indicated this position did not change. The orphans ranked fourth and fifth in this social order. Robinson (1962) reported that the social position of food-deprived white-tailed deer (*Odocoileus virginianus*) fawns was directly related to physical condition. On February 9, 1967, both kids, apparently in good health, were seen in a herd of 18 pronghorns.

Opponents of September pronghorn hunting seasons contend that young of the year may not survive if their mothers are shot. Observations of survival and maintenance of physical condition by these two pronghorn kids orphaned at age 7 weeks, plus supporting information, indicate that kids are likely to survive the death of their mother during a September hunting season.

[1] Work partially financed by the Montana Cooperative Wildlife Research Unit, University of Montana. National Bison Range (U. S. Bureau of Sport Fisheries and Wildlife), and Montana State Fish and Game Department provided additional assistance.

LITERATURE CITED

ROBINSON, W. L. 1962. Social dominance and physical condition among penned white-tailed deer fawns. J. Mammal. 43(4):462–469.

Received for publication March 17, 1967.

IMMOBILIZATION OF PRONGHORN ANTELOPES WITH SUCCINYLCHOLINE CHLORIDE[1]

DONALD M. BEALE, Utah State Department of Fish and Game, and Utah State University, Logan

ARTHUR D. SMITH, Department of Range Science, Utah State University, Logan[2]

Abstract: Succinylcholine chloride was administered intramuscularly by Cap-Chur gun to eight pronghorn antelopes (*Antilocapra americana*). The animals were confined to a 40-acre enclosure which permitted repeated dosages on some animals. Effective doses ranged from 6.05–9.93 mg/100 lb of body weight. No mortality resulted, and no complications were observed. The drug seems an effective immobilant for this species.

Succinylcholine chloride has been widely used for immobilizing a variety of wild and domestic animals. Native American ungulates upon which it has been used are: elk, Flook et al. (1962) and Harper (1965); mule deer, Boyd (1962) and Pearson et al. (1963); mule deer, black-tailed deer, and white-tailed deer, Cowan et al. (1962); caribou and moose, Bergerud et al. (1964). In addition it has been used on mountain lions, grizzly bears and black bears, and a number of species of African wildlife. Marked interspecific differences have been found (Harthoorn 1965:43). Only two reports were found of the drug's use on pronghorn antelopes. Thomas (1961) reported its use on two captive animals and Hepworth and Blunt (1966:27) mentioned its use on antelopes in Wyoming.

Our tests to gather additional data on the response of antelopes to succinylcholine chloride were conducted between July 15 and December 6, 1965, with eight antelopes at the Desert Experimental Range, Milford, Utah. Six of the antelopes had been trapped the previous fall and placed in a 40-acre enclosure. The other two were twin fawns born and raised in the pasture.

The diet of these animals at the time of the test consisted of forage obtained from the pasture, primarily Russian thistle (*Salsola kali*), globemallow (*Sphaeralcea grossulariaefolia*), and rabbit brush (*Chrysothamnus viscidiflorus*). Alfalfa hay and a small amount of cottonseed-meal pellets were also provided. The antelopes were wild but because they were accustomed to humans it was possible to lure them into Cap-Chur gun range with feed.

MATERIALS AND METHODS

The drug was administered with the Cap-Chur gun, model 50 (Palmer Chemical and Equipment Co. Inc., Douglasville, Georgia). Automatic syringe projectiles (2 cc) with the Cap-Chur charge were used. Needles were of the collared type (1½ inch, 12 gauge) with 1 inch between collar and point. A second collar of smaller diameter was added to some of the needles at ½ inch from the point. The smaller collar penetrated the skin with greater ease and acted as a barb.

The succinylcholine chloride used ("Sucostrin," E. R. Squibb and Sons) was in aqueous solution of 20 mg/cc. Physiological saline solution was used to dilute the drug to obtain desired strengths.

All shots were made when the animals came to feed, at distances ranging from 20–

[1] The work reported was completed in connection with Pittman-Robertson Project W-105-R.

[2] Present address: Public Land Law Review Commission, Washington, D. C.

Table 1. Responses of eight pronghorn antelopes to injections of succinylcholine chloride administered by Cap-Chur gun and automatic syringe.

Animal Number	Sex	Age	Date Injected (1965)	Live Weight (lb)	Total Dosage (mg)	Dosage (mg/ 100 lb)	Minutes to Collapse	Minutes Immo- bilized	Needle- collar Type
1	M	mature	July 22	127	7.7	6.05	6	23	single
2	M	2 years	July 26	110*	6.4	5.82	no effect		single
			July 27	110*	6.4	5.82	no effect		single
			July 28	110*	6.6	6.00	no effect		double
			Sept. 17	114	7.0	6.18	7	42	double
			Oct. 5	108	7.0	6.52	3	30	double
3	M	1 year	July 21	85*	5.0	5.88	no effect		single
			July 28	85*	7.5	8.82	no effect		single
			Oct. 5	87	7.1	8.21	4	31	double
			Oct. 6	87	6.2	7.17	5	29	double
4	M	1 year	July 20	90*	6.4	7.11	no effect		single
			Aug. 6	92	7.5	8.13	8	23	double
5	F	mature	Dec. 2	118	7.5	6.36	6	25	double
6	F	1 year	Aug. 10	76	7.6	9.93	7	21	double
			Dec. 2	87	7.5	8.62	no effect		single
			Dec. 3	87	7.5	8.62	6.5	25	double
7	M	fawn	Dec. 6	63	4.0	6.35	6	25–30	double
8	F	fawn	Dec. 5	54	5.0	9.26	3.5	30	double

* Weights estimated later after animals had been immobilized and actually weighed.

30 yards. A barn in the corner of the pasture served as a blind and made it possible to operate from those ranges. All shots, with one exception, were made in the hip region. The weight of the animals was determined with a platform scale following the first immobilization. Follow-up observations were made to see if adverse effects resulted from immobilization.

RESULTS AND DISCUSSION

The results obtained (Table 1) show that succinylcholine chloride was an effective drug for immobilizing pronghorn antelopes under existing conditions. Their body condition was believed comparable to that of antelopes on the open range.

A total of 11 cases of immobilization was achieved and no mortality or apparent complications resulted. In three instances, apparently slight overdoses were given, and in those cases artificial respiration was given for approximately 10 minutes. This procedure was used by Talbot and Lamprey (1961).

When the automatic projectile syringes were used with standard collared needles, the syringe would instantly bounce off the animal upon impact. This action was believed due to the back pressure caused by the injection of fluid and the failure of the collar to penetrate the skin. Consequently, the entire dosage may not have entered the muscle tissue. Similar observations were made by Pearson et al. (1963). Many of the shots were at the extreme range of the gun and that may have been a factor in the failures when the larger collar was used. Prolonged penetration was attained by using needles with smaller collars. All but one of the successful shots were made with the modified needle.

Effective immobilization dosages ranged from 6.05–9.93 mg/100 lb of body weight. Not enough tests were made to establish accurately the minimum effective and maximum safe doses. Also, animals on different feeds or in various degrees of physical condition may respond differently. Under the conditions of the tests, the higher dosages were probably close to the maximum that was safe.

The antelopes used in these tests were not under severe stress and since shots were made from a blind, they were not highly alarmed at the time the drug was injected. Usually they were feeding on the hay at the time shots were made. The general response, after a shot was fired, was for the entire group to run 100–200 yards toward the center of the pasture and resume feeding in a minute or two. On several occasions they immediately returned to feed on the hay and the one which received the injection collapsed at the feeding area.

Effects of the drug were not apparent until 2 or 3 minutes before collapse. At that time they would stop eating and show signs of relaxation of the neck muscles followed by unsteadiness in the shoulders.

One limitation in using this technique to capture pronghorn antelopes under field conditions is the limited range of the gun. The CO_2-powered gun used was not accurate at more than 30 to 35 yards.

The time lapse between injection and immobilization has been reported as a major shortcoming of the drug in field use, because the animal may escape to cover. In our tests the latent period ranged from 3 to 8 minutes, well within the time periods for other species. The time lapse might be of less concern with pronghorn antelopes because of the open range the species inhabits.

LITERATURE CITED

BERGERUD, A. T., A. BUTT, H. L. RUSSELL, AND H. WHALEN. 1964. Immobilization of Newfoundland caribou and moose with succinylcholine chloride and Cap-Chur equipment. J. Wildl. Mgmt. 28(1):49–53.

BOYD, R. J. 1962. Succinylcholine chloride for immobilization of Colorado mule deer. J. Wildl. Mgmt. 26(3):332–333.

COWAN, I. McT., A. J. WOOD, AND H. C. NORDAN. 1962. Studies in the tranquilization and immobilization of deer (*Odocoileus*). Canadian J. Comp. Med. and Vet. Sci. 26(3):57–61.

FLOOK, D. R., J. R. ROBERTSON, O. R. HERMANRUDE, AND H. K. BUECHNER. 1962. Succinylcholine chloride for immobilization of North America elk. J. Wildl. Mgmt. 26(3):334–336.

HARPER, J. A. 1965. Immobilization of Roosevelt elk by succinylcholine chloride. J. Wildl. Mgmt. 29(2):339–345.

HARTHOORN, A. M. 1965. Application of pharmacological and physiological principles in restraint of wild animals. Wildl. Monogr. 14. 78pp.

HEPWORTH, W., AND F. BLUNT. 1966. Research findings on Wyoming antelope. Wyoming Wildl. 30(6):24–29.

PEARSON, H. A., A. D. SMITH, AND P. J. URNESS. 1963. Effects of succinylcholine chloride on mule deer. J. Wildl. Mgmt. 27(2):297–299.

TALBOT, L. M., AND H. F. LAMPREY. 1961. Immobilization of free-ranging East African ungulates with succinylcholine chloride. J. Wildl. Mgmt. 25(3):303–310.

THOMAS, W. D. 1961. Chemical immobilization of wild animals. J. Am. Vet. Med. Assoc. 138(5):263–265.

Received for publication July 6, 1966.

BRIEFER ARTICLES

FOODS OF KANSAS ANTELOPES RELATED TO CHOICE OF STOCKING SITES[1]

BILL D. HLAVACHICK, Kansas Forestry, Fish and Game Commission, Hays

Abstract: Forage habits of Kansas antelopes (*Antilocapra americana*) were investigated from September, 1963, to August, 1964. A total of 323 minutes of antelope feeding time were recorded on 13 species of plants at 10 stations during the summer, fall, and winter. Forbs accounted for 36 percent of the observed antelope diet, browse 2 percent, cactus 40 percent, and grasses 22 percent. No accurate estimate of winter wheat consumption could be made, but antelopes spend considerable time on winter wheat in the late fall, winter, and spring. The selection of transplant sites in Kansas will not be restricted to areas where browse is available but can include sites where forbs, cactus, and grass are abundant. In several such areas, cooperative transplant agreements have been made. The presently occupied range of roughly 250,000 acres appears able to support several hundred antelopes.

The purpose of this study was to determine the foods of antelopes in Kansas in order to facilitate the choosing of future transplant sites.

Observations were made in extreme western Kansas, at 10 feeding areas in Wallace and Sherman counties, the winter range of 80 antelopes and the summer range of approximately 50. Records were kept of 323 minutes of antelope feeding time.

METHODS

The antelope-minute technique described by Buechner (1950), as adapted for use in this study, included the following steps: (1) direct observation with binoculars, spotting scope, or the unaided eye of antelopes feeding on various plant species; (2) pinpointing the exact spots of feeding activity on individual plants; (3) spotting a small area where at least 30 seconds of feeding time took place; and (4) attempting to locate all freshly clipped plants and estimating the amount of time spent on each species. Time estimates were based on the

amount of freshly clipped plants, especially where it was obvious that the animals had spent more time feeding on a particular plant than had been observed directly.

Each small feeding area was located and identified by using tall outstanding vegetation such as yucca (*Yucca* sp.), sand sage (*Artemisia filifolia*), and snow-on-the-mountain (*Euphorbia marginata*) as boundary markers. The feeding area was methodically searched to locate all freshly clipped plants. Feeding areas were not of similar size because antelopes move steadily while feeding and the vegetation used as markers to define an area was not arranged in a fashion conducive to standardization.

Observations were made at all times during the daylight hours, whenever and wherever antelopes were located. The animals are not so abundant as to assure their being observable at a specific time and place.

Antelopes usually moved out of visual range when they sighted the observer. I would wait a few minutes, then using the topography as a shield, approach to where I could see the feeding area without being observed by the animals.

[1] A contribution of the Federal Aid in Wildlife Restoration Act, Kansas Project W-23-R.

Table 1. Summary of recorded forage consumption by Kansas pronghorn antelopes, by species, from September, 1963, to August, 1964.

SPECIES	FREQUENCY AT 10 STATIONS	ANTELOPE-MINUTES	PERCENT
Forbs			
Artemisia kansana	6	50.5	16
Aster multiflorus	1	28.5	9
Euphorbia marginata	1	18.0	6
Lygodesmia juncea	1	12.0	4
Sphaeralcea coccinea	2	3.5	1
Psoralea argophylla	1	1.5	tr*
Psoralea tenuiflora	1	2.0	tr
Total forbs	13	116.0	36
Browse			
Artemisia filifolia	1	6.0	2
Total browse	1	6.0	2
Grass			
Bouteloua curtipendula	1	30.0	9
Sporobolus cryptandrus	3	19.5	6
Bouteloua gracilis	2	16.0	5
Aristida longiseta	2	5.5	2
Total grass	8	71.0	22
Cacti			
Opuntia macrorhiza	5	130.0	40
Total cacti	5	130.0	40
Totals		323.0	100

* Less than 1 percent.

RESULTS AND DISCUSSION

Thirteen species of plants were utilized as pronghorn forage during the observation periods. In all, seven species of forbs, four species of grass, and one species each of browse and cactus were identified as pronghorn forage (Table 1).

The 2 percent browse utilization figure reflects the paucity of browse plants, while the greater percentage use of grass indicates its dominance in the habitat.

During 1963 a habitat evaluation study was conducted to determine percent composition of major species of vegetation throughout the occupied antelope range. The results indicated a composition of 72 percent grass, 2 percent shrubs, 3 percent forbs, 1 percent cactus, and 22 percent bare ground (Hlavachick 1963).

Antelopes appear to use more grass in Kansas than in other states such as Colorado (Hoover et al. 1959), Wyoming (Wyoming Game and Fish Commission 1956), and Texas (Buechner 1950). Grass makes up 72 percent of the pasture habitat in the Kansas study area; perhaps the preponderance of grass in the diet of the Kansas antelopes is due to high availability.

Sand sage, the only shrub observed utilized as forage, makes up only 2 percent of the diet even though many antelopes wintered along stream valleys where sand sage is most abundant. This tends to confirm the suggestion of Deming (1963) that antelopes use sagebrush because it is available and not because they prefer it.

Cactus and forb consumption rated as 1 and 2 respectively in utilization (Table 1), with cactus being used on a seasonal basis only and forbs utilized throughout the year.

Antelopes use considerable winter wheat, especially in winter and early spring, but their consumption of this crop could not be accurately estimated because the wheat fields afforded no concealment for observing. Three bands of antelopes numbering 8, 15, and 25 were known to spend all or part of the winter months on wheat fields.

Spring and summer forage species included many-flowered aster (*Aster multiflorus*), silver psoralea (*Psoralea argophylla*), scarlet globemallow (*Sphaeralcea coccinea*), and sagewort (*Artemisia kansana*). Sand sage was the only browse species utilized. Blue grama (*Bouteloua gracilis*), sand dropseed (*Sporobolus cryptandrus*), and red three-awn (*Aristida longiseta*) were the grasses used. Antelopes actively sought the fruits of the prickly pear (*Opuntia macrorhiza*), especially in late summer and fall. Forbs accounted for 40 percent of the observed spring and summer diet, browse 4 percent, grass 16 percent, and cactus 40 percent. A total of 135 antelope-minutes of feeding time was recorded on nine species of plants.

Plants taken in the fall included few-flowered scurfpea (*Psoralea tenuiflora*), scarlet globemallow, sagewort, blue grama, and cactus. Prickly pear made up the bulk of the fall diet. Fruits of this species are then mature, succulent, and tasty, and antelopes seemed to prefer these fruits to all other plants.

Blue grama, growing close to patches of cactus, was not used by cattle in this area. This fact tended to assure that grama matured and produced more seed heads than would be found without the protection afforded by the cactus. Antelopes ate these seed heads, secondarily, I feel, while feeding on the cactus, taking more blue grama than they would have if the cactus had not been close by.

Forage consumption during the fall included forbs 9 percent, grass 15 percent, and cactus 76 percent. Five species of plants were taken and 100 minutes of feeding time were recorded.

During December and January, 88 minutes of feeding time were recorded on six plants, with forbs making up 60 percent of the diet and grass 40 percent. Plants taken were skeleton weed (*Lygodesmia juncea*), snow-on-the-mountain, sagewort, sand dropseed, red three-awn, and sideoats grama (*Bouteloua curtipendula*). More grass was used in winter than at any other season, a fact related to its abundance and also to the drying up of forbs and cactus fruits.

MANAGEMENT IMPLICATIONS

The area where this study was conducted consists of approximately 250,000 acres, and is the only presently occupied antelope range in Kansas. In November, 1964, 72 antelopes were released within this area;

subsequent aerial and ground surveys show that they have increased. In the most recent survey, conducted during the summer of 1967, 186 antelopes were counted. Landowners' reports indicate that antelopes occur outside the area covered in aerial transects, and 200 antelopes is probably an accurate total estimate. A favorable buck:doe:fawn ratio of 51:100:70 was observed among the 186 animals counted in 1967.

Thus, the stocking attempt has been successful. I think that this range is capable of supporting several hundred antelopes, provided that landowners maintain their tolerance toward antelopes feeding on winter wheat.

Based on the success of the stocking program and the results of my food habits study, I feel that transplant sites in Kansas will not need to be restricted to areas where browse species are available. Instead, they may be chosen where forbs, cactus, and grass are abundant on relatively large expanses of rangeland, 10,000 acres or more. Several such areas are located in the southwest, central, and south-central parts of Kansas, and cooperative transplant agreements have been entered into with farmers and ranchers in these regions.

LITERATURE CITED

BUECHENER, H. K. 1950. Life history, ecology, and range use of the pronghorn antelope in Trans-Pecos Texas. Am. Midland Naturalist 43(2):257–354.

DEMING, O. V. 1963. Antelope and sagebrush. Trans. Interstate Antelope Conf. 14:55–60.

HLAVACHICK, B. D. 1963. Habitat evaluation. Kansas Forestry, Fish and Game Comm. Job Completion Rept., P.-R. Project W-23-R. 14pp. Mimeo.

HOOVER, R. L., C. E. TILL, AND S. OGILVIE. 1959. The antelope of Colorado. Colorado Dept. Game and Fish Tech. Bull. 4. 110pp.

WYOMING GAME AND FISH COMMISSION. 1956. Quarterly progress report, Federal Aid Project W-27-R-9. 24pp.

Received for publication June 26, 1967.

AGE DETERMINATION OF PRONGHORNS BY THE INCISOR CEMENTUM

HENRY E. McCUTCHEN, Department of Zoology, University of Montana, Missoula

Abstract: An examination of stained sections of the first permanent incisor teeth of pronghorns (*Antilocapra americana*) showed that the number of cementum annuli is correlated with age. Ten known-age pronghorns from 1½ to 6⅓ years of age were used to confirm the technique.

This paper reports the results of a study in which the annular structure of the cementum in the first permanent incisor teeth of pronghorn antelope was correlated with age.

In recent years a number of artiodactyls have been aged by annuli in the cementum of the teeth. This technique was used by Sergeant and Pimlott (1959) on moose (*Alces alces*), by McEwan (1963) on caribou (*Rangifer tarandus*), by Low and Cowan (1963) on mule and black-tailed deer (*Odocoileus hemionus*), by Mitchell (1963) on red deer (*Cervus elaphus*), and by Ransom (1966) and Gilbert (1966) on white-tailed deer (*Odocoileus virginianus*).

Dow and Wright (1962) used known-age pronghorns to organize age classes based on tooth eruption and wear. Kolenosky and Miller (1962) using pronghorns aged by tooth eruption and wear, found that lens weight increased with age.

I acknowledge the help of P. L. Wright, University of Montana, who directed the study and provided the known-age specimens. I also thank R. W. Fields, G. F. Weisel, B. W. O'Gara and R. P. Stoneberg for giving advice and materials for the study.

MATERIALS AND METHODS

The first permanent incisor (Pil) was chosen for the study because it is easy to remove and is the first permanent incisiform tooth to erupt (Dow and Wright 1962). The incisors from 10 known-age prong-

Table 1. Known-age pronghorns used to confirm cementum aging technique. All specimens from Montana and Wyoming.

COLLECTION NUMBER	SEX	DATE OF DEATH	AGE (YEARS)
B95	F	Jan. 27, 1966	1½
E16	M	Sept. 26, 1953	2⅓
E17	M	Oct. 27, 1953	2⅓
E18	M	Oct. 8, 1954	3⅓
E19	F	Dec. 20, 1954	3½
H3560–61	M	Aug. 11, 1965	4¼
E20	M	Sept. 21, 1955	4⅓
E21	M	Sept. 27, 1955	4⅓
E22	M	Sept. 7, 1956	5⅓
E23	M	Sept. 18, 1957	6⅓

horns from 1½ to 6⅓ years of age were used to establish the technique for cementum aging (Table 1). In addition to these, the incisors of over 100 unknown-age pronghorns were prepared and examined. All the animals were collected from Montana and Wyoming. All of the known-age animals were from the collection of S. A. Dow, Jr. and P. L. Wright.

The incisors were removed from the mandibles and sagittal or cross sections were cut from the roots with a tooth saw. The sections were ground to a thickness of about 20 microns with carborundum paper using the method suggested by Frost (1958). Each section was washed in a mild detergent solution, decalcified in nitric acid, neutralized in a saturated solution of lithium carbonate and alcohol, rinsed in distilled water, fixed to a microscope slide and stained in hematoxylin and eosin.

RESULTS AND DISCUSSION

A gross inspection of the incisors revealed that the cementum covered all of the root and was thicker on the lingual side and toward the tip of the root. Microscopic examination of the stained sections showed alternating light-staining and dark-staining bands in the cementum. I found that each pair of alternating bands represent 1 year

Fig. 1. Sagittal section of the incisor of a 2⅓-year-old known-age pronghorn killed in the fall. *A* is dentine; *B*, dentino-cemental interface, and *C* is cementum formed during the 2nd summer of life. *D* is cementum formed during the 2nd fall and winter; *E*, cementum formed during the 3rd spring and summer; *F* is cementum formed during the 3rd fall of life.

of growth. The light-staining bands represent spring and summer growth; the dark-staining bands fall and winter growth.

By sectioning a series of first incisors from the unerupted through the fully erupted stage I determined that the cementum begins to form just prior to eruption. The time of cementum formation will vary as Dow (1952) found that the eruption time of PiI varied from 14 to 17 months of age.

A stained section of an incisor from a 2⅓-year-old known-age pronghorn killed in the fall is shown in Fig. 1. The letter **A** marks the dentine and B marks the dentino-cemental interface. The extremely narrow, light-staining band, C, represents the initial,

JWM 33(1): 174

Fig. 2. Sagittal section of the incisor of a 5⅓-year-old known-age pronghorn killed in the fall. Count was begun at 1⅓ years in the area of the initial formation of the first dark-staining fall-winter band, and continued to the fifth fall-winter band which was forming on the outside edge at about 5⅓ years. A is dentine; B, dentino-cemental interface; W indicates two dark-staining bands formed in one annulus; and L indicates fainter-staining lamellae.

Fig. 3. Cross section of the incisor of an unknown-age pronghorn killed in the fall; age estimated at 9⅓ years by cementum annuli. A is dentine; B, dentino-cemental interface; X is an area of annuli discontinuity.

limited summer growth of cementum which formed at around 14 months of age during the second summer of the pronghorn's life. The narrow, dark-staining band, D, which formed at about 1⅓ years of age, was added during the second fall and winter. The wide, light-staining band, E, represented the period of growth during the third spring and summer. The outside, dark-staining band, F, formed at about 2⅓ years in the third fall just before the animal's death.

In Montana, the pronghorns are hunted in the fall, about ⅓ year past their average birth date of June 1 (Dow and Wright 1962). Fig. 2 depicts a method of correlating the number of cementum annuli with age in a 5⅓-year-old known-age pronghorn killed in the fall.

Although the cementum annuli of known-age pronghorns up to 6⅓ years of age were correlated with age, a series of 7-year and older known-age incisors should be examined to help confirm the cementum-aging technique for this species. A number of incisors of old, unknown-age pronghorns were examined. Fig. 3 shows the cementum of a pronghorn killed in the fall estimated

at 9⅓ years by the cementum annuli. The maximum age estimate of any pronghorn in the collection was 12⅓ years by this technique.

It was difficult to determine the exact month when the dark-staining and light-staining bands began to form during the year. The light-staining band appears to form in early spring as animals collected in mid-May had a very narrow, light-staining band forming on the outside of the cementum. The time of the formation of the dark-staining band appears to vary from late August through November.

In some sections each annulus contained two dark-staining bands lying closely together (Fig. 2). This condition was easily recognized and did not cause any difficulty in aging. The cause of these is unknown. Low and Cowan (1963) and Gilbert (1966) noted a similar phenomenon in deer cementum. Fainter-staining lamellae (Fig. 2) were also observed within the cementum annuli.

Difficulty in aging by the cementum was occasionally experienced with poorly stained sections and with sections in which the cementum annuli were wholly discontinuous.

LITERATURE CITED

Dow, S. A., Jr. 1952. An evaluation of some criteria for age determination of the pronghorn (*Antilocapra americana* Ord). M.S. Thesis. Montana State Univ., Missoula. 71pp.

Dow, S. A., Jr., and P. L. Wright. 1962. Changes in mandibular dentition associated with age in pronghorn antelope. J. Wildl. Mgmt. 26(1):1–18.

Frost, H. M. 1958. Preparation of thin undecalcified bone sections by rapid manual method. Stain Tech. 33(6):273–277.

Gilbert, F. F. 1966. Aging white-tailed deer by annuli in the cementum of the first incisor. J. Wildl. Mgmt. 30(1):200–202.

Kolenosky, G. B., and R. S. Miller. 1962. Growth of the lens of the pronghorn antelope. J. Wildl. Mgmt. 26(1):112–113.

Low, W. A., and I. McT. Cowan. 1963. Age determination of deer by annular structure of dental cementum. J. Wildl. Mgmt. 27(3): 466–471.

McEwan, E. H. 1963. Seasonal annuli in the cementum of the teeth of barren ground caribou. Canadian J. Zool. 41(1):111–113.

Mitchell, B. 1963. Determination of age in Scottish red deer from growth layers in dental cement. Nature 198(4878):350–351.

Ransom, A. B. 1966. Determining age of white-tailed deer from layers in cementum of molars. J. Wildl. Mgmt. 30(1):197–199.

Sergeant, D. E., and D. H. Pimlott. 1959. Age determination in moose from sectioned incisor teeth. J. Wildl. Mgmt. 23(3):315–321.

Received for publication March 11, 1968.

RUMINO RETICULAR VFA CONTENT OF PRONGHORN ANTELOPE

JULIUS G. NAGY, Department of Fishery and Wildlife Biology and Department of Animal Science, Colorado State University, Fort Collins

GARY L. WILLIAMS, Colorado State University, Fort Collins

Abstract: Molar concentrations and percentage distributions of short chain fatty acids obtained from various age-classes and sexes of pronghorn antelope (*Antilocapra americana*) were investigated. The concentrations of the acids and their percentage distribution seem to correspond to data obtained on domestic ruminants on somewhat comparable diets. Some statistically significant differences ($P < 0.05$) were obtained on the percentage distribution of the acids of adults and fawns.

Volatile fatty acids (VFA) are metabolites produced by the microbial fermentation of forages in the rumino-reticulum of ruminant animals. Once thought to be of minor significance, these acids are known now to supply the major source of energy to the ruminant.

A considerable amount of information is available on VFA production, concentration, and the ratios of individual acids in the rumen of domestic animals (Annison and Lewis 1959), but less is known concerning wild ruminants. Short et al. (1966) presented data on seasonal variations in VFA in the rumen of mule deer *Odocoileus hemionus*.

The purpose of this paper, therefore, is to present some information on the concentration and ratios of VFA in different age classes of the pronghorn antelope.

The authors wish to acknowledge the help of the Colorado Department of Game Fish and Parks personnel and the excellent cooperation of Colorado hunters.

METHODS

Rumen contents were obtained from 25 antelope killed September 19, 1964, in northwestern Colorado on an area considered good antelope range. A variety of grasses, forbs, and shrubs, mainly bitterbrush (*Purshia* sp.) and sagebrush (*Artemisia* sp.), are available for the herd on this range. The animals were collected by hunters who removed the whole compound stomachs, placed them in plastic bags, and turned in the material at the check station. Time lapse between killing the animals and

Table 1. Total VFA content and molar percentages of individual volatile fatty acids from antelope rumen contents according to age-class and sex.

		MEANS (STANDARD ERRORS IN PARENTHESES)					TOTAL VFA CONC. m mole/L	
VARIABLE	SAMPLE SIZE	Acetic	Propionic and iso-butyric	Butyric	Isovaleric	Valeric	Mean	Interval
Age Class								
Fawns	11	69.1(±0.65)	17.1(±0.35)	8.4(±0.27)	1.7(±0.11)*	3.7(±0.20)	105.5	±19.2
Yearlings	5	69.9(±0.83)	17.4(±0.54)	7.9(±0.37)*	1.4(±0.12)	3.3(±0.21)*	122.2	±17.2
Adults	9	69.9(±0.39)	16.5(±0.58)	8.6(±0.32)	1.4(±0.08)	3.6(±0.07)	117.7	±15.9
Sex								
Males	8	69.8(±0.50)	16.6(±0.59)	8.6(±0.32)	1.4(±0.08)	3.6(±0.10)	120.2	±15.1
Females	17	69.5(±0.84)	17.1(±0.25)	8.2(±0.06)	1.5(±0.08)	3.5(±0.14)	114.6	± 8.4

* Value significantly different from other age-class, $P < 0.05$.

receiving the rumen contents was approximately 2–4 hours. At the check station, the rumen was opened, the contents mixed, and approximately 200 g placed in jars. The samples were frozen immediately with ample amounts of dry ice and remained frozen until processing in the laboratory.

Rumen fluid was prepared in the laboratory by straining each sample through cheese cloth. Ten ml of the strained fluid was mixed with 2 ml of 25 percent meta-phosphoric acid. The mixture was frozen and later centrifuged at 16,000 rpm for 45 minutes. Short-chain-fatty-acid content and composition was determined by gas chromatography using a hydrogen flame detector. The procedure was identical to that described by Nagy et al. (1964:787). The rumen contents of 8 males and 17 females comprised of 11 fawns (approximately 4 months old), 5 yearlings, and 9 adults were examined. Data presented are based on three replications of 18 injections into the gas chromatograph performed upon the rumen fluid of each antelope.

RESULTS AND DISCUSSION

The VFA composition of antelope rumen content samples were similar to those reported for free-grazing cows (Balch and Rowland 1957), for sheep feeding on wheaten hay (Gray and Pilgrim 1952), and for deer feeding on browse diets (Nagy et al. 1964, Short et al. 1966). Work with domestic ruminants showed that relative proportions of the acids in the rumen are somewhat influenced by the diet of the ruminant. Acetic acid predominates under most dietary regimes, but substantial amounts of propionic and butyric acids are also formed. Diets rich in easily digestible carbohydrates, such as glucose or starch, favor propionic acid production, while high fiber diet would show an increase of acetate in the percentage composition of the acids (Annison and Lewis 1959:60). Hence, the ratio of acetic acid to propionic acid can be used in many cases to make inference about the digestibility of the diet.

No statistically significant differences were found in the total VFA content among various age-classes and sexes (Table 1). The percentage distribution of the acids was found to be the same for male and females but differed significantly in some cases, that is, low butyric and valeric acids in yearlings and high isovaleric acids in fawns. It should be emphasized, however, that microbial fermentation continued after death while absorption of VFA stopped when the animals were killed. We had no control over the time lapse between killing the animal and freezing the rumen contents nor over the time of kill after feeding. Therefore, data should be interpreted with caution. We might conclude, however, that by an estimated 4–5 months of age, antelope fawns are functionally ruminants and probably developed the same functional microorganisms as the adults. Bryant et al. (1958) found that calves, reared on commercial starter, obtained at 9–13 weeks of age the characteristic microflora of the adult bovine. The data of Lengemann and Allen (1955), who made a study of rumen function in dairy calves, suggest that the usual adult proportions of the short chain fatty acids are obtained only after 6 months of age.

Although more data are needed on the short-chain-fatty-acid content and composition of wild ruminants, it seems that their gross pattern does not differ greatly from their domestic counterparts. It seems also, since VFA content and percentage distribution can reflect previous dietary regimes, examination of rumen contents of wild animals, especially during winter, might prove a valuable tool in determining the nutritional level of the diet of the animal.

LITERATURE CITED

Annison, E. F., and D. Lewis. 1959. Metabolism in the rumen. Methuen & Co. Ltd., London and John Wiley & Sons Inc., New York. 184pp.

Balch, D. A., and S. J. Rowland. 1957. Volatile fatty acids and lactic acid in the rumen of dairy cows receiving a variety of diets. British J. Nutrition 11(3):288–298.

Bryant, M. P., Nola Small, Cecelia Bouma, and I. Robinson. 1958. Studies of the composition of the ruminal flora and fauna of young calves. J. Dairy Sci. 41(12):1747–1767.

Gray, F. V., and A. F. Pilgrim. 1952. Fermentation in the rumen of the sheep. III. Intermediate stages in the fermentation of wheaten hay *in vitro* by micro-organisms from the rumen. J. Expt. Biol. 29(1):54–56.

Lengemann, F. W., and N. N. Allen. 1955. The development of rumen function in the dairy calf. I. Some characteristics of the rumen contents of cattle of various ages. J. Dairy Sci. 38(6):651–656.

Nagy, J. G., H. W. Steinhoff, and G. M. Ward. 1964. Effects of essential oils of sagebrush on deer rumen microbial function. J. Wildl. Mgmt. 28(4):785–790.

Short, H. L., D. E. Medin, and A. E. Anderson. 1966. Seasonal variations in volatile fatty acids in the rumen of mule deer. J. Wildl. Mgmt. 30(3):466–470.

Received for publication October 31, 1968.

WINTER FOOD HABITS, RANGE USE, AND HOME RANGE OF ANTELOPE IN MONTANA[1]

STEPHEN R. BAYLESS, Montana Department of Fish and Game, Havre

Abstract: A study of the food habits, range use, and home range of pronghorn antelope (*Antilocapra americana*) with emphasis on the winter period was conducted in 1966–67 in Montana. Quantitative measurements of canopies and densities of taxa were made in five of the eight vegetation types available to antelope. The sagebrush–grassland type received most of the use by antelope, both in summer and winter. Most winter observations were in vegetation types where sagebrush was common. The winter diet, determined by plant utilization, consisted of 93 percent shrubs, 6 percent forbs, and a minor amount of grass. The diet, determined by analysis of rumen contents, consisted of 78 percent shrubs, 19 percent forbs, and a small amount of grass. Big sagebrush (*Artemisia tridentata*) provided 45 percent of the antelope food in winter. Results of five summer aerial censuses showed 32 male antelope per 100 females and 74 fawns per 100 females. Poor body condition of antelope and some fawn mortality in winter was possibly related to quality of sagebrush in the diet. Winter home-range size was determined for each of 16 individually marked antelope, three using telemetry. Eight of the marked antelope "shifted" their home range at least once. A yearling female had a home-range size of 5,574 acres and a yearling male, 4,160 acres. Six adult females had an average home-range size of 2,841 acres; three fawn females, 2,417 acres; and five fawn males, 1,580 acres.

Information on the winter food and range-use habits of pronghorn antelope in Montana is somewhat limited. Cole (1956) reported the results of a comprehensive study of food and range-use habits with special reference to alfalfa, but data for winter were less comprehensive than for other seasons. Cole and Wilkins (1958) studied food and range use in reference to the effects on production of winter wheat. Martinka (1967) reported on mortality and food habits during a severe winter. Prominent among reports for other states are those of Einarsen (1948) and Buechner (1950) who gave information for Oregon and Texas, respectively.

The principal objectives of my study, conducted during the summer of 1966 and winter of 1966–67, were to obtain quantitative data on food habits, range use, and home range of pronghorns in winter to help evaluate current management practices (Bayless 1967). An additional parameter of the investigation was concerned with the effects of sagebrush removal on wildlife. The summer period was largely devoted to studies of the vegetation. The use of telemetry in winter greatly aided the study of habitat relationships and behavior.

To the following, I wish to extend appreciation for their contributions: D. C. Quimby, Montana State University, for technical supervision and guidance in preparation of the manuscript; R. J. Mackie, formerly with the Montana Department of Fish and Game, for initial project planning; W. E. Booth, Montana State University, for verification of my identification of plant specimens; N. S. Martin, D. Pyrah, T. W. Mussehl, R. R. Knight, and P. Schladweiler, Montana Department of Fish and Game, for assistance during various phases of the study; personnel of the Bureau of Land Management, Lewistown District Office, for their cooperation; and to my wife, Judy, for encouragement and assistance.

[1] A joint contribution from Montana State University, Agricultural Experiment Station, Project No. 400, Paper No. 934 Journal Series and the Game Management Division, Project Nos. W-98-R-6 and 7, Montana Fish and Game Department.

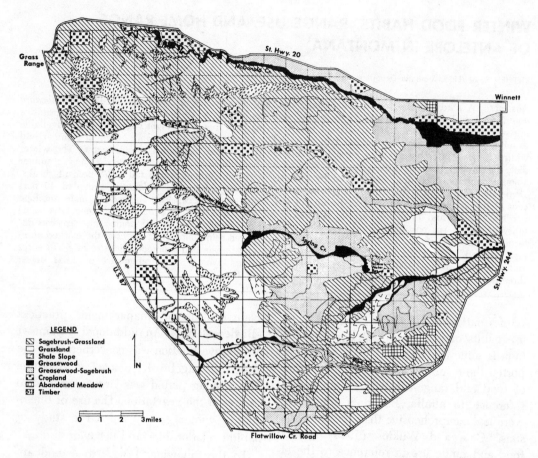

Fig. 1. The Yellow Water Triangle Study Area in central Montana showing vegetation types.

LEGEND

⬚ Sagebrush-Grassland
☐ Grassland
▨ Shale Slope
■ Greasewood
▥ Greasewood-Sagebrush
▦ Cropland
▤ Abandoned Meadow
▨ Timber

N

0   1   2   3 miles

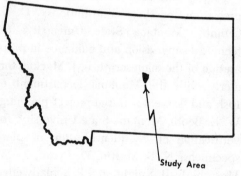

Study Area

STUDY AREA

The study area, composed of about 268 square miles, was located in central Montana approximately 40 miles east of Lewistown (Fig. 1). The principal economy of the area is stock raising, integrated with grain, alfalfa, and forage production. Privately owned lands constitute 67.3 percent of the area; publicly owned lands 32.7 percent. Public lands are administered by the U. S. Bureau of Land Management, U. S. Fish and Wildlife Service, and the State of Montana.

The characteristic physiographic features are sharply rolling upland plains, shale slopes, and bottomlands (Cole 1956). The latter two occur where erosion has dissected the upland plain. Several creeks, many stock water ponds, and the Yellow Water Storage Reservoir, occur on the area.

Gieseker (1940:15) describes the climate as semiarid, ". . . characterized by moderately low rainfall, great extremes in summer and winter temperatures, many sunny days and relatively low humidity." The average annual precipitation at Flat Willow, on the east edge of the study area, is 12.57 inches (U. S. Dept. of Commerce 1967). The mean average annual temperature is 45.4 F. Temperature extremes during the study period were 105 F in July, 1966, and –13 F in March, 1967.

METHODS

Survey of Vegetation

Classification of the vegetation was adapted from Mackie (1965) and Cole (1956). Scientific and common plant names are from Booth (1950) and Booth and Wright (1962). The method of vegetation analysis was a modification of the method of Daubenmire (1959), whereby 2- × 5-dm plots were systematically placed within a relatively homogenous and undisturbed portion of each vegetation stand. The percent canopy-cover of each species, and percentages of bare ground, rock, and lichens, were recorded for each plot. Classes were: Class 1, 0–5 percent; Class 2, 5–25 percent; Class 3, 25–50 percent; Class 4, 50–75 percent; Class 5, 75–95 percent; and Class 6, 95–100 percent. The mid-point of each class was the value used in data tabulations. Taxa occurring within each vegetation stand, regardless of whether they occurred in any of the plots, were also recorded.

Twenty 2- × 5-dm plots within each of thirty-nine 20- × 50-ft sample units on the various vegetation types were evaluated in summer. Thirty sample units located at antelope feeding sites and consisting of ten 2- × 5-dm plots along a 100-ft line were evaluated in winter.

To measure sagebrush density on the sagebrush–grassland type, I recorded the number and canopy intercept of all sagebrush plants encountered along transect lines. Each of the 27 200-ft transects measured in summer was composed of four 50-ft lines equidistant across the greatest length of a 20- × 50-ft sample unit. Several sagebrush plants were measured in each one-third of the sample unit to obtain the average maximum height and average height for the stand. In winter, the number, canopy coverage, and height of all sagebrush plants occurring along each of 16 100-ft transects were recorded.

Range Use

Aerial censuses were conducted in late June, mid-July, early August, mid-August, and early September, 1966, and early February, 1967. Each flight across the study area during a census period permitted the coverage of a 1-mile-wide strip. Starting at the northwest corner, antelope were classified in each north–south strip until the entire area had been covered. All flights started shortly after sunrise on calm, clear days, and were terminated after approximately 3 hours because of observer fatigue.

The relation between the occurrence of antelope and vegetation types in winter was evaluated by recording the type where each of the animals was first observed. Observations from the ground were made with the aid of a 15–60× spotting scope and 7- × 35-mm binoculars during 75 observation days between December 9 and March 23, while traversing the area in a four-wheel-drive vehicle over essentially the same routes. Data from aerial censuses were used in summer.

Food Habits

One-quart rumen samples were collected from each of 18 antelope and analyzed according to the method of Cole (1956). Recognizable items were volumetrically measured and expressed as percentages. Feeding-site examinations supplemented rumen content analyses in determining food preferences. Each "bite" from a plant was recorded as one instance of use on a feeding site, as described by Knowlton (1960). The percentage of the diet for each plant used was computed for each rumen and feeding site. These percentages were totaled and averaged by month, using the aggregate percent method (Martin et al. 1946).

To compare availability of plant species with their respective percentages in the diet, ten 2- × 5-dm plots placed along a 100-ft line were examined at each feeding site not covered with snow to determine the percent canopy coverage of each plant species. When snow cover made the use of the above method impractical, shrub canopies were measured along 100-ft line transects.

Marking and Home Range

Nineteen antelope, including seven adult females, one yearling female, four fawn females, one yearling male, and six fawn males, were trapped on December 9, 1966. They were driven a maximum distance of 7 miles by helicopter into an oval-shaped trap (McLucas 1956). The following day they were individually marked and released.

Neckbands constructed of plastic-impregnated nylon ("Saflag") backed with nylon webbing, similar to those used by Knight (1966) for elk, were stapled around the necks of 16 antelope. Various symbols and color combinations for individual bands facilitated recognition. Depending on light conditions, individual bands were identifiable at distances of ½ to ¾ of a mile; some patterns, however, were more easily recognizable than others.

Three antelope were each equipped with two-stage, crystal-controlled transmitters mounted on ⅛-inch thick leather collars riveted around the animals' necks. Transmitters operated in the 151 Mc range. Two emitted steady signals, and the third, a pulsating signal. The transmitters with steady signals were more easily heard than was the one with a pulsating signal when high winds caused noise in the earphones of the receiver. Receivers were the double conversion, crystal-controlled, superheterodyne type, with sensitivity better than 0.1 microvolt. Radio equipment was supplied by Markusen Electronic Specialties, Esko, Minnesota.

Banded and radio-equipped antelope were located daily when possible. Transmitter signals were heard from as far away as 7 miles under optimum conditions, but depressions and/or ridges hindered reception.

Locations of individual antelope were recorded in 0.1-mile intervals by day and month on a 0.5-inch scale map. To estimate home-range size, a line was drawn around the outside points of observation for each individual antelope. The area enclosed was calculated with the aid of a Polar Planimeter.

RESULTS AND DISCUSSION

Vegetation

The vegetation of the study area is included in the Temperate Grassland Biome (Odum 1959) and the Mixed Grass Prairie Association (Oosting 1948). The present analysis, with slight modification, follows Cole's (1956) vegetation descriptions, but makes use of quantitative measurements for five of the eight vegetation types. The Cropland, Abandoned-Meadow, and Woodland vegetation types were of little importance to antelope and were therefore deleted from quantitative analysis.

Table 1. Percentage distribution by month of 9,345 antelope observations on the Yellow Water Triangle Study Area on five vegetation types in winter, 1966–67.

Month	Sagebrush-Grassland	Grass-Land	Grease-Wood	Greasewood-Sagebrush	Crop-Land	Number Observations		
						Singles	Groups	Total Antelope
December	67	4	10	13	6	5	76	1,810
January	86	4	5	3	2	7	84	2,682
February[a]	62	6	–	31	–	9	161	3,204
March	70	7	–	23	–	1	75	1,649
Average	71	5	4	18	2			
Total						22	396	9,345

[a] Data from an aerial census on February 9, when 441 antelope observations were recorded, are combined with data from ground observations.

Although a pronounced difference occurred in composition and crown cover of forbs between summer and winter, composition of shrubs and grasses between the seasons remained similar. The occurrence and distribution of vegetation types are shown on Fig. 1.

Sagebrush–Grassland Vegetation Type.— This type occupied 51.3 percent of the study area. Various degrees of association and dominance occurred between big sagebrush, grasses, and forbs. These appeared to characterize differences in topography, soils, and/or intensity of livestock grazing.

Big sagebrush was the dominant plant, both in aspect and occurrence, but its density and height varied throughout the type. Sagebrush heights averaged 11 inches throughout the type, and canopies averaged 10 inches in diameter. Western wheatgrass (*Agropyron smithii*), bluebunch wheatgrass (*Agropyron spicatum*), blue grama (*Bouteloua gracilis*), Junegrass (*Koeleria cristata*), and Sandberg bluegrass (*Poa secunda*) were the dominant native grasses. Dominant forbs included fringed sagewort (*Artemisia frigida*), plains prickley pear (*Opuntia polyacantha*), spindle plantain (*Plantago spinulosa*), and Selaginella (*Selaginella densa*).

Grassland Vegetation Type.—This type

occupied 16.6 percent of the study area. Broom snakewood (*Gutierrezia sarothrae*) was the most common shrub. Bluebunch wheatgrass, blue grama, Junegrass, and needle-and-thread (*Stipa comata*) were the most important grasses, but various degrees of association and dominance occurred among the grasses. Important forbs included northern androsace (*Androsace septentrionalis*), fringed sagewort, spindle plantain, slimflower scurfpea (*Psoralea tenuiflora*), and Selaginella.

Shale Slope Vegetation Type.—This type, occupying 1.6 percent of the area, was confined to slopes below shale ridges. Big sagebrush, rubber rabbitbrush (*Chrysothamnus nauseosus*), broom snakeweed, and Arkansas rose (*Rosa arkansana*) were the dominant shrubs. Western wheatgrass, bluebunch wheatgrass, prairie sand reedgrass (*Calamovilfa longifolia*), longleaf sagebrush (*Artemisia longifolia*), slimflower scurfpea, and prairie thermopsis (*Thermopsis rhombifolia*) were also characteristic.

Greasewood Vegetation Type.—This type, occupying 2.8 percent of the area, was confined to stream bottoms. Greasewood (*Sarcobatus vermiculatus*) was dominant, but big sagebrush was also present. Western wheatgrass, bluebunch wheatgrass, blue grama, desert saltgrass (*Distichlis stricta*), and Sandberg bluegrass were the most common grasses. Common forbs included northern androsace, fringed sagewort, spindle plantain, and Selaginella.

Greasewood–Sagebrush Vegetation Type.—This type was the second most extensive, covering 14.2 percent of the area. It was confined to bottomland flats and adjacent gentle slopes between the sagebrush–grassland and greasewood vegetation types. Big sagebrush, Nuttall saltbush (*Atriplex nuttallii*), and greasewood were dominant shrubs. Dominant grasses included thickspike wheatgrass (*Agropyron dasystachyum*), western wheatgrass, bluebunch wheatgrass, and Sandberg bluegrass. Among forbs, northern androsace, hoary aster (*Aster canescens*), plains prickly pear, and spindle plantain were important.

Other Vegetation Types.—Vegetation types of little importance to antelope, but occurring on the study area, were the cropland type (alfalfa, hay, wheat), the abandoned-meadow type, and the woodland type (*Pinus ponderosa*).

Pronghorn Population Characteristics

The highest total count of 529 antelope was made in mid-July. Data from the September and February flights were not reliable for sex and age-class composition because does and fawns were difficult to distinguish from the air after August. During the June, July, and two August censuses, 1,925 antelope were classified. There were 32 males per 100 females, and 74 fawns per 100 females. The fawn/female figure includes yearling females. Some workers, including Einarsen (1948), have reported that antelope females do not breed until their second year, while others have reported breeding of fawns (Buechner 1950, Wright and Dow 1962).

During the winter, seven female antelope

were collected. They were aged according to mandibular dentition (Dow and Wright 1962). No yearlings were collected. Except for one with a single fetus, all females were carrying twins.

Distribution and Use of Vegetation Types

Winter (December, January, February, March).—The sagebrush–grassland vegetation type received most of the antelope use regardless of month (Table 1) or weather conditions. During each month, 62 percent or more of the observations occurred in this type, and for the entire winter, 71 percent. The sagebrush–grassland and greasewood–sagebrush types combined provided 80 percent or more of the observations in each month and 89 percent for winter. The grassland, greasewood, and cropland types received minor use, and no use was recorded for the shale slope, timber, or abandoned-meadow types. There was some evidence, from individually marked antelope, of movement from grassland to sagebrush types during periods when snow covered the ground.

The density of sagebrush plants at each antelope observation site recorded from the ground was determined (Table 2). Density values were assigned on an ocular-estimate basis resulting from experience gained while cover mapping. Most of the antelope observations were in vegetation types where sagebrush density was estimated as "common": that is, 21–40 plants intercepted per 200 ft of line transect. Measurements of canopy coverages of sagebrush in this density category ranged from 10–24 percent (Bayless 1968).

From December 10 through March 22, 9,323 antelope were observed in 396 groups of two or more animals. Group sizes averaged 23 antelope on the sagebrush–grassland vegetation type, 23 on the grassland type, 48 on the greasewood type, 34 on the

Table 2. Percentage distribution by month of 8,904 antelope observations in relation to sagebrush density in winter, 1966–67.

	SAGEBRUSH DENSITY				TOTAL NUMBER OBSERVATIONS
MONTH	1 Rare	2 Scattered	3 Common	4 Dense	
December	9[a]	29	50	12	1,810
January	7	28	53	12	2,682
February	7	38	45	10	2,763
March	7	17	48	28	1,649
Average	7.5	28.0	49.0	15.5	
Total					8,904

[a] Percentages are based on 100 percent for each month.

greasewood–sagebrush type, and 50 on the cropland type. The average group size for all types was 23.5.

Groups were largest on the cropland type, but only 2 percent of the total antelope observations occurred here. Dirschl (1963) believed that the extent and quality of the winter range were the factors determining group size for antelope.

Group size increased steadily from approximately 20 individuals, when the ground was dry, to about 31 when snow covered the ground. No correlation between group size and temperature was established, except that groups were slightly larger with warmer temperatures.

Summer (June, July, August, September). —Use of vegetation types in summer was evaluated from 2,305 observations of ante-

lope during five aerial censuses (Table 3). The sagebrush–grassland type received more use than did any other type during June, July, August, and for the entire summer, but intensities of use during this period were significantly less than for the winter months (Table 1). Use of this type steadily decreased through the summer. In September, the grassland and cropland types each received greater use than sagebrush–grassland. Cole (1956) found that sagebrush–grassland was used more by antelope than other vegetation types prior to midsummer, but after this time, use of this type decreased and use of greasewood and shale slope types increased. He also indicated that use of alfalfa fields sharply increased after mid-August, reaching a maximum in late September.

A total of 2,249 antelope in 238 groups, averaging 9.4, was observed during the five aerial censuses in summer. Groups were largest on the cropland vegetation type, but only 8 percent of the total groups were seen here. Most of the groups observed were in sagebrush–grassland, where the average group size was 8.2. Groups averaged 11 antelope on the grassland type, 8 on the shale slope type, 6 on the greasewood type, 8 on the greasewood–sagebrush type, 14 on the cropland type, and 9 on the abandoned-meadow type. Female-fawn groups, bache-

Table 3. Percentage distribution by month of 2,305 antelope observations on seven vegetation types in summer, 1966, as determined by five aerial censuses.

								NUMBER OBSERVATIONS		
MONTH	SAGEBRUSH-GRASSLAND	GRASS-LAND	SHALE SLOPE	GREASE-WOOD	GREASEWOOD SAGEBRUSH	CROP-LAND	ABANDONED MEADOW	Singles	Groups	Total Antelope
June	52	24	2	5	9	6	2	24	60	428
July	50	24	–	2	6	17	–	11	60	529
August[a]	44	31	–	1	16	8	–	11	85	968
September	16	45	–	1	17	22	–	10	33	380
Average	41	31	tr	2	12	13	tr			
Total								56	238	2,305

[a] Data for this month are the result of two aerial censuses on August 3 and August 9.

Table 4. Winter food habits of antelope by month as indicated by 13,758 instances of plant use at 28 feeding sites on the Yellow Water Triangle Study Area.

TAXA[a]	JANUARY 9 Feeding Sites			FEBRUARY 12 Feeding Sites			MARCH 7 Feeding Sites		
	Use[b]	Percent of Diet	Percent of Veg. Available	Use	Percent of Diet	Percent of Veg. Available	Use	Percent of Diet	Percent of Veg. Available
Shrubs									
Artemisia cana	910	19	7[c]	257	4	tr	367	11	3
Artemisia tridentata	4,309	76	13	3,378	79	13	3,096	78	13
Chrysothamnus nauseosus	–	–	–	129	3	tr	254	5	1
Symphoricarpos occidentalis	–	–	–	–	–	–	95	3	1
Total Shrubs	5,266	96	–	3,795	87	–	3,852	97	–
Forbs									
Artemisia frigida	7	tr	tr	332	11	6	94	3	tr
Aster canescens	214	2	2	–	–	–	–	–	–
Total Forbs	289	3	–	339	11	–	94	3	–
Grasses									
Poa compressa	–	–	–	80	2	tr	–	–	–
Total Grasses	43	tr	–	80	2	–	–	–	–

[a] Only those species which comprised 1 percent or more of the diet for at least one month are included. Others occurring were: *Agropyron spicatum* (January), *Artemisia longifolia* (March), *Atriplex* spp. (January and February), *Eurotia lanata* (February), *Grindelia squarrosa* (January), *Opuntia polyacantha* (January and February), *Phlox hoodii* (February), and *Poa secunda* (January).
[b] Refers to the number of instances of use.
[c] As determined by canopy coverage.

lor herds, and territorial males, as described by Cole (1956), were observed.

Winter Food Habits

Shrubs constituted the most important forage class in the antelope diet during winter, averaging 93 percent of the total use at feeding sites, and 78 percent by volume of the total identifiable material in rumen samples (Tables 4 and 5). Among shrubs, big sagebrush was the most important, both at feeding sites, where it averaged 78 percent of the total instances of use, and in rumens, where it averaged 45 percent by volume of the total identifiable material. Its use at feeding sites appeared to be greatly in excess of its abundance. Cole (1956), working in the same area, found that browse species, including big sagebrush and silver sagebrush, formed the major portion of rumen samples in December,

January, and February. Many authors have indicated the importance of browse in winter antelope diets (Ferrel and Leach 1952, Yoakum 1958, Dirschl 1963).

Forbs were the next most important forage class, both in rumens and at feeding sites. They averaged 6 percent of the diet on feeding sites and 19 percent by volume of the total identifiable material in rumens. Fringed sagewort was the most important forb at feeding sites. Fringed sagewort and prickly pear cactus were the important forbs in rumens. Antelope were observed to paw prickly pear cactus on several occasions, apparently for the purpose of breaking off the upper, spiny portion of the plant in order to eat the base.

Grass was unimportant, both at feeding sites and in rumens, but was eaten by antelope during green-up periods in warm weather. In the April rumen sample, grass,

Table 5. Frequency of occurrence and volume percentages of plant taxa and forage classes among 18 antelope rumen samples collected over a 5-month period in winter, 1966–67.

TAXA[a]	MONTH					
	December	January	February	March	April	Unknown[b]
Shrubs	(3)[c]	(2)	(3)	(6)	(1)	(3)
Artemisia cana	33/3[d]	50/T		17/T		
Artemisia tridentata	100/50	100/57	100/47	100/38	100/22	100/54
Atriplex spp.	67/T	100/3	33/T	17/T		33/T
Chrysothamnus nauseosus	67/7	50/21	33/9	67/3	100/9	
Unidentified shrubs	100/12	100/10	100/15	100/23	100/47	100/33
Total Shrubs	100/73	100/92	100/71	100/64	100/78	100/87
Forbs						
Artemisia frigida	67/14	50/T	67/15	83/5		67/1
Aster canescens		50/3				
Leptodactylon pungens	67/4			17/T		67/4
Opuntia polyacantha	100/5	100/3	67/7	100/19		100/T
Oxytropis spp.						33/1
Unidentified forbs	100/4	100/T	100/6	100/8		100/4
Total Forbs	100/27	100/7	100/28	100/33		100/11
Grass and grass-like plants	100/1	100/1	67/T	100/2	100/22	67/1

[a] Only those taxa which comprised 1 percent or more of the volume for at least one month are included. Others occurring were: *Antennaria rosea* (December, February, March, and Unknown), *Artemisia longifolia* (Unknown), *Allium textile* (March), *Juniperus* spp. (March), and Lichens (March).
[b] Includes three rumen samples from fawns found dead on the study area in February or March.
[c] Number of rumen samples in parenthesis.
[d] Percent frequency/aggregate percent of total volume. T indicates values less than 1 percent.

largely green, formed 22 percent by volume of the total identifiable material.

Two dead fawn antelope were found in February and one in March. The gelatinous condition of the marrow in the femur bones indicated malnutrition (Cheatum 1949). The rumen contents of these fawns did not vary significantly from those of other rumens. Little or no subcutaneous fat was visible on females and fawns collected for rumen samples, and the amount of fat inside the body cavities was observed to steadily decline with each successive collection during the winter. The rumen contents of the antelope which apparently died of malnutrition did not vary significantly from those of other rumens.

Thirteen and three-tenths percent of 511 sagebrush plants measured on feeding sites were decadent (25 percent or more of the crown was dead). On many feeding sites, big sagebrush plants were severely hedged. Martinka (1967), reporting on mortality of Montana pronghorns in a severe winter, suggested that malnutrition may have been related to a lack of sufficient quantities of shrubby sagebrush in the diet. The poor body condition and fawn mortality noted in this study possibly was related to quality of sagebrush in the diet. The relatively low fawn/female ratio may also be indicative.

Winter Home Range

A total of 579 locations of individually marked and/or radio-equipped antelope was obtained between December 9 and March 23. When released, all 18 successfully marked antelope returned to the same general area from which they were originally driven during the trapping operation.

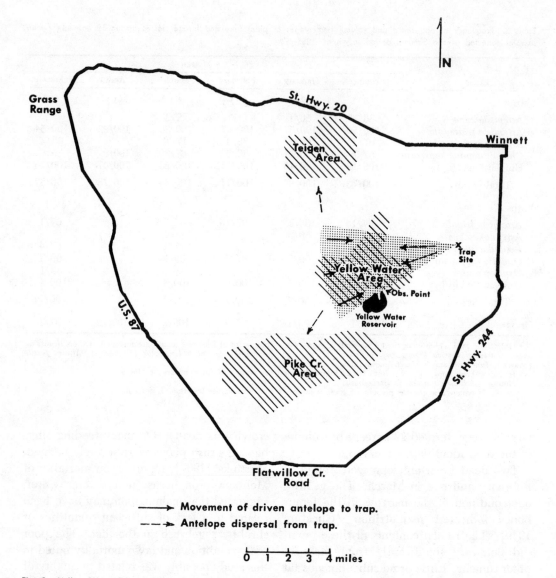

Fig. 2. Yellow Water Triangle Study Area showing antelope trapping pattern and winter concentration areas for marked antelope.

Eight, including one with a radio, remained on this area (Yellow Water Area) through the winter study period; five, including one with a radio, moved approximately 7 miles north to the Teigen Area after remaining in the Yellow Water Area for only 3 days; one radio-equipped yearling male moved 3 miles south to the Pike Creek Area after spending 3 days in the Yellow Water Area; and two banded antelope shifted their home range to the Teigen Area after spending approximately 1 month in the Yellow Water Area (Fig. 2). Data for two antelope were too incomplete for further conclusions.

Table 6. Summary of movement data for 16 individually marked antelope on the Yellow Water Triangle Study Area in winter, 1966–67.

			DISTANCE (MILES)				
			Maximum	First	From Center of Range[b]		Estimated
	No. of	SHIFT (MILES) BETWEEN	Between	to last			Home Range
ANTELOPE	OBSERV.	HOME RANGES[a]	Observ.	Observ.	Mean	Max.	(acres)
Adult F (4002)	11		4.08	2.66	1.41	2.42	1,510.4
	10	4.97	2.62	0.88	0.83	1.36	1,369.6
	14	1.47	2.05	0.23	0.65	1.28	870.4
Adult F (4004)	39	–	3.17	1.76	1.00	1.75	2,924.8
Adult F (4005)	39	–	3.96	1.76	1.08	2.78	3,776.0
Adult F (4014)	39	–	3.96	1.91	1.09	2.70	3,840.0
Adult F (1301)	58	–	3.16	1.35	0.98	1.74	2,835.2
Adult F (1374)	35	–	4.27	2.54	1.29	2.85	3,929.6
	14	1.56	2.12	0.20	0.60	1.35	915.2
Yearling F (4003)	41	–	5.02	2.20	1.16	4.10	5,574.4
Fawn F (4008)	5		1.40	1.13	0.59	0.80	409.6
	13	1.90	2.11	1.00	0.63	1.32	915.2
Fawn F (4009)	14		4.27	0.45	1.22	2.85	1,644.8
	4	4.82	1.60	1.15	0.58	0.52	134.4
Fawn F (4010)	38	–	4.80	1.90	1.12	3.32	4,691.2
Yearling M (1372)	22		6.82	1.85	1.98	3.64	5,209.6
	19	3.64	4.37	1.64	0.97	3.13	3,110.4
Fawn M (4006)	37	–	3.18	2.64	1.04	2.30	2,560.0
Fawn M (4007)	7		1.90	1.00	0.68	0.98	1,011.2
	13	1.90	2.10	1.00	0.62	1.31	960.0
Fawn M (4011)	5		1.40	1.13	0.56	0.80	428.8
	13	1.89	2.10	1.00	0.63	1.33	960.0
Fawn M (4012)	5		1.40	1.13	0.56	0.80	428.8
	12	1.99	1.70	1.00	0.55	1.00	723.2
Fawn M (4015)	42	–	1.17	1.90	1.01	1.75	2,668.8

[a] Center to center distance.
[b] Central point of the area within which the animal was observed, calculated geometrically (Hayne 1949).

One fawn male was deleted from home-range calculations because only five observations were recorded. Eight of the 16 for which home ranges were calculated "shifted" their home range, seven once and one twice (Table 6). A home range "shift" was defined as a movement from one area of activity to another with no subsequent return.

The yearling female had the largest home range of all sex and age groups for which data were available, followed by the yearling male, adult females, fawn females, and fawn males, respectively (Table 7). No data were available for adult males. Movements for each of two adult females are shown graphically in Figs. 3 and 4.

For those groups where more than one animal was available, home-range sizes were tested with a standard analysis of variance, one-way classification, $P > 0.05$ (Li 1965). The hypothesis tested was:

Table 7. Average winter home-range size for each of five sex and age-groups of individually marked antelope on the Yellow Water Triangle Study Area in winter, 1966–67.

AGE AND SEX GROUP	No. OF ANTE-LOPE	AV. HOME RANGE SIZE (ACRES)[a]	RANGE
Adult F	6	2,841.4	1,250.1–3,840.0
Yearling F	1	5,574.4	–
Fawn F	3	2,417.1	915.2–4,691.2
Yearling M	1	4,160.0	–
Fawn M	5	1,579.5	723.2–2,668.8

[a] Eight antelope had home range "shifts." The average of the home ranges for each of these antelope was used in calculating average home-range size, except for four where the number of observations for one of the home ranges was less than six. For these four the home range resulting from six or more observations was used.

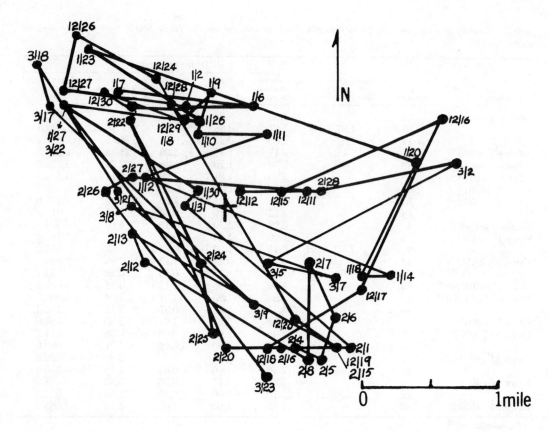

+ geometric center of home range

—— joins successive observations on home range

Fig. 3. Individual locations of an adult female (1301) by day and month in the Yellow Water Area with no home range shifts.

there was no significant difference between the mean home-range size of adult females, fawn females, and fawn males. Whether the assumptions were satisfied in this test was questionable, but the resulting F-value of 1.4898 with 2 and 11 degrees of freedom led to acceptance of the hypothesis. A *t*-test applied to the three group means also led to acceptance of the hypothesis that no significant difference existed (11 degrees of freedom, $P > 0.05$).

Fawn females had the most variable home-range sizes, followed by adult females and fawn males, respectively. Since home-range data were available for only one yearling female and one yearling male, no conclusion could be made about the variability of the home ranges for these sex and age groups.

Adult females used a larger area on the sagebrush–grassland vegetation type than on the greasewood–sagebrush type. Fawn

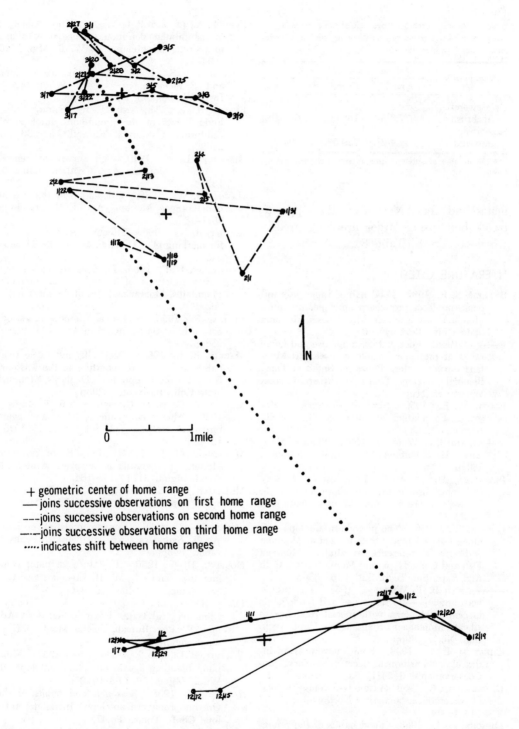

Fig. 4. Individual locations of an adult female (4002) by day and month showing two home range shifts. The first home range was in the Yellow Water Area; the second and third in the Teigen Area.

JWM 33(3): 551

Table 8. Average area used by each of three sex and age groups of individually marked antelope in relation to vegetation types in winter, 1966–67.

VEGETATION TYPE	AVERAGE AREA USED (ACRES)		
	Adult F	Fawn F	Fawn M
Greasewood-sagebrush	2,977.3(5)[a]	3,168.0(2)	2,614.4(2)
Sagebrush-grassland	3,542.4(2)	729.6(2)	1,504.0(3)

[a] The number of antelope used in calculations in parenthesis.

males and females showed the opposite trend, both using larger areas on greasewood–sagebrush (Table 8).

LITERATURE CITED

BAYLESS, S. R. 1967. Food habits, range use and home range of pronghorn antelope in central Montana during winter. M.S. Thesis, Montana State Univ., Bozeman. 65pp.

———. 1968. Food habits, range use and home range of pronghorn antelope in central Montana during winter. Paper presented at Third Biennial Antelope States Workshop, Casper, Wyoming. 11pp.

BOOTH, W. E. 1950. Flora of Montana. I. Research Foundation at Montana State Coll., Bozeman. 232pp.

———, AND J. C. WRIGHT. 1962. Flora of Montana. II. Montana State Coll., Bozeman. 280pp.

BUECHNER, H. K. 1950. Life history, ecology and range use of the pronghorn antelope in Trans-Pecos Texas. Am. Midland Naturalist 43(2):257–354.

COLE, G. F. 1956. The pronghorn antelope—Its range use and food habits in central Montana with special reference to alfalfa. Montana Fish and Game Dept. and Montana State Coll. Agr. Expt. Sta. Tech. Bull. 516. 63pp.

———, AND B. T. WILKINS. 1958. The pronghorn antelope—Its range use and food habits in central Montana with special reference to wheat. Montana Fish and Game Dept. Tech. Bull. No. 2. 39pp.

CHEATUM, E. L. 1949. Bone marrow as an index of malnutrition in deer. New York State Conservationist 3(5):19–22.

DAUBENMIRE, R. 1959. A canopy-coverage method of vegetational analysis. Northwest Sci. 33 (1):43–64.

DIRSCHL, H. J. 1963. Food habits of the pronghorn in Saskatchewan. J. Wildl. Mgmt. 27(1): 81–93.

DOW, S. A., JR., AND P. L. WRIGHT. 1962. Changes in mandibular dentition associated with age in pronghorn antelope. J. Wildl. Mgmt. 26 (1):1–18.

EINARSEN, A. S. 1948. The pronghorn antelope and its management. 1st ed. Wildl. Mgmt. Inst., Washington, D. C. 238pp.

FERREL, CAROL M., AND H. R. LEACH. 1950. Food habits of the prong-horn antelope of California. California Fish and Game 36(1): 21–26.

GIESEKER, L. F. 1940. Soil survey of central Montana. Montana Agr. Expt. Sta. Bull. 9. 133pp.

HAYNE, D. W. 1949. Calculation of the size of home range. Montana Agr. Expt. Sta. Bull. 30:1–18.

KNIGHT, R. R. 1966. Effectiveness of neckbands for marking elk. J. Wildl. Mgmt. 30(4):845–846.

KNOWLTON, F. F. 1960. Food habits, movements and populations of moose in the Gravelly Mountains, Montana. J. Wildl. Mgmt. 24(2): 162–170.

LI, J. C. R. 1965. Statistical inference I. 1st ed. Edwards Brothers, Inc., Ann Arbor, Michigan. 658pp.

MACKIE, R. J. 1965. Deer, elk, and cattle food habits and range relationships in the Missouri River Breaks. Unpubl. Ph.D. thesis, Montana State Coll., Bozeman. 229pp.

MARTIN, A. C., R. H. GENSCH, AND C. P. BROWN. 1946. Alternative methods in upland game bird food analysis. J. Wildl. Mgmt. 10(1):8–12.

MARTINKA, C. J. 1967. Mortality of northern Montana pronghorns in a severe winter. J. Wildl. Mgmt. 31(1):159–164.

McLUCAS, J. 1956. Antelope trapping procedure. Spec. Rep. to Game Mgmt. Div., Montana Dept. Fish and Game, Helena.

ODUM, E. P. 1959. Fundamentals of ecology. W. B. Saunders Co., Philadelphia, Pennsylvania. 546pp.

OOSTING, H. J. 1956. The study of plant communities. 2nd ed. W. H. Freeman and Co., San Francisco, California. 440pp.

U. S. DEPT. OF COMMERCE. 1967. Montana Climatological Data. Environ. Sci. Serv. Admin., Weather Bureau, Helena, Montana. (Personal communication.)

WRIGHT, P. L., AND S. A. DOW, JR. 1962. Minimum breeding age in pronghorn antelope. J. Wildl. Mgmt. 26(1):100–101.

YOAKUM, J. 1958. Seasonal food habits of the Oregon pronghorn antelope. Interstate Antelope Conf., Trans. Pp.47.

Received for publication November 5, 1968.

CLOSTRIDIUM PERFRINGENS ENTEROTOXEMIA IN HAND-REARED ANTELOPE[1]

JULIUS G. NAGY, Department of Fishery and Wildlife Biology and Department of Animal Science, Colorado State University, Fort Collins

THOMAS A. BARBER, Department of Fishery and Wildlife Biology, Colorado State University, Fort Collins

ALBERT E. McCHESNEY, Department of Pathology, Colorado State University, Fort Collins

Abstract: Enterotoxemia caused by *Clostridium perfringens* was responsible for the death of a 2-month-old hand-reared antelope (*Antilocapra americana*). This case of enterotoxemia and other digestive upsets occurred as a group of antelope fawns began to consume solid food along with their milk diet. Symptoms of the disease and preventive treatment given to the animals is discussed.

Susceptibility of young pen-reared wild ruminants, used in wildlife research, to diseases of domestic animals which are kept nearby or have previously occupied the same pens has been little investigated. Occasional clinical reports and necropsies of wild animals brought into diagnostic laboratories provide a large part of the present knowledge.

Cl. perfringens organisms were cultured from the intestinal contents of a bottle-raised 2-month-old pronghorn antelope kid which died after approximately 36 hours of illness. Immediately prior to the time of the animal's death, its diet included milk, leaves of alfalfa hay, and commercial calf starter which was being used as a means of transition from milk to solid food.

Early symptoms observed were abdominal tensing and a moderate watery diarrhea. Before death the animal lay down with its legs drawn up, extending its head onto the ground, and was unable to rise. Findings of a necropsy, performed within 1 hour of the animal's death, included extensive hemorrhagic enteritis with blotchy hemorrhages throughout the gastrointestinal tract, blood clots in the peritoneal cavity, and degenera-

tion of kidney structure. Antitoxin–toxin neutralization tests in mice with *Cl. perfringens* types C and D diagnostic serums showed the toxin produced to be of the D type; the organism producing this toxin is responsible for enterotoxemia in domestic livestock in the same geographical area.

Symptoms, necropsy findings, and a consideration of diet and feeding, indicate that this animal was affected with enterotoxemia in a manner similar to domestic and feedlot lambs. Accumulation of partly digested low roughage feeds in the intestine of these young animals allows the rapid proliferation of the type D organism and the reproduction of high levels of toxin (Newsom and Thorpe 1938). Digestive disorders among hand-raised antelope have been described by Einarsen (1948:114). Honess and Winter (1956:43) found that enterotoxemia occurred in adult mule deer (*Odocoileus hemionus*) fed alfalfa hay but not among young animals which were fed milk or rations normally given to mature deer.

Immediately following the death of the first animal, the five remaining kids of the group received three doses of 1 ml of chloromycetin at 8-hour intervals, a single dose of 20 ml of *Cl. perfringens* type D antitoxin subcutaneously, and 3 and 10 days later, 1 ml of *Cl. perfringens* type C toxoid.

[1] This study was financed under National Science Foundation Grant GB-7824 and is part of the International Biological Program, Grassland Biome Sub-program.

JWM 33(4): 1033

At the time of initial treatment all of the animals weighed between 20 and 25 lbs.

Despite treatment all of the animals showed symptoms of intestinal disorder. In all cases the feces became soft with the pellets mucous-covered or watery. The two most severely affected animals were those which ordinarily consumed the largest amounts of food. These two antelope, with a severe watery diarrhea, were isolated from the rest and their previous diet of whole cow's milk was changed to 12 oz of a 1:4 dilution of Similac[2] in water given four times daily. At each feeding, 100 mg of chloromycetin, one powdered 0.5 g sulfathaladine tablet, and 2 to 3 ml of Kaopectate[3] were mixed in the formula. One-pound quantities of oats treated with recommended therapeutic levels of feed additive terramycin were offered.

The condition of the latter two animals improved within a day after treatment was initiated. Treatment was continued for 5 days and at the end of this time the drugs were removed from the formula and the amount of Kaopectate decreased; within 3

---

[2] Product of Ross Laboratories, Columbus, Ohio.
[3] Product of Upjohn Pharmaceuticals, Kalamazoo, Michigan.

days after the cessation of medication, the symptoms returned and more treatment was necessary. From this time until milk was completely eliminated from their diet these two animals suffered sporadic relapses and the treatment was reinstituted. In spite of this somewhat continuous gastro-intestinal tract disorder, both of these animals were apparently in excellent condition at weaning and of the same weight as their untreated pen-mates.

Previous experience of the authors with raising mule deer fawns in captivity has indicated that the period of change from monogastric to ruminant digestion is critical. Loss of this antelope due to enterotoxemia and digestive upsets evidenced by the surviving kids show that such may also be the case with young pen-raised antelope.

LITERATURE CITED

EINARSEN, A. S. 1948. The pronghorn antelope and its management. The Wildlife Management Institute, Washington, D. C. 238pp.

HONESS, R. F., AND K. B. WINTER. 1956. Diseases of wildlife in Wyoming. Wyoming Game and Fish Comm. Bull. 9. 279pp.

NEWSOM, J., AND M. THORPE. 1938. The toxicity of intestinal filtrates from lambs dead of overeating. J. Am. Vet. Med. Assoc. 93:165–168.

Received for publication March 13, 1969.

JWM 34(2): 470

DERIVATION OF WHOLE WEIGHTS FOR THE PRONGHORN[1]

BART W. O'GARA,[2] Department of Zoology, University of Montana, Missoula

Abstract: Manipulation of whole and partial weights of 133 pronghorns (*Antilocapra americana*) indicated that the approximate whole weights of adults and yearlings could be derived from partial weights with less than 2 percent error (95 percent confidence interval.) Derivation of whole weights for fawns involved a maximum error of 7 percent.

Whole weights of game animals are often of interest or value to sportsmen and biologists. Whole weights are generally secured during scientific collections but only eviscerated or carcass weights are obtained by checking station personnel and hunters. The object of this paper is to establish approximate values by which whole weights of pronghorns can be derived from partial weights.

I wish to thank P. L. Wright for his advice and help throughout this study.

METHODS AND MATERIALS

For the purpose of this paper, whole weights are defined as weights which were taken just after the animals were shot and

bled. Eviscerated weights are the weights of animals from which all of the viscera had been removed. Carcass weights are the weights of animals with the viscera, heads, feet, and skins removed.

Between August, 1965, and October, 1967, 137 pronghorns were shot on the National Bison Range, Moiese, Montana, and in Yellowstone National Park. These animals were collected during all months of the year for a study of the reproductive cycle of the female pronghorn (O'Gara 1969), but slightly more than half of them were collected during the months of August, September, and October. Most of the animals were shot between sunrise and 2 hours after sunrise but some were collected during all hours of the day. Four animals are not included in this paper.

Whole, eviscerated, and carcass weights were taken to the nearest lb; heads were weighed to the nearest 0.25 lb; the feet were weighed to the nearest 5 g. Reproductive tracts were removed from females

[1] A contribution from the National Defense Education Act, the Montana State Fish and Game Department, the Bureau of Sport Fisheries and Wildlife, the National Park Service, and the University of Montana.

[2] Present address: Montana Cooperative Wildlife Research Unit, University of Montana, Missoula.

before whole weights were taken. The volume of each rumen's contents was determined, to the nearest pint, by emptying the contents into a graduated, 12-quart bucket. Rumen volume was later converted to weight by multiplying the volume by 2.5 lb/qt. Average rumen weights for each sex and age-class were determined. The whole weight of each animal was adjusted by subtracting or adding the difference between the individual's rumen weight and the average weight for the particular age- and sex-class.

RESULTS AND DISCUSSION

The average whole weights of adult animals in this collection (110.7 ± 9.9 lbs for 90 does and 126.9 ± 8.9 for 14 bucks) are higher than those reported in California, Colorado, Oregon, and Wyoming, and less than those reported from Alberta (Bear 1967, Edwards 1958, Mason 1952, McLean 1944, Mitchell 1965). Larger numbers of old animals in this collection may account for the heavier weights.

McLean (1944:239) reported an 18-percent loss of weight when pronghorns which he collected in California were eviscerated. Einarsen (1948:41) stated that a dressed-out pronghorn with its feet removed weighed 20 percent less than its whole weight, apparently basing this conclusion on McLean's weights. One hundred and four adult animals collected in Montana averaged 28-percent loss from evisceration (O'Gara 1968:137); Bear (1967:118–120) reported an average loss of 27 percent in Colorado; adult females in Wyoming averaged 31-percent loss. It is possible that the light weights often reported for pronghorns result from the use of Einarsen's (1948) method of computing whole weights from partial weights.

Percent of weight lost by evisceration is not a convenient way in which to deter-

Table 1. Average multipliers by which whole weights could be derived from partial weights of pronghorns.[a]

		MULTIPLIER		95 PERCENT CI
Female Fawns (8)				
EV	×	1.35	= WW	1.34–1.36
EV − Ft	×	1.41	= WW	1.40–1.42
EV − Hd	×	1.44	= WW	1.43–1.45
EV − Ft & Hd	×	1.51	= WW	1.50–1.52
Carcass	×	1.77	= WW	1.66–1.88
Male Fawns (5)				
EV	×	1.38	= WW	1.35–1.41
EV − Ft	×	1.44	= WW	1.41–1.47
EV − Hd	×	1.48	= WW	1.46–1.50
EV − Ft & Hd	×	1.56	= WW	1.52–1.60
Carcass	×	1.78	= WW	1.75–1.81
Female Yearlings (12)				
EV	×	1.35	= WW	1.34–1.36
EV − Ft	×	1.40	= WW	1.39–1.41
EV − Hd	×	1.44	= WW	1.43–1.45
EV − Ft & Hd	×	1.49	= WW	1.48–1.50
Carcass	×	1.68	= WW	1.66–1.70
Male Yearlings (4)				
EV	×	1.36	= WW	1.35–1.37
EV − Ft	×	1.41	= WW	1.39–1.43
EV − Hd	×	1.45	= WW	1.44–1.46
EV − Ft & Hd	×	1.50	= WW	1.49–1.51
Carcass	×	1.73	= WW	1.72–1.74
Female Adults (90)				
EV	×	1.39	= WW	1.38–1.40
EV − Ft	×	1.45	= WW	1.44–1.46
EV − Hd	×	1.48	= WW	1.46–1.50
EV − Ft & Hd	×	1.54	= WW	1.52–1.56
Carcass	×	1.73	= WW	1.71–1.75
Male Adults (14)				
EV	×	1.39	= WW	1.38–1.40
EV − Ft	×	1.44	= WW	1.43–1.45
EV − Hd	×	1.50	= WW	1.49–1.51
EV − Ft & Hd	×	1.56	= WW	1.55–1.57
Carcass	×	1.75	= WW	1.73–1.77

[a] Mult = Multiplier; CI = Confidence Interval; EV = Eviscerated Weight; WW = Whole Weight; Hd = Head; Ft = Feet; ( ) = Sample Size.

mine the whole weights of animals. Table 1 lists the average numbers by which partial weights of pronghorns of various sex and age-groups had to be multiplied in order to arrive at their whole weights. Weights of necks, which are often removed by hunters, were not taken in 1965–66. During this collection, the heads were removed at the atlas, therefore the whole neck contributed to the eviscerated and carcass weights. In 1967, I secured the following weights of necks which were severed at the atlas and sawed off immediately in front of the shoulders: 8 adult does averaged 116 lbs, their necks—2.94 lbs; 1 buck (3½ years old) weighed 126 lbs, his neck —3.75 lbs. Thus a multiplier of 0.03 added to any multiplier in Table 1 would roughly compensate for the removal of the neck.

Rumen contents varied from 3 to 16 pints but no relationship was apparent between the time of day that an animal was shot and its rumen volume. Confidence intervals for deriving whole weights from partial weights without taking the rumen contents into consideration were too large to have practical application. Ten 1-quart samples of fresh rumen contents averaged 2.56 lb/qt. Weighing rumens, with their contents, in the field would have been more convenient and accurate than measuring the volume of their contents and later converting it to weight.

The large confidence interval (± 0.11) associated with carcass weights of female fawns probably resulted from errors in taking field weights. Three carcass weights are the source of the wide variation. Since the confidence interval associated with other weights for the same animals is much smaller (± 0.02), it is improbable that the carcass weights actually varied to the extent indicated.

All of the whole weights were biased slightly because the animals were bled be-fore whole weights were taken. Eviscerated and carcass weights were taken soon after the death of the animals in this collection. Thus dehydration of an eviscerated animal or a carcass would increase the bias toward a low estimate of the whole weight when using a multiplier. Since hunter-killed pronghorns are usually transported considerable distances through dry prairie country, this bias would be large if the eviscerated animal or carcass was weighed after a hunter returned home with his kill.

LITERATURE CITED

BEAR, G. D. 1967. Antelope investigations. Colorado Game Research Rept. Proj. No. W-40-R-7, 1. Pp.45–131.

EDWARDS, W. C. 1958. Reproductive potential of big game animals. Wyoming Game and Fish Dept., Proj. No. FW-3-R-5. Pp.33–57.

EINARSEN, A. S. 1948. The pronghorn antelope and its management. The Wildlife Management Institute, Washington, D. C. 238pp.

McLEAN, D. C. 1944. The pronghorned antelope in California. California Fish and Game Dept. 30(4):221–241.

MASON, E. 1952. Food habits and measuremens of Hart Mountain antelope. J. Wildl. Mgmt. 16(3):387–389.

MITCHELL, G. J. 1965. Natality, mortality and related phenomena in two populations of pronghorned antelope in Alberta, Canada. Ph.D. Thesis. Washington State Univ., Pullman. 111pp. Multilithed.

O'GARA, B. W. 1968. A study of the reproductive cycle of the female pronghorn (*Antilocapra americana* Ord). Ph.D. Thesis. Univ. Montana, Missoula. 161pp. Multilithed.

———. 1969. Unique aspects of reproduction in the female pronghorn (*Antilocapra americana* Ord). Am. J. Anat. 125(2):217–232.

Received for publication January 20, 1969.

JWM 34(3): 570

FORAGE USE, WATER CONSUMPTION, AND PRODUCTIVITY
OF PRONGHORN ANTELOPE IN WESTERN UTAH[1]

DONALD M. BEALE, Utah State Division of Fish and Game, Salt Lake City[2]

ARTHUR D. SMITH, Department of Range Science, Utah State University, Logan

Abstract: A study of herbage production, forage use, water consumption, and productivity of pronghorn antelope (*Antilocapra americana*) was conducted from 1961 through 1969, on semi-desert range in western Utah. Most of the data were obtained from a small herd of antelope confined by a fence to 10,000 acres. Herbage production on the study area ranged from 114–321 lbs of air-dried herbage per acre over a 5-year period. During the same period, annual precipitation ranged from 4.24–11.13 inches. During summers of above-average rainfall, forbs provided over 90 percent of the diet at the peak of their production. Conversely, in years of below-average summer rainfall, forbs were often scarce and contributed less than 20 percent, browse making up the remainder. Grass was commonly utilized by antelope in early spring, and occasionally in late summer and fall if new growth appeared. Succulence appeared to be the major characteristic of the forage sought by the antelope. During late fall and winter when nearly all forbs were dry, their diet was over 90 percent browse, mostly black sagebrush (*Artemisia nova*). Antelope water consumption varied inversely with the quantity and succulence of preferred forage species. When forbs were abundant and their moisture content was 75 percent or more, the antelope did not drink water even though it was readily available. As vegetation lost succulence, water consumption began, reaching 3 quarts of water per animal per day during extremely dry periods. Fawn:doe ratios on the study area ranged from 100:100 to 181:100. These ratios are for mature does. A statistical analysis of fawn production to precipitation received during the previous summer months indicated a significant relationship and gave statistical values of $t = 4.42$ ($P < 0.01$); $r = 0.722$ ($P < 0.05$).

Pronghorn antelope are not abundant in Utah despite their wide distribution within the state. Approximately 1,200 head range in small herds over roughly 15,000 square miles of semi-desert range similar to that on the study area. Historical evidence indicates that antelope were once more numerous than they have been in recent years (Udy 1953). Seton (1927:424) cited one report that numerous antelope were seen in Utah, but the specific area of Utah was not identified. By 1922 they had been reduced to less than 1,000 head (Nelson 1925:56). Concern over the apparent low productivity and the now relatively static population trend of this species led to its study on the semi-desert ranges of western Utah.

These semi-desert ranges are primarily used for winter grazing by sheep and cattle. A few areas are also grazed in summer by cattle. Heavy grazing by livestock in the past has altered vegetative composition over much of the range and many browse species have been eliminated over large areas (Stewart et al. 1940). Some of these were preferred antelope forage. The adoption of improved management practices and the replacement of sheep by winter cattle grazing has resulted in recovery of browse plants, particularly black sagebrush, on some of these range lands. Hutchings and Stewart (1953:36) report considerable increase in herbage production from black sagebrush as a result of improved grazing practices.

Special thanks are extended to personnel of the Intermountain Forest and Range Experiment Station for their cooperation and assistance. The authors are particularly grateful to R. C. Holmgren who provided

[1] A contribution from Utah Federal Aid Project W-105-R, Department of Range Science, Utah State University, in cooperation with the Intermountain Forest and Range Experiment Station, Forest Service, U. S. Department of Agriculture.

[2] Stationed at Utah State University, Logan.

considerable help and encouragement throughout the study.

THE STUDY AREA

The study area is located 50 miles west of Milford, Utah, on the Desert Experimental Range of the Intermountain Forest and Range Experiment Station, U. S. Forest Service. For purposes of this study, a small herd of antelope was confined by a fence to a range of approximately 10,000 acres. The number of antelope in the herd varied from 15 to 53 but for the most part approximated 35 head. The area is moderately grazed by approximately 1,800 sheep between January 1 and March 31. The actual number of sheep-days use are adjusted to Forest Service calculations of forage production each year.

The study area is typical of many intermountain valleys in western Utah and central Nevada. It ranges in elevation from 5,200–8,500 ft above sea level, but the antelope seldom go above 6,500 ft. The chief topographical feature consists of long alluvial fans cut by shallow drainages that extend from the mountains to the valley bottom. Above the alluvial fans is an area of steep slopes and below, a small area of lacustrine sediments. Most topographic situations where antelope have been seen in western Utah are represented in the study area. The vegetation is comprised of various communities of the northern desert shrub formation of Shantz (1925). Major shrub species present in the enclosure include shadscale (*Atriplex confertifolia*), winterfat (*Eurotia lanata*), little rabbitbrush (*Chrysothamnus stenophyllus*), black sagebrush, and bud sagebrush (*A. spinescens*). Desert almond (*Prunus fasciculata*), big rabbitbrush (*Chrysothamnus nauseosus*), and Mohave brickellia (*Brickellia oblongifolia*) are common along drainages.

The most abundant grasses are Indian ricegrass (*Oryzopsis hymenoides*), galleta (*Hilaria jamesii*), sand dropseed (*Sporobolus cryptandrus*), blue grama (*Bouteloua gracilis*), and squirreltail (*Sitanion hystrix*). A sparse overstory of Utah juniper (*Juniperus osteosperma*) occurs on the higher benchlands above 6,000 ft elevation. A large number of annual and perennial forbs such as globemallow (principally *Sphaeralcea grossulariaefolia*), chaenactis (*Chaenactis macrantha*), and wild buckwheat (*Eriogonum hookeri*) are present. The abundance of the annuals depends a great deal on spring and summer rainfall (Hutchings 1954).

The climate of the area is characterized by low humidity, low precipitation, and widely ranging temperatures diurnally and seasonally. Maximum temperatures during summer frequently exceed 95 F and minimum temperatures in winter often drop to –20 F. Annual precipitation averages approximately 6 inches, but it is highly variable. The precipitation in the central part of the study area ranged from 4.24–11.13 inches over the 9 years of record (Table 1). Most of the summer rainfall comes as thunderstorms during July and August. Snowfall is normally light and accumulated depths seldom exceed 6 inches.

METHODS

Herbage Production

Herbage production of all species on the study area was determined in November each year from 1962–1966. Supplemental forage inventories were made at other periods during the summer to obtain data on the ephemeral species. Transects were randomly located in areas frequented by antelope, as determined by observation and pellet count. Circular plots 96 ft² were located at random along these transects.

Table 1. Average monthly precipitation measured at four gauges on the study area on the Desert Experimental Range.

YEAR	Jan.	Feb.	Mar.	Apr.	May	June	July	Aug.	Sept.	Oct.	Nov.	Dec.	TOTAL
1961	0.41	0.29	0.42	1.06	0.13	0.35	0.54	2.33	1.52	0.55	0.15	0.22	7.97
1962	0.31	1.35	0.19	0.00	0.94	0.53	0.03	0.00	0.01	0.52	0.00	0.36	4.24
1963	0.00	0.45	0.33	1.00	0.37	1.41	0.03	1.45	1.60	0.70	0.85	0.38	8.57
1964	0.19	0.10	0.43	1.11	0.76	0.54	0.38	0.51	0.08	0.18	0.83	0.64	5.75
1965	0.08	0.28	0.70	0.73	1.64	0.38	0.49	3.95	0.78	0.03	0.88	1.19	11.13
1966	0.20	0.28	0.19	0.15	0.20	0.11	0.08	0.62	1.04	0.29	0.04	1.64	4.84
1967	0.38	0.04	0.08	1.46	1.21	2.08	1.86	0.38	1.96	0.05	0.09	0.21	9.80
1968	0.04	0.45	0.49	1.50	0.63	0.69	0.86	0.80	0.21	0.46	0.09	0.17	6.39
1969	0.76	0.39	0.70	0.24	0.13	1.07	1.72	1.11	0.25	0.59	0.20	0.27	7.43

The number of plots used was such as would provide an estimate for the major perennial browse and grass species within 10 percent of the mean and ranged from 146–430. Herbage production was determined using the weight-estimate method (Pechanec and Pickford 1937b).

Forage Use

Two methods were used to determine forage preference and use: (1) random observations at feeding sites; (2) ocular estimates of use on sample plots. During the spring and summer, most of the data were obtained from the examination of feeding sites. The procedures were similar to those followed by Buechner (1950) and Cole (1956). Feeding antelope were located by aid of a spotting scope and the site identified by some recognizable feature. When the antelope left or ceased feeding, the sites were examined and estimates made of the amounts of available forage and the percentage of forage removed by species, using a modification of the procedure suggested by Pechanec and Pickford (1937a).

Ocular estimates of utilization (Pechanec and Pickford 1937a) were made concurrently within the same plots used for the taking of herbage production data in the fall. Additional utilization estimates were made in winter using the same methods of location of 96-ft² plots as were employed in the production estimates.

Seven rumen samples were collected from the study area to augment the feeding site data and provide additional qualitative information.

In addition, 31 rumen samples were collected from male antelope killed near the study area during hunting seasons. These samples provided information on late summer and fall forage use by antelope outside the study area.

Dirschl (1962) reported that there was very little difference in plant composition data obtained from antelope rumen samples washed with screens ranging from 2.83 to 5.66 mm in mesh size. The larger screens, however, retained materials which were more easily identified. Accordingly, our samples were washed through screens of 5.66-mm and 4.00-mm mesh.

The material retained in the screen was allowed to stand in the laboratory until it became air dry, then was separated by species (using plant collections as reference material), weighed, and the percentages of each plant species determined.

Water Consumption

Data on antelope water consumption were obtained during a 4-year period, 1962–65. Water was available only in 100-

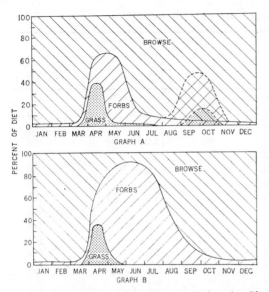

Fig. 1. Diet of antelope in southwestern Utah under different moisture regimes. A. Dry season. Dotted lines indicate change in diet in late summer when summer rains occur. B. Wet season. Diets under high precipitation during spring and summer.

gallon-capacity troughs spaced throughout the area. The troughs had covers over three-fourths of their area to minimize evaporation. At one location, an identical trough was fenced from antelope to provide means of correcting for evaporational loss. No correction was made for precipitation since it was assumed that it would be equal in both protected and open troughs and would be accounted for in the evaporation measurement. Each trough was equipped with a pointed water level marker similar to those in open pan evaporimeters.

At each refilling, the amount of water required to bring the water to the level defined by the marker was determined. The difference between the amounts required to fill the unprotected and the protected troughs divided by the number of animals in the study area gave the consumption per animal. Fawns were given fractional values based on weight so that the data are in terms of adult animals.

Fawn Production and Survival

Natality of the antelope herd was determined by close observation of the does in early morning hours throughout the fawning period. Observations were made from towers and natural lookout points, using a spotting scope. Some of the does in the herd had individual markings which facilitated matching does and fawns. In some years, some of the fawns also were marked as an aid in determining fawn survival. Information regarding survival of fawns was obtained from periodic fawn/doe counts. In some instances, a total count of the herd was possible. Where this was not possible, survival indices were derived from fawn/doe ratios and fawn counts among the marked does.

RESULTS AND DISCUSSION

Herbage Production

Over a 5-year period (1962–66), the total herbage production at the time of the November inventory ranged from 113–321 lbs/acre and averaged 164 lbs/acre, air-dry weight (Table 2). Those forbs, many preferred by antelope, which had matured and disappeared before fall estimates were made, were not represented in the data.

Total forage production on semi-desert range is directly related to the amount of precipitation (Hutchings and Stewart 1953), although for individual species, the seasonal occurrence of precipitation is important and particularly so for many of the forage species preferred by antelope. Many of the perennial forbs on the study area responded to available moisture anytime from spring through fall. Some annuals grow best during the spring, while others are favored by summer moisture. Unless moisture is available during these periods, species normally present are reduced in volume or entirely absent. For example,

Table 2. Herbage production on the Desert Experimental Range, November, 1962–1966.

	HERBAGE PRODUCTION POUNDS/ACRE AIR DRIED		
SPECIES	Low Year (1963)	High Year (1965)	Five-Year Average (1962–1966)
Shrubs			
Atriplex confertifolia	19.7	61.6	33.6
Eurotia lanata	9.0	31.2	12.2
Artemisia nova	6.1	15.9	9.9
Gutierrezia sarothrae	3.8	23.2	9.7
Chrysothamnus spp.	3.8	13.6	6.6
Ephedra nevadensis	2.5	9.8	3.5
Artemisia spinescens	4.3	4.7	3.3
Tetradymia spinosa	1.0	0.8	0.8
Prunus fasciculata	0.6	1.5	0.6
Petradoria pumila	0.2	0.8	0.4
Cercocarpus intricatus	0.3	1.0	0.3
Polygala acanthoclada	0.2	0.2	0.3
Brickellia oblongifolia	0.3	0.1	0.2
Cowania stansburiana	0.1	0.1	0.1
Salvia carnosa	0.1	0.3	0.1
Subtotal, shrubs	52.0	164.8	81.6
Forbs, perennial			
Sphaeralcea spp.	3.5	9.4	3.6
Eriogonum spp.	1.9	5.3	2.0
Cryptantha spp.	2.2	2.1	1.2
Oenothera caespitosa	0.8	0.4	0.3
Penstemon spp.	0.5	0.6	0.3
Enceliopsis nudicaulis	0.4	0.2	0.2
Erigeron pumilus	0.2	0.5	0.2
Haplopappus nuttallii	0.1	0.5	0.2
Linum lewisii	0.1	0.3	0.2
Astragalus spp.	0.1	0.1	0.1
Hymenopappus filifolius	0.1	0.2	0.1
Forbs, annual			
Halogeton glomeratus	1.2	19.4	4.1
Phacelia crenulata	0.5	1.1	1.7
Chaenactis macrantha	0.1	0.6	0.8
Lappula redowskii	0.6	1.5	0.6
Lepidium montanum	0.3	1.2	0.5
Townsendia florifer	0.2	0.3	0.2
Aster spp.	0.1	0.2	0.1
Chenopodium spp.	0.0	0.1	0.1
Euphorbia ocellata	0.1	0.1	0.1
Eriogonum spp.	0.0	0.2	0.1
Gilia spp.	0.0	0.1	0.1
Machaeranthera canescens	0.0	0.2	0.1
Salsola kali	0.1	0.3	0.1
Subtotal, forbs	13.1	44.9	17.0

Table 2. (Continued).

SPECIES	HERBAGE PRODUCTION POUNDS/ACRE AIR DRIED		
	Low Year (1963)	High Year (1965)	Five-Year Average (1962–1966)
Grasses			
Oryzopsis hymenoides	16.6	48.3	28.0
Hilaria jamesii	14.7	23.5	16.1
Sporobolus spp.	10.0	21.7	11.9
Bouteloua gracilis	4.0	9.8	4.5
Sitanion hystrix	1.3	5.5	2.1
Stipa comata	0.7	1.0	1.5
Bromus tectorum	0.6	0.8	0.6
Aristida spp.	0.3	0.3	0.2
Poa sandbergii	0.1	0.2	0.1
Subtotal, grasses	49.3	111.1	65.0
Total Vegetation	113.4	320.8	163.6

during the drought years of 1962 and 1966, forbs produced almost no forage during July and August. During the summer of 1967, rainfall for April–June was 4.75 inches (Table 1) and summer-growing forbs were abundant. At the height of their growth in July, forbs produced 43 lbs of forage/acre, air-dry, on the portion of the study area used by antelope. Of this amount, chaenactis, eriogonums, and globemallow made up 16, 11, and 6 lbs/acre, respectively. These data were from 200 plots located at random on permanent transects. In 1969, rainfall for the same 3-month period was 1.44 inches and only 2 lbs of forbs/acre, air-dry, were produced on the same transects, nearly all globemallow.

Yearlong Forage Use

The approximate seasonal diets of antelope in southwestern Utah during above-average and below-average precipitation (based upon data obtained from fall and winter utilization estimates and examination of feeding sites), are shown in Fig. 1. The data obtained from utilization esti-

mates were plotted on graph paper by months and curves were drawn through them. Monthly precipitation from year to year was so erratic, especially in summer, that in any one year, wide departures from these generalized forage-use patterns occurred. For example, no precipitation was recorded in August, 1962; in 1965, 3.95 inches fell. Even in years of above-normal precipitation, individual months can be expected to be below normal, as in 1963, when the annual precipitation was 8.57 inches but only 0.03 inches fell in July.

Yearlong, browse supplied two-thirds to three-fourths of the forage, grass contributed about 5 percent, and forbs the remainder. The herbaceous species were important forage sources, April through September, under the most favorable conditions. During dry years they were of little consequence except during the period April through June.

The yearlong and seasonal ratings shown in Table 3 are to a considerable extent subjective, but indicate our judgement of the importance of each to antelope. The seasonal ratings do not imply that the species

JWM 34(3): 576

Table 3. Forage preference and use by antelope on the Desert Experimental Range.

SPECIES	PREFER-ENCE[a]	FORAGE USED BY ANTELOPE AS DETERMINED BY OBSERVATIONS AT FEEDING SITES (1962–1968)[b]					
		Spring March–May	Summer June–Aug.		Fall Sept.–Nov.		Winter Dec.–Feb.
			Dry Year	Wet Year	Dry Year	Wet Year	
Shrubs							
Artemisia nova	3	H	H	L	H	M	H
Artemisia spinescens	3	H					L
Atriplex confertifolia	1		L				L
Brickellia oblongifolia	2		M	L	M	L	L
Cercocarpus ledifolius	1						L
Chrysothamnus spp.	1				L		L
Cowania stansburiana	2		L		L	L	L
Ephedra nevadensis	3	M		M			
Eurotia lanata	1						L
Gutierrezia sarothrae	1				L	L	
Prunus fasciculata	3	M	M	H	M	L	
Salvia carnosa	2	L	L	L	L	L	L
Forbs, perennial							
Astragalus spp.	1	L					
Cryptantha spp.	1	L					
Enceliopsis nudicaulis	1	L	M				
Erigeron pumilus	2	M	L	M		L	
Eriogonum spp.	3	H	L	H	L	H	
Haplopappus nuttallii	2	L		L			
Hymenopappus filifolius	2	M		L			
Linum lewisii	3		L	H		H	
Oenothera caespitosa	3	H		H		L	
Penstemon spp.	3	H	L	H		L	
Sphaeralcea spp.	3	H	L	H	L	H	L
Forbs, annual							
Aster spp.	3	L		L			
Chaenactis macrantha	3	H		H			
Chenopodium spp.	1	L		L		L	
Eriogonum spp.	3	M		H		H	
Euphorbia ocellata	3	L		H		H	
Gilia spp.	3	L		M			
Lepidium montanum	1	L					
Machaeranthera canescens	3	L		M		H	
Phacelia crenulata	1	L					
Salsola kali	3	L	L	H	L	M	
Townsendia florifer	3	L		M		M	
Grasses							
Bouteloua gracilis	1	L					
Bromus tectorum	3	M			L		
Oryzopsis hymenoides	2	M					
Poa sandbergii	3	H			L		
Sitanion hystrix	2	M					
Sporobolus spp.	1	L					
Stipa comata	1	L					

[a] Forage preference: 3 = High—selected over other plants during some stage of growth or consistently used at all seasons of the year; 2 = Moderate—eaten in moderate amounts whenever available; 1 = Low—eaten but lightly.
[b] Relative volumes of forage: H = high; M = moderate; L = light.

maintains this importance throughout the entire period. For example, grasses are mainly important during the month of April, providing little forage in March and May.

Seasonal Change in the Use of Forage

Winter diets differed little irrespective of the moisture conditions. Throughout the 4- or 5-month period beginning in November and extending to the latter part of March, browse plants made up over 90 percent of the diet. Black sagebrush supplied most of this regardless of the proportions of other browse plants present. During this season, small amounts of other browse species were eaten and they seldom made up more than 10 percent of the diet. Winterfat, brickellia, and little rabbitbrush were the most important of these secondary species. Usually there were small amounts of perennial forbs present and when fall moisture was adequate, the rosettes of winter annuals appeared. These were eaten but they contributed little to the forage supply.

Based upon our feeding site observations in March, black sagebrush and bud sagebrush were the species most heavily used. Our observations gain support from a rumen sample collected from the study area on March 25 which contained 94 percent bud sagebrush. After bud sagebrush was fully leafed out, its use decreased but it continued to be eaten until it passed the full flowering state. Apparently antelope have a seasonal preference for bud sagebrush much the same as sheep. Hutchings (1954:5) reported that bud sagebrush is most readily eaten by sheep in late winter at the early stage of growth.

By late March, grass usually had started to grow and young shoots were readily used by antelope. Sandberg bluegrass (*Poa sandbergii*) and Indian ricegrass were the most preferred grasses. Sandberg bluegrass was similarly used by antelope in the Red Desert region of Wyoming (Severson and May 1967). Spring was usually the only time of year when grass was important in the diet of antelope on the study area even though grass made up 40 percent of the total average herbage produced annually (Table 2).

As forbs became available, they replaced grass and, by May, made up a major part of the antelope's diet. Throughout the study period, soil moisture was adequate during early spring for at least moderate growth of forbs so that until early May, diets differed very little from year to year.

Differences in the diet due to variations in the amount of moisture and, hence, the amount of forbs present, began to be evident in May. In June of dry years, forbs provided little forage and their use gradually declined further—unless August rains occurred, in which case they again assumed substantial importance. Under favorable moisture conditions, forbs were the principal source of the diet.

Succulent forbs were especially abundant in 1967, an unusually wet year, constituting 95 percent of the antelope's diet during June and July. Of this, 86 percent was contributed by four species: globemallow, 34 percent; chaenactis, 30 percent; eriogonums, 12 percent; and gilia (*Gilia hutchinsifolia*), 10 percent. More commonly, forbs declined in volume and succulence by late June and browse became the major item of the diet. Black sagebrush was the most important browse plant, followed by desert almond and Mohave brickellia. The use of desert almond was variable from year to year and depended upon the twig growth. When twig growth was ample, antelope used desert almond heavily, as in 1965, when two rumen samples collected from yearling males in early August contained 49 and 69 percent of this species.

Table 4. Percent composition by weight of forage samples from the rumens of 31 antelope collected near the Desert Experimental Range in late August and early September.

SPECIES	YEAR AND NUMBER OF SAMPLES							
	1961 (7)	1962 (7)	1963 (4)	1964 (5)	1965 (3)	1966 (3)	1967 (2)	AVERAGE (31)
Shrubs								
Artemisia frigida	1	1						0.4
Artemisia nova	68	32	52	47	18	50	80	48.6
Artemisia tridentata		17						3.8
Atriplex canescens						6		0.6
Cowania stansburiana			1					0.1
Crysothamnus spp.			1					0.1
Ephedra nevadensis						T		T
Eriogonum microthecum	4	8						2.7
Gutierrezia sarothrae						1		0.1
Juniperus osteosperma	2	T	T		1			0.7
Prunus fasciculata	T		4	T	T			0.5
Symphoricarpos sp.		2						0.4
Subtotal	75	60	58	47	19	57	80	58.0
Forbs								
Amaranthus graecizans	1							0.2
Aster sp.			1	1	1			0.4
Astragalus sp.	T			3	8		1	1.3
Chaenactis spp.						2		0.2
Chenopodium album			1					0.1
Cordylanthus ramosus				3			3	0.7
Cryptantha sp.	T			2	12			1.5
Eriogonum spp.	7		3	7	2		4	3.5
Euphorbia ocellata	1	12	10	5	26			7.5
Franseria sp.		4		10				2.5
Gilia sp.				1				0.2
Iva axillaris	T	4		10	4			2.9
Linum lewisii	T							
Machaeranthera canescens	1	T	T	T		3		0.5
Mentzelia sp.	T	T						T
Opuntia spp.	4	2	2	1	1	28		4.6
Penstemon spp.				4			5	1.0
Salsola kali	10	9	2	3	16	5	6	7.5
Sphaeralcea grossulariaefolia	1	9	5	2	9	5		4.6
Solanum triflorum		18						2.3
Solidago sp.				1				0.1
Subtotal	25	40	42	53	79	43	19	41.7
Grass	T	T	T	T	T		T	0.3

Globemallow is one of the more drought resistant forbs on the study area, commonly remaining green throughout the summer. Consequently, it was available and used by antelope when few other forbs were. This species also responds well to late summer precipitation as does flax (*Linum lewisii*). Both were prominent in the diet.

Rains in late July and August resulted in abundant forb growth in local areas which antelope selected for feeding. Annuals such as wild buckwheat, glandular eriogonum (*E. glandulosum*), and Russian thistle (*Salsola kali*) were often abundant approxi-

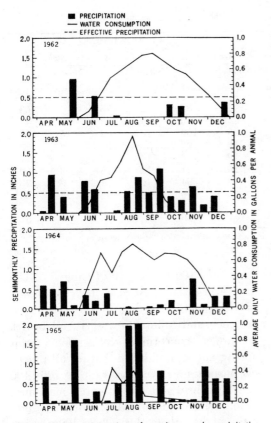

Fig. 2. Water consumption of antelope and precipitation on the Desert Experimental Range.

The forbs most commonly found were Russian thistle (most consistently present), spurge (*Euphorbia ocellata*), globemallow, and various eriogonums.

The variability in the presence of individual forbs was great. Often a single forb would predominate in a rumen, spurge making up 77 percent of one sample. From year to year, the importance of individual species varies greatly. Although the numbers of samples are small and may not represent a fair sample of the diet, they do identify species that are important. Moreover, they illustrate the variation in species availability from year to year as a result of variable and erratically distributed precipitation.

By October, except for 1963 when forbs persisted on the study area through November, browse became the principal source of forage. Occasionally when moisture was adequate in late fall, cheatgrass (*Bromus tectorum*) germinated on favorable sites and produced green herbage which the antelope used. This occurred infrequently and browse formed the major part of the antelope diet after mid-October. Black sagebrush was the species most used, followed by brickellia and desert almond.

Water Consumption

Water consumption from 1962 through 1965 was closely related to the succulence of available forage which was in turn related to the amount of precipitation (Fig. 2). From Russia, Bannikov et al. (1967) reported similar results from studies with the saiga (*Saiga tatarica*), an animal much like the pronghorn antelope in behavior and food habits. When forbs were abundant and their moisture content 75 percent or more, the antelope on our study area did not drink water even though it was readily available. In the summer of 1962, when the forage was dry (the browse

mately 2 weeks after such rains, and they were used extensively by antelope. If forbs were not available, antelope selected the most succulent browse available. Similar observations were reported by Dirschl (1963:88) in southern Saskatchewan. At no time were antelope observed to use dry mature grass.

Browse averaged 58 percent of the contents of 31 rumen samples taken from male antelope killed by hunters in late August and early September on the open range near the study area (Table 4). On the average, black sagebrush provided 49 percent, but some individual rumens contained over 90 percent sagebrush. Prickly pear (*Opuntia* sp.) was a common component.

Table 5. Antelope fawn production and survival on the study area on the Desert Experimental Range.

	FAWN PRODUCTION			FAWNS MARKED		FAWN SURVIVAL TO:[a]					
						Late June		Late July		November	
YEAR	Total Breeding Does	Fawns Dropped	Fawns/ 100 Does	Number	Fawns Probably Abandoned	Number of Fawns	Percent Survival	Number of Fawns	Percent Survival	Number of Fawns	Percent Survival
1962	10	10	100	4	2	7	88	6	75	5	63
1963	15	15	100	9	6	5	56	4	44	4	44
1964	16	29	181	9	5	24	100	20	83	15	63
1965	15	20	133	0	0	19	95	13	65	6	30
1966	15	24	160	0	0	19	79	10	42	4	17
1967	14	20	143	9	4	13	81	12	75	8	50
1968	11	19	173	15	2	16	94	12	71	9	53
1969	16	29	181	23	3	25	96	24	92	22	85
Average			153				86		68		51

[a] Based on production minus marked fawns which were immediately lost presumably as a result of handling.

plants making up the diet averaged 39 percent moisture), water consumption averaged approximately 3 quarts per animal per day. In October, when temperatures were lower, the consumption of water declined but was never below 2 quarts per day until the first snowfall in November. In 1963 and 1965, consumption of water was relatively high during the early portion of the summer, but when the amount of succulent forage increased as a result of heavy summer precipitation, water consumption rapidly decreased to zero. The highest intake observed was under 1 gallon per day, a figure less than that reported by Sundstrom (1968). From these investigations, it appears that under excellent forage conditions, antelope would benefit little from water developments; but when forage is dry, drinking water might be advantageous. During dry years, water developments may encourage better distribution of antelope on range lands where natural water sources are limited or absent.

Fawn Production

The average fawn : doe ratio at birth, over an 8-year period, for the antelope on the study area was 153 : 100 and ranged from 100 : 100 to 181 : 100 (Table 5). The low ratio of the first year may have been biased downward due to observer inexperience and failure to observe all fawns.

Studies concerning fetus : doe ratios among antelope indicate that for all practical purposes a fawn : doe ratio of 200 : 100 can be considered the potential maximum ratio. Larsen (1964:144) reported a fetal ratio higher than this (208 : 100) based upon pregnant does at approximately 39 days of gestation. However, if all mature does examined had been used in the calculation, the ratio would have been 192 : 100. Hoover et al. (1959:25) found a fetal ratio of 193 : 100 in 42 does examined between 2 and 8 months gestation. The highest postparturition ratio reported in the same study was 168 : 100. This ratio was based on the number of does known to have produced at least one fawn, and there is no assurance that all mature does were identified or that all fawns were observed. Thus it appears that the 181 : 100 fawn : doe ratio we observed in 1969 was close to the maximum obtainable. We have no way of knowing whether our fetal ratios were less than those reported in the studies cited above. Whether we had pre-parturition loss, or whether there were post-parturition losses, could not be determined.

Fawn Mortality

The weight and apparent vigor of fawns seemed to indicate healthy animals at birth. Live weights of 24 fawns caught for marking at 1–3 days of age averaged 8.4 lbs. This compares favorably with fawn weights from other states. Weights reported for 1-day old fawns in Colorado by Hoover et al. (1959:41) were 7.05 lbs for males and 6.51 lbs for females.

Despite the apparent good health of the fawns, considerable mortality occurred between birth in May and November (Table 5). Twenty-two of the 69 fawns marked died within a few days of handling. It is presumed that abandonment by does was the prime cause, although it is difficult to assess this factor. Early disappearance of marked fawns could be detected, but there was no check possible on unmarked fawns until a total tally could be made in late June. Abandonment was positively affirmed for the 5 fawns lost following marking in 1968 and 1969.

The 22 fawns presumed or known to be abandoned were excluded from the calculation of survival shown in Table 5 in June, July, and November, since it was felt this procedure would more accurately represent survival in an undisturbed population.

The losses for all years averaged 14, 18, and 17 percent for the May–June, July, and August–November periods, respectively. Individual years departed from this. For example, in 1965, the losses were 5, 30, and 35 percent during the same consecutive periods. By contrast, only one fawn died after the June count in 1963. The survival of fawns to November, excluding those presumed to have been abandoned, averaged 51 percent and varied from 30 percent in 1965 to 85 percent in 1969.

Effect of Forage Condition on Fawning and Survival

It was hypothesized that the condition of forage during late summer and fall, which on the desert responds to above-normal precipitation, could influence both breeding activity and successful gestation of the does and size of the fawn crop. Accordingly, a regression analysis was made of the ratios of fawns dropped to breeding does for the years 1963–1969, and the 4-months precipitation, June through September of the preceding year. This analysis resulted in the following equation and tests of significance: $Y = 120.97 + 9.807X$; $t = 4.42$ $(P < 0.01)$; $r = 0.722$ $(P < 0.05)$.

There is less evidence that forage conditions affected fawn survival. When succulent forbs were abundant during June, July, and August, the physical condition and growth of fawns, as determined from general observations, appeared markedly better than during years when there were few succulent forbs. However, fawn mortality that occurred could not be attributed to poor forage conditions alone, for in 1965, high June–November losses occurred despite good summer forage conditions.

Predation may be a more important factor than previously thought. During the 1966–69 period, eight fawns on the study area were known to have been killed by predators, seven by bobcats, and one by coyotes. Indirectly, poor forage conditions may increase losses from predation. During dry years, the antelope tend to move to higher elevations among the hills where the terrain is broken and fawns may be more vulnerable to predation.

LITERATURE CITED

Bannikov, A. G., L. V. Zhirnov, L. S. Lebedeva, and A. A. Fandeev. 1967. Biology of the saiga. (Translated from Russian.) Israel Program for Sci. Transl., Jerusalem. 252pp.

JWM 34(3): 582

BUECHNER, H. K. 1950. Life history, ecology, and range use of the pronghorn antelope in Trans-Pecos Texas. Am. Midland Naturalist 43(2):257–354.

COLE, G. F. 1956. The pronghorn antelope— its range use and food habits in Central Montana with special reference to alfalfa. Montana State Coll., Agr. Expt. Sta., Tech. Bull. 516. 62pp.

DIRSCHL, H. J. 1962. Sieve mesh size related to analysis of antelope rumen contents. J. Wildl. Mgmt. 26(3):327–328.

———. 1963. Food habits of the pronghorn in Saskatchewan. J. Wildl. Mgmt. 27(1):81–93.

HOOVER, R. L., C. E. TILL, AND S. OGILVIE. 1959. The antelope of Colorado. Colorado Dept. Game and Fish, Tech. Bull. 4. 110pp.

HUTCHINGS, S. S. 1954. Managing winter sheep range for greater profit. U. S. Dept. Agr., Farmer's Bull. 2067. 46pp.

———, AND G. STEWART. 1953. Increasing forage yields and sheep production on Intermountain winter ranges. U. S. Dept. Agr., Circ. 925. 63pp.

LARSEN, P. 1964. Some basic reproductive characteristics of pronghorn antelope in New Mexico. Proc. Western Assoc. State Fish and Game Commissioners, San Francisco. 44:142–145.

NELSON, E. W. 1925. Status of the pronghorned antelope, 1922–24. U. S. Dept. Agr., Bull. 1346. 64pp.

PECHANEC, J. F., AND G. D. PICKFORD. 1937a. A comparison of some methods used in determining percentage utilization of range grasses. J. Agr. Res. 54(10):753–765.

———, AND ———. 1937b. A weight estimate method for the determination of range or pasture production. J. Am. Soc. Agron. 29(11):894–904.

SETON, E. T. 1927. Lives of game animals. Vol. III. Doubleday, Doran and Co., Inc., Garden City, New York. 413pp.

SEVERSON, K. E., AND M. MAY. 1967. Food preferences of antelope and domestic sheep in Wyoming's red desert. J. Range Mgmt. 20(1):21–25.

SHANTZ, H. L. 1925. Plant communities in Utah and Nevada. In I. Tidestrom (Editor), Flora of Utah and Nevada. Contrib. U. S. Natl. Herbarium, Smithsonian Inst. 25:12–23.

STEWART, G., W. P. COTTAM, AND S. S. HUTCHINGS. 1940. Influence of unrestricted grazing on northern salt desert plant associations in western Utah. J. Agr. Res. 60(5):289–316.

SUNDSTROM, C. 1968. Water consumption by pronghorn antelope and distribution related to water in Wyoming's red desert. Proc. Third Biennial Antelope States Workshop. Casper, Wyoming. Pp. 39–46. Processed.

UDY, J. R. 1953. Effects of predator control on antelope populations. Fed. Aid. Div., Utah State Dept. Fish and Game, Pub. 5. 48pp.

Received for publication December 19, 1969.

ENERGY FLUX AND WATER KINETICS IN YOUNG PRONGHORN ANTELOPE[1]

D. E. WESLEY, Department of Fishery and Wildlife Biology, Colorado State University, Fort Collins

K. L. KNOX, Department of Animal Science, Colorado State University, Fort Collins

J. G. NAGY, Department of Fishery and Wildlife Biology, Colorado State University, Fort Collins

Abstract: Energy flow trials with four pronghorn antelope (*Antilocapra americana*) ranging from 108 to 182 days of age, produced results similar to those described for other ruminants with the possible exceptions of total heat production and fasting metabolic rate. The comparatively high heat production may be related to the higher metabolism of younger animals. Fasting metabolic rates were above the interspecies mean of 70 kcal/kg$^{0.75}$/24 hours; similar results have occurred with other wild ruminants. Pronghorn antelope, under the conditions tested, had a slightly higher content of body water than reported for other ruminants. This is feasible since pronghorn probably have a lower fat content than do most domestic or laboratory animals. Water flux in antelope is similar to that in domestic sheep and mule deer (*Odocoileus hemionus*). Noticeable differences existed between water kinetics of male and female pronghorn.

Several studies of pronghorn food habits have been reported (Hoover et al. 1959, Buechner 1950, Scarvie and Arney 1957). However, little is known about the ability of the pronghorn to utilize food resources to fulfill energy requirements. The importance of energy in the diet of wild ruminants has been recognized. Both direct and extrapolated values have been reported. Energy deficiency markedly influences growth and antler development in white-tailed deer (*Odocoileus virginianus*) (French et al. 1955). Fasting metabolic rates of white-tailed deer have been measured (Silver et al. 1969), and were found to be greater than the interspecies value reported by Kleiber (1961:215). Similar studies have been conducted with the eland (*Taurotragus oryx*) and wildebeest (*Connochaetes* sp.) (Rogerson 1968) and revealed comparable results.

Big-game management may be enhanced by an awareness of the rates at which foods are made metabolically available to the wild ruminant. It is necessary to establish the relative energy flux in antelope before the importance of diet quality and quantity for this animal can be ascertained.

Studies of eland and oryx (*Oryx beisa*) (Taylor 1969), have shown that water conservation is important to survival of certain wild ruminants. Pronghorn, having evolved in an arid environment, may have an unusual capacity to regulate water metabolism. Before this possibility can be explored, water kinetic values must be established under defined conditions.

METHODS

Two male and two female antelope, raised in captivity from birth and trained to laboratory conditions, were placed alternately in a metabolic cage at 21 C. Prior to the trial, the antelope were allowed 72 hours in the laboratory room and cage. During the trials, which lasted 160–240 hours, water and a mixed concentrate feed, composed mainly of corn, rolled barley and milo, and protein supplement, were available ad libitum. In addition, each animal was given approximately 450 ml of whole milk daily. Moisture content of the con-

[1] Financed under Nat. Sci. Found. Grant GB-7824 and is part of the U. S. Int. Biol. Program, Grassland Biome Sub-program.

centrate was approximately the same for all trials. During confinement, energy flow and water-kinetic data were collected simultaneously.

Energy Flow

Consumption of dry matter was measured for each animal during the trials. Urine and feces produced during trials were collected and sampled for determination of dry matter. Periodically the cages were sealed with Plexiglas and respiration was recorded for 3 hours at 21 C to measure heat production by indirect calorimetry (Kleiber 1961:124). This procedure was repeated to allow each animal at least 12 hours of respiratory-measurement time during each trial and at least 3 additional hours under fasting conditions. Respiration was recorded for each animal after a 48-hour fast. In addition, respiration was recorded for one animal at 24-hour increments during 72 hours of fasting.

Energy consumed by an animal can be partitioned into apparent digestible, metabolizable, and net energy (Crampton and Harris 1969:62). Apparent digestible energy was determined by subtracting the energy content of the feces from the gross energy intake of the animal. Metabolizable energy is that portion of chemical energy available for production of heat, body substances, and work. It is measured by subtracting the energy loss in urine and methane from the apparent digestible energy. By convention and for convenience, methane energy is included as part of digested energy. In reality, however, much of the methane never enters the animal's body per se. Net energy is the energy used for maintenance only or for maintenance plus production. Net energy for maintenance, measured by indirect calorimetry as fasting metabolic rate, is the

fraction of total net energy expended to keep the animal in energy equilibrium. Net energy for production in our study is the fraction of net energy required for movement, growth, etc. Total net energy available to the animal is derived by subtracting heat increment from metabolizable energy. The heat increment, or calorigenic effect of food consumed, is defined as the increase in heat production following consumption of food by an animal in a thermoneutral environment. An estimation of heat increment is derived by subtracting the fasting heat production of a resting animal under thermoneutral conditions, from its total heat production. Later trials have shown that 21 C is in the thermoneutral range for the pronghorn. Total heat production is measured by the indirect calorimetry technique with a fed animal.

Water Kinetics

The isotope dilution technique (Foy and Schnieden 1960) was used to study water kinetics. Each antelope was injected intravenously with 2 ml of tritiated water (specific activity of 200.9 $\mu c/ml$) and placed in a metabolic cage. Urine samples were collected in early morning and late afternoon. The time of excretion of each sample was estimated at the mid-point ($\bar{x}$) between successive collection times and recorded as hours post-injection. A 20-ml aliquot was taken from each urine sample, refluxed with activated charcoal and filtered to provide a clear filtrate for determining specific activity. A 0.05-ml aliquot of the filtrate from each sample was pipetted into dioxane-based scintillation solution and its activity was determined using a scintillation spectrometer. The specific activity of each sample (expressed as $\mu c/ml$ × 10^{-4}) was plotted against time of excretion on semi-logarithmic coordinates and

Table 1. Comparison of energy utilization by young dairy calves and pronghorn antelope.

	Average Age (Days)	Age Range (Days)	Average Gross Energy Intake/Day/Kg (Kcal)	Digestible Energy (Percent of Gross Intake)	Metaboliz-able Energy (Percent of Digestible Energy)	Net Energy (Percent of Digestible Energy)
Dairy Calves[a]	160	143–187	100.5	70[b]	87	64
Pronghorn	139	108–182	113.1	78[b]	94	73

[a] Ritzman, E. G. and N. F. Colovos, 1943.
[b] Differences between digestible energy values, in particular, may have been affected by differences between diets.

the best-fitting straight line was calculated by the method of least squares.

The water kinetic relationships involved are illustrated in the formula $Y = ae^{b\bar{x}}$ where Y is the specific activity at any time. The specific activity at time zero is represented by a and is determined by extrapolation. The slope of the line (the constant rate of water uptake) is represented as b and $\bar{x}$ is the mean time (post-injection) of any urine sample.

Other calculations included total body water or pool size (P), determined by dividing the μc of tritiated water injected by the specific activity of the urine sample extrapolated to time zero. The water turnover rate was calculated as $ln\ 2/b$. The water flux (amount of water leaving the pool per unit time per unit of metabolic size) is equal to $p \times b/kg^{0.75}$.

RESULTS AND DISCUSSION

Energy Flow

A primary problem in interpreting results of this experiment involves the ages of our antelope. Any comparison with other ruminants requires cognizance of possible age differences because animals less than 1 year of age possess higher metabolic rates (Blaxter 1962:96). Ritzman and Benedict (1930:12) showed that fasting metabolic rates of domestic lambs and sheep decreased rapidly with age until the animals were 4 to 6 months old. After 1 year, their fasting metabolic rates seemed relatively stable. Ritzman and Colovos (1943:42) found that young growing cattle reached a relatively stable basal metabolism after approximately 8 months.

The apparent digestible, metabolizable, and net energy values calculated for the four antelope are similar to values given for young dairy calves (Table 1). Rogerson (1968) found metabolizable energy to range from 49 to 59 percent of gross energy intake for the eland and from 51 to 59 percent for the wildebeest. With improved diets, these values increased for both species. It was found that these wild ruminants were generally more efficient at

Table 2. Energy flux characteristics of pronghorn antelope.

Sex	Age (Days)	Wt (Kg)	Percent of Gross Energy Intake			Fasting Metabolism (Kcal/Kg$^{0.75}$/day)
			Total Heat Production	Net Energy (Maintenance)	Net Energy (Production)	
M$_1$	108	18.8	55	51	16	106
M$_2$	182	25.7	56	26	18	61
F$_1$	143	19.8	62	49	6	92
F$_2$	122	18.5	48	32	27	110

Table 3. Water kinetic characteristics of pronghorn antelope.

Sex	Age (Days)	Wt (Kg)	Body Water (Percent of Body Weight)	Turnover (Percent/day)	Biological Half-life (Days)	Flux (ml/kg$^{0.75}$/day)
M$_1$	108	18.8	77	11	6.3	178
M$_2$	182	25.7	73	12	5.6	205
F$_1$	143	19.8	82	15	4.5	264
F$_2$	122	18.5	80	16	4.4	261

using metabolizable energy for production than were cattle and sheep.

The fasting heat production of antelope averaged 92 and ranged from 61 to 110 kcal/kg$^{0.75}$/day (Table 2). Considering variation that exists among species and within species (Blaxter 1962:86), this range is not unusual. These values for fasting metabolic rate may represent the range for pronghorn and are not intended for extrapolation to the entire population. Some discrepancies among results of various experiments may be due to varying lengths of fasting periods. Silver et al. (1969) found that a 48-hour fast produced reliable fasting metabolic rates with adult white-tailed deer.

Since the energy requirements of an animal are directly related to its fasting metabolic rate, the data indicate that the total energy demand of the pronghorn relative to body size is greater than that of most domestic ruminants and as a result, the pronghorn may undergo greater stress during food shortage.

Water Kinetics

Water turnover rates, percent body water and flux were similar for antelope of the same sex, however, differences between sexes were prominent (Table 3). Similar sex-related results were found in chickens (Chapman and Black 1967). With the exception of body water, these values are similar to values for mule deer (Knox et al. 1969). Water content of the body varies

inversely with fat content (Prentice et al. 1952) and younger animals tend to have a higher percent body water than do older animals (Edelman and Leibman 1959, Phillips et al. 1970). These factors may account for the high values found with pronghorn. The biological half-life of water (T½) in antelope was also similar to that of sheep (Anand and Parker 1966). Since the T½ value is a function of body size (Foy 1964), these results are quite reasonable.

Amounts of water consumed averaged 84 and 107 ml per day/kg body weight for the two females, while these values for the two males were 64 and 52.

Results of this study should be interpreted with caution, as evidenced by the increased turnover rate, half-time and flux in closely confined deer when compared to less confined deer (Knox et al. 1969).

Richmond et al. (1962) suggested that water flux and metabolic rate were related. The fasting metabolic rate of each of the four antelope was plotted against the water flux for that particular animal. The variation among the points precluded any statement of relationship between the two factors.

The data suggest that the pronghorn is an energetically expensive ruminant to maintain because of its high metabolic rate. The antelope, however, is a selective feeder and is thus able to obtain maintenance energy from vegetation which is generally not utilized extensively by domestic ruminants (Hoover et al. 1959, Free 1969).

No conclusive statements can be made concerning the ability of the pronghorn to conserve water since no experiments have been conducted with water restriction.

Perhaps with an extension of the type of data presented, predictions can be made as to the carrying capacity of the pronghorn's range as well as its capacity to survive under conditions of food and water shortage.

LITERATURE CITED

ANAND, R. S., AND H. R. PARKER. 1966. Total body water and water turnover in sheep. Am. J. Vet. Res. 27(19):899–902.

BLAXTER, K. L. 1962. The energy metabolism of ruminants. Charles C. Thomas, Springfield, Illinois. 329pp.

BUECHNER, H. K. 1950. Life history, ecology and range use of the pronghorn antelope in Trans-Pecos, Texas. Am. Midland Naturalist 43(3):256–354.

CHAPMAN, T. E., AND A. L. BLACK. 1967. Water turnover in chickens. Poultry Sci. 46 (3):761–765.

CRAMPTON, E. W., AND L. E. HARRIS. 1969. Applied animal nutrition. 2nd ed. W. H. Freeman and Co., San Francisco. 753pp.

EDELMAN, I. S., AND J. LEIBMAN. 1959. Anatomy of body water and electrolytes. Am. J. Med. 27:256–277.

FREE, J. C. 1969. Comparison of two methods for determining dry matter intake by large herbivores. M.S. Thesis. Colorado State Univ., Fort Collins, Colorado. 33pp.

FOY, J. M. 1964. The biological half-life of tritiated water in the mouse, rat, guinea-pig and rabbit under tropical conditions and the effect of climate and saline drinking on biological half-life of tritiated water in the rat. J. Cellular and Comp. Physiol. 64:279–282.

———, AND H. SCHNIEDEN. 1960. Estimation of total body water (virtual tritium space) in the rat, cat, rabbit, guinea-pig, and man, and of the biological half-life of tritium in man. J. Physiol. 154(1):169–176.

FRENCH, C. E., L. C. MCEWEN, N. D. MAGRUDER,

R. H. INGRAM, AND R. W. SWIFT. 1955. Nutritional requirements of white-tailed deer for growth and antler development. Pennsylvania Agr. Expt. Sta. Bull. No. 600. 50pp.

HOOVER, R. L., C. E. TILL, AND S. OGILVIE. 1959. The antelope of Colorado. Colorado Dept. Fish and Game, Denver. Tech. Bull. No. 4. 110pp.

KLEIBER, M. 1961. Fire of life: an introduction to animal energetics. John Wiley & Sons, New York. 454pp.

KNOX, K. L., J. G. NAGY, AND R. D. BROWN. 1969. Water turnover in mule deer. J. Wildl. Mgmt. 33(2):389–393.

PHILLIPS, R. W., L. D. LEWIS, AND K. L. KNOX. 1970. Alterations in body water turnover and distribution in neonatal calves with acute diarrhea. Ann. of the New York Acad. Sci. Conf. on Neonatal Enteric Infections Caused by *Escherichia coli*. May 18, 19, 20 (In Press).

PRENTICE, T. C., W. SIRI, N. I. BERLIN, G. M. HYDE, R. J. PARSONS, E. E. JOINER, AND J. H. LAWRENCE. 1952. Studies of total body water with tritium. J. Clin. Invest. 31:412–418.

RICHMOND, C. R., W. H. LANGHAM, AND T. T. TRUJILLO. 1962. Comparative metabolism of tritiated water by mammals. J. Cellular and Comp. Physiol. 59(1):45–53.

RITZMAN, E. G., AND F. G. BENEDICT. 1930. The energy metabolism of sheep. New Hampshire Expt. Sta. Tech. Bull. No. 43. 23pp.

———, AND N. F. COLOVOS. 1943. Physiological requirements and utilization of protein and energy by growing dairy cattle. Univ. New Hampshire Tech. Bull. No. 80. 59pp.

ROGERSON, A. 1968. Comparative nutrition of wild animals. M. A. Crawford (Editor), Symposia of the Zoological Society of London No. 21. Academic Press, New York. 429pp.

SCARVIE, O., AND J. ARNEY. 1957. Food habits of pronghorn antelope, *Antilocapra americana*, in October in northern Colorado. J. Lee Dean Memorial Library, Colorado State Univ. 9pp.

SILVER, HELENETTE, N. F. COLOVOS, J. B. HOLTER, AND H. H. HAYES. 1969. Fasting metabolism of white-tailed deer. J. Wildl. Mgmt. 33(3): 490–498.

TAYLOR, C. R. 1969. The eland and the oryx. Sci. Am. 220(1):89–95.

Received for publication March 30, 1970.

MEASUREMENTS, WEIGHTS, AND CARCASS YIELDS OF PRONGHORNS IN ALBERTA

GEORGE J. MITCHELL, Department of Lands and Forests, Edmonton, Alberta[1]

Abstract: Standard body measurements (117 specimens), whole weights (216 specimens), hog-dressed weights (1,210 specimens), and dressed weights (40 specimens) obtained from pronghorn antelopes (*Antilocapra americana americana*) in southern Alberta were analyzed and compared with data published for specimens of the *americana*, *mexicana*, and *oregona* subspecies in other regions. The average total lengths of pronghorns in this study are longer than those of pronghorns for all regions except California. Alberta pronghorns have the shortest ear lengths. Mean shoulder heights are equivalent to those for Montana pronghorns but are shorter than for pronghorns in other regions. The maximum whole weight attained by a mature male (155 lb) in late summer in Alberta exceeds the maximum weight previously reported. Although pronghorns in this study are heavier than those in most regions, their mean body weights are similar to *americana* specimens in Wyoming, and *oregona* animals in Oregon and California. The relatively lighter winter body weight in Alberta probably reflects the severe conditions on that northern range. The physical features of the pronghorn appear to comply with both Allen's Rule and Bergmann's Rule. Mean hog-dressed weights in this study exceed those for Idaho, Montana, and Wyoming, but are smaller than those reported for California and North Dakota. They range from 66 to 75 percent of whole weights. Mean dressed carcass yields range from 51 to 57 percent and correspond closely to the yield values reported for other wild ungulates. Whole weights can be estimated by applying the conversion factors 1.36 and 1.51 to the hog-dressed weights of mature males and females, respectively, and 1.78 and 1.95 to the dressed weights. Also, the linear regressions between whole and hog-dressed weight for yearling and mature males ($y = 16.7496 + 1.1732x$) and females ($y = 38.7119 + 0.9501x$), and the linear regressions between whole weight and heart girth for immature and older males and females ($y = 0.3043x - 179.4817$), mature males and females ($y = 0.2545x - 126.6853$), and submature males and females ($y = 0.2484x - 136.6747$), can be used to provide useful estimates of whole weights.

This paper reports on age- and sex-specific body measurements and seasonal weights of pronghorns in Alberta at the northern limit of their continental distribution. Body measurements and weights, carcass yields, and the percentage of whole weights comprised by internal and external offal are considered. The relationships between various body weights are compared with data from other regions, and criteria are established for estimating whole weights using hog-dressed and dressed weights and heart girths.

This study was conducted on the western extremity of the Canadian Great Plains in Alberta between lat 49° and 51° N. The steppe of this region is a relatively uniform, undulating to gently rolling till plain characterized by a mean annual precipitation of less than 14 inches, high rates of evaporation, prolonged periods of drought, and great extremes in temperature. Most soils are classed as Brown Soil Group (Chernozems) by Bowser et al. (1963) and support a mixed prairie vegetation (Coupland 1950, 1961). Needle-and-thread (*Stipa comata*), blue grama (*Bouteloua gracilis*), western wheatgrass (*Agropyron smithii*), Junegrass (*Koeleria cristata*), pasture sagewort (*Artemisia frigida*), and sagebrush (*Artemisia cana*) are dominant on many upland sites (Clarke et al. 1942, Coupland 1950, 1961, Smoliak 1956). Most pronghorns examined in this study were shot or trapped in plant communities classified as *Stipa comata–Agropyron smithii / Bouteloua gracilis*, and *Stipa comata / Bouteloua gracilis* habitat types (Mitchell 1965).

[1] Present address: Biology Department, University of Saskatchewan, Regina Campus, Regina.

I thank staff members of the Alberta Department of Lands and Forests, particularly Fish and Wildlife Officers J. G. Pelchat and C. A. Gordon, for their cooperation during this study. R. W. Trueblood, J. McLucas, and T. B. Knopp, Montana Fish and Game Department, provided a portable trap, support facilities, and expert field assistance during livetrapping, tagging, and weighing in November 1962. L. G. Sugden, Canadian Wildlife Service, offered constructive criticisms of the manuscript.

METHODS

Body Measurements

Body measurements were obtained from 117 freshly killed antelopes collected regularly by the investigator and colleagues from 1962 through 1966. The animals were hunted on foot or by car, killed with a rifle, and immediately measured. Linear body measurements to the nearest 5 mm were taken with a flexible steel tape. These measurements, taken before necropsy, have been described by Anderson (1948:44–47) for total length, tail length, and hind foot length. In addition, the following linear measurements were recorded:

EAR LENGTH—The length from the base of the ear notch to the ear tip.

HEART GIRTH—The circumference of the chest immediately posterior to the front legs.

SHOULDER HEIGHT—The distance from the top of the shoulder above the scapula to the ventral midpoint of the digital pad.

Body Weights

Hog-dressed weights were obtained by a systematic examination of 1,197 hunter-killed antelopes at 30 wildlife checking stations from 1956 to 1965. A carcass was weighed on a tripod-mounted beam scale to the nearest 0.5 pound. Sex and the location of the kill were recorded. Mandibles and eye lenses were collected whenever possible. Age determinations were made at the checking stations on the basis of physical characteristics and mandibular tooth replacement and wear (Dow and Wright 1962), or later in the laboratory using this mandibular method and/or the eye-lens technique described by Kolenosky and Miller (1962). Whole, hog-dressed, and dressed weights were also taken from freshly killed pronghorns collected for the present study using a tripod-mounted beam scale. Animals livetrapped in November 1962 and weighed on a platform scale, and net-captured neonatal kids provided most of the live weight measurements. A single live weight was recorded from an adult female immobilized with 500 mg of dart-projected succinylcholine chloride in June 1960.

In this paper the term "whole weight" is used to designate both whole carcass weight and live weight. Equating these two body weights is considered valid inasmuch as all whole carcass weights were taken immediately after each animal was shot, and in every instance the loss of blood, body fluids, and other tissues appeared negligible.

The hog-dressed weight is the whole weight less the viscera, stomach contents, and diaphragm (internal offal). The dressed weight is the hog-dressed weight less the hide, head, and, in the case of males, the testes (external offal). The carcass yield is the dressed weight expressed as a percentage of whole weight. Animals 4–12 months of age are termed *immature*. *Yearling* refers to antelopes 12–24 months of age. Pronghorns designated as *mature* are 2 years old and older.

The data were treated statistically by means of linear regression analyses and *t*

Table 1. Body measurements and whole weights of 117 pronghorn antelopes in Alberta, 1962–66.

	Total Length (mm)	Tail Length (mm)	Hind Foot Length (mm)	Ear Length (mm)	Heart Girth (mm)	Shoulder Height (mm)	Whole Weight (lb)
Neonatal males[a]							
$\bar{x}$	600.3	50.1	265.1	83.6	372.2	463.3	8.4
$S_{\bar{x}}$	5.35	1.17	2.11	1.03	5.24	7.65	0.24
n	37	37	37	36	36	36	34
Range	543–661	24–61	230–285	70–97	295–430	375–552	4.9–10.7
Neonatal females[a]							
$\bar{x}$	598.3	53.9	265.2	84.0	379.3	453.1	8.6
$S_{\bar{x}}$	6.81	1.21	2.18	0.95	5.14	6.18	0.26
n	38	42	42	42	41	37	40
Range	460–670	32–77	230–290	65–96	283–448	388–532	4.6–12.0
Immature males[b]							
$\bar{x}$	1,260.0	116.7	406.7	135.0	880.0	865.0	80.0
n	3	3	3	2	3	3	2
Range	1,250–1,280	90–140	390–420	130–140	860–890	825–900	80.0
Immature females[b]							
$\bar{x}$	1,317.5	127.5	391.0	145.0	860.0	802.5	78.0
n	2	2	2	2	2	2	2
Range	1,310–1,325	125–130	387–395	140–150	850–870	755–850	74.5–81.5
Yearling males[c]							
$\bar{x}$	1,391.7	129.7	401.7	141.7	973.3	856.7	112.8
n	3	3	3	3	3	3	3
Range	1,360–1,450	109–145	395–410	130–150	965–980	800–895	100.0–122.0
Yearling females[d]							
$\bar{x}$	1,362.0	118.0	399.0	142.0	954.2	852.0	97.6
$S_{\bar{x}}$	17.79	11.68	7.14	2.55	18.06	13.28	3.59
n	5	5	5	5	5	5	4
Range	1,310–1,400	90–142	380–420	135–150	900–1,005	825–900	91.0–107.5
Mature males[e]							
$\bar{x}$	1,415.7	105.2	404.9	143.1	969.7	874.5	124.4
$S_{\bar{x}}$	10.23	5.15	4.09	1.78	10.98	9.25	3.79
n	16	15	15	15	15	11	16
Range	1,360–1,495	85–145	380–440	133–160	875–1,050	830–920	102.5–155.0
Mature females[f]							
$\bar{x}$	1,405.6	96.9	397.1	141.6	954.0	860.3	111.4
$S_{\bar{x}}$	9.18	7.90	4.38	1.85	10.40	11.39	2.94
n	9	8	9	9	8	9	7
Range	1,360–1,440	70–135	380–420	132–150	905–985	800–910	103.5–124.0

[a] Weighed in late May and early June.
[b] Weighed in January and February.
[c] Weighed in January, April, and October.
[d] Weighed in March and October.
[e] Weighed in all months except November and December.
[f] Weighed in January, March, April, June, and November.

Table 2. Mean body measurements of two races of mature antelopes as reported in the literature.[a]

RACE AND SEX	SAMPLE SIZE	TOTAL LENGTH (mm)	TAIL LENGTH (mm)	HIND FOOT LENGTH (mm)	EAR LENGTH (mm)	SHOULDER HEIGHT (mm)	LOCATION	AUTHORITY
americana								
Male	36	1,340	134	376	150	873	Montana	Buck (1947)
Female	12	1,360	126	366	150	830	Montana	Buck (1947)
Male	16	1,416	105	405	143	874	Alberta	This study
Female	9	1,406	97	397	142	860	Alberta	This study
oregona								
Male	251–359	1,459	112	451	163		California	McLean (1944)
Male	21	1,344	104	430	155	946	Oregon and Nevada	Mason (1952)

[a] Measurements from the literature were converted to millimeters and rounded.

tests (Steel and Torrie 1960:161–182). Significance was $P < 0.05$.

RESULTS AND DISCUSSION

Body Measurements

Body measurements were obtained from 38 immature and older pronghorns and 79 neonatal kids (Table 1). Male and female neonates showed no differences in measurements. Immature animals showed a rapid growth from birth to 7–8 months of age.

The data compiled by Buck (1947) for *americana* in Montana, when analyzed, showed average total length measurements shorter than those for Alberta (Table 2). Similarly, maximum total lengths for males and females in Montana (1,410 and 1,422 mm) are less than those observed in this study (1,495 and 1,440 mm). In Alberta the mean and maximum hind foot lengths are longer, while tail length, ear length, and maximum shoulder height are shorter than those for Montana animals. The body measurements reported by Einarsen (1948:229) for one *americana* from North Dakota are similar to those in this study except that the total length is shorter than the average Alberta measurement. Alberta specimens have greater mean total and tail lengths than two *mexicana* animals from Texas as reported by Buechner (1950:284). California *oregona* measurements (McLean 1944) are consistently larger than those for Alberta. In Oregon and Nevada (Mason 1952) the *oregona* race exhibits body measurements that exceed those in the present study, except that tail length is similar and the mean total length of *oregona* is shorter.

Body Weights

Whole, hog-dressed, and dressed weights were obtained for 216, 1,210, and 40 pronghorns, respectively. Neonatal males and females showed similar weights in May and comparable weight gains of approximately 60 pounds during their first summer and fall (Table 3). By their second winter, yearlings weighed between 91 and 116 pounds, and corresponded to mature animals in body weight. Mature males increased in weight during spring and summer, and attained their heaviest weights in late summer. The 155-lb male shot on September 1 probably approximates the maximum whole weight attained by free-ranging pronghorns in prime condition in Alberta. Between October and March, the body weights of mature

JWM 35(1): 80

Table 3. Mean whole weights (lb) of 216 Alberta prong-horn antelopes by sex, age-class, and season.

	APRIL–JUNE	JULY–SEPT.	OCT.–DEC.	JAN.–MARCH
Immature males				
$\bar{x}$	8.4[a]	–	72.2	75.0
$S_{\bar{x}}$	0.24	–	1.54	–
n	37	–	16	3
Range	5–11	–	60–81	65–80
Immature females				
$\bar{x}$	8.7[a]	–	70.7	78.0
$S_{\bar{x}}$	0.28	–	1.71	–
n	41	–	14	2
Range	5–12	–	59–83	74–82
Yearling males				
$\bar{x}$	–	–	104.8	108.2
$S_{\bar{x}}$	–	–	2.70	–
n	–	–	12	2
Range	–	–	91–122	100–116
Yearling females				
$\bar{x}$	–	–	102.3	100.7
$S_{\bar{x}}$	–	–	2.25	3.97
n	–	–	9	5
Range	–	–	91–112	91–112
Mature males				
$\bar{x}$	116.7	134.2	115.9	110.5
$S_{\bar{x}}$	3.82	5.47	4.26	3.25
n	5	7	19	4
Range	104–126	119–155	104–133	102–116
Mature females				
$\bar{x}$	109.1	–	103.8	110.9
$S_{\bar{x}}$	4.36	–	1.37	4.49
n	4	–	32	4
Range	100–118	–	91–120	104–124

[a] Mean weight for neonatal kids in May.

males decreased slightly. Mature males weighed more than females at all seasons except during winter.

Data for *americana* in Wyoming (Edwards 1958) show that whole weights are in close agreement with those obtained in Alberta (Table 4). Maximum whole weights of yearling and mature females in Wyoming

in the fall–spring period (121 and 138 lb) are greater than those for corresponding females in Alberta (112 and 124 lb). However, these differences are not significant. Mean weight data in my study agree with those presented by McLean (1944), Einarsen (1948), and Mason (1952) for *oregona*. However, the maximum weights of males (140 lb) in winter and spring in Oregon were not attained by Alberta antelopes during these seasons. The relatively light winter body weight in Alberta may reflect the severe conditions and nutritional stresses on pronghorns on this northerly range. The average weight of males in Alberta in winter is significantly greater (approximately 18 pounds difference) than winter weights reported for Colorado (Hoover et al. 1959: 20). The weights for *mexicana* from Texas reported by Buechner (1950) are also less than those from Alberta considered for this study.

In Alberta, the mean hog-dressed weight of mature males (85 lb) collected in fall was significantly higher than hog-dressed weights for other age groups (Table 5). The fall weights for Alberta exceeded fall weights calculated from data given by Shaw (1960, 1961) for Idaho, Buck (1947) for Montana, and Hepworth (1965) for Wyoming animals, but are less than those reported by McKean (1951) for North Dakota, and McLean (1944) for California pronghorns. These variations may reflect differences in season of collection or variations in the method of measuring rather than actual differences in weights characteristic of each population.

The progressive loss in body weights of males between October and March, observed in the present study, probably occurs in pronghorns in other regions. This phenomenon has been reported by Blood and Lovaas (1966) in Manitoba elk (*Cervus*

Table 4. Mean whole weights (lb) of three races of antelopes as reported in or determined from data in the literature.

RACE AND AGE	SEASON	MALE	FEMALE	LOCATION	AUTHORITY
americana					
Yearling	Fall-spring		103 (10)[a]	Wyoming	Edwards (1958)
Mature	Fall-spring		111 (60)	Wyoming	Edwards (1958)
Yearling	Winter	86 (7)	82 (3)	Colorado	Hoover et al. (1959)
Mature	Winter	92 (6)	90 (8)	Colorado	Hoover et al. (1959)
Yearling	Fall-winter	105 (14)	102 (14)	Alberta	This study
Mature	All year[b]	119 (35)	100 (40)	Alberta	This study
mexicana					
Yearling	Fall	64 (20)	62 (24)	Texas	Buechner (1950)
Mature	Fall	91 (166)	87 (188)	Texas	Buechner (1950)
oregona					
Mature	Spring-summer	113 (67)		California	McLean (1944)
Mature	Fall	114 (?)	92 (?)	Oregon	Einarsen (1948)
Yearling	Fall		95 (1)	Oregon	Mason (1952)
Mature	All year	124 (19)	105 (1)	Oregon	Mason (1952)

[a] Sample sizes are in parentheses.
[b] The females were collected in fall and spring.

canadensis manitobensis), and Kelsall (1968) in barren ground caribou (*Rangifer tarandus grönlandicus*), and others, and is presumably related to rutting activities.

The paucity of published data precludes a critical appraisal of the sizes and weights of pronghorns in different regions. My attempt to evaluate the morphology and weight changes of antelopes throughout their large latitudinal range, and their conformity to Allen's Rule and to Bergmann's Rule (Allee et al. 1949:119–120) is preliminary in nature, and must be considered tentative until more data are collected and reported.

In terms of mean values, the data suggest that Alberta pronghorns exhibit (1) the longest total lengths with the exception of California animals; (2) intermediate tail lengths; (3) intermediate hind foot lengths; (4) shortest ear lengths; (5) shortest shoulder heights, with the exception of Montana animals, which are similar; and (6) heaviest body weights, with the exception of Oregon pronghorns, which are similar, and Califor-

nia and North Dakota animals, which are similar or heavier. In addition, the maximum weight attained by a male in Alberta exceeds that previously reported for pronghorns.

Approximate mean annual temperatures

Table 5. Mean hog-dressed weights (lb) of 1,210 Alberta pronghorns in fall.

CATEGORY	n	$\bar{x}$	$S_{\bar{x}}$	RANGE
Immature male	142	51.1	0.48	34.0–63.0
Immature female	130	50.7	0.44	38.0–67.0
	272	50.9	0.33	34.0–67.0
Yearling male	148	76.7	0.49	60.0–92.5
Yearling female	131	72.1	0.54	55.0–88.0
	279	74.6	0.39	55.0–92.5
Mature male	320	85.0	0.29	67.0–110.5
Mature female	191	76.6	0.46	61.0–100.0
	511	81.9	0.31	61.0–110.5
Mature and yearling				
Male	93	82.0	0.93	60.0–111.0
Female	55	76.9	1.02	60.0–92.0
	148	80.1	0.73	60.0–111.0

Table 6. Hog-dressed weights (lb) expressed as mean percentages of whole weights of 40 pronghorn antelopes collected from all seasons in Alberta.

CATEGORY	n	HOG-DRESSED WEIGHT				DRESSED WEIGHT			
		Percentage	$S_{\bar{x}}$	Range	CF[a]	Percentage	$S_{\bar{x}}$	Range	CF[a]
Immature male	3	69.9	4.23	62.5–77.1	1.43	55.0	4.93	47.5–64.3	1.82
Immature female	2	68.8	1.70	67.1–70.5	1.45	52.1	2.45	49.7–54.6	1.92
Yearling male	3	75.0	1.14	73.0–75.1	1.33	57.1	0.43	56.5–57.9	1.75
Yearling female	5	70.6	0.62	69.2–72.7	1.42	54.5	0.52	52.7–55.8	1.83
Mature male	16	73.6	1.04	66.3–81.3	1.36	56.0	0.84	49.6–61.9	1.78
Mature female	11	66.1	1.41	60.4–73.2	1.51	51.2	1.10	46.4–56.3	1.95

[a] Conversion factor = the reciprocal of the mean percentage.

for Alberta and 13 western states (Canada Year Book 1969:45–47, Golenpaul 1970:855–857, Long 1970:224), show a decrease between coastal and continental regions (California: 65 F, New Mexico: 57 F), and a decrease with increasing latitudes (Texas: 66 F, Colorado: 50 F, Montana: 44 F, North Dakota: 41 F, southern Alberta: 39 F). It thus appears that the physical features of pronghorns comply with both Allen's Rule and with Bergmann's Rule, showing a reduction in size of protruding parts (ears and total leg length) and an increase in body size (total length and body weight) with decreasing ambient temperatures. The outstanding contradiction to this statement is found in the total lengths and body weights of pronghorns in Oregon and California. The reasons for this nonconformity to Bergmann's Rule require further study.

The relationships between whole, hog-dressed, and dressed carcass weights for 40 antelopes collected at all seasons are shown in Table 6. The hog-dressed to whole weight percentages are consistent between age groups; none of the differences between age-classes by sex or sexes by age-class are significant, with the exception of the difference between mature males and females. The relatively smaller mean hog-dressed weight percentage in females was related to pregnancy and the development of fe-

tuses in the nine pregnant females in this sample. The ratio of visceral weight to whole weight increased from 27 percent in females in November to 40 percent in a female at term pregnancy in June. Whole carcasses of mature animals averaged 29 percent weight loss when reduced to the hog-dressed condition. O'Gara (1970) reported 28 percent loss to Montana antelope carcasses when eviscerated.

In Alberta, hog-dressed weights of *americana* in June and September represented an average of 77 percent of the mean whole weight. During the same months in California (McLean 1944:239), the hog-dressed weight was significantly larger at 82 percent of the whole weight. The hog-dressed percentages in Alberta decreased to 66 percent in February, and then showed a marked increase between March and June.

Average dressed weights also show a consistent relationship to whole weights, ranging from 51 to 57 percent. The mean carcass yield for immature and older pronghorns was 54.3 percent. This corresponds closely to the mean yields of 52.5 percent for white-tailed deer (*Odocoileus virginianus*), 54.2 percent for Rocky Mountain elk (*Cervus canadensis*), 56.6 percent for Uganda kob (*Adenota kob*), and 50.0 percent for moose (*Alces alces*) reported by Hamerstrom and Camburn (1950), Quimby

Table 7. Carcass weights, yields, and offal percentages for 40 pronghorn antelopes from Alberta.

	IMMATURE MALE (n = 3)			YEARLING MALE (n = 3)			MATURE MALE (n = 16)		
	$\bar{x}$	$S_{\bar{x}}$	Range	$\bar{x}$	$S_{\bar{x}}$	Range	$\bar{x}$	$S_{\bar{x}}$	Range
Whole weight (lb)	76.7	3.33	70.0–80.0	106.2	5.20	100.0–116.5	119.1	2.53	102.5–134.0
Hog-dressed weight (lb)	53.3	1.76	50.0–56.0	79.7	3.98	74.5–87.5	87.6	2.03	68.0–99.0
Dressed weight (lb)	41.8	2.05	38.0–45.0	60.7	3.44	56.5–67.5	66.7	1.73	52.5–76.5
Carcass yield[a]	55.0	4.93	47.5–64.3	57.1	0.43	56.5–57.9	56.0	0.84	49.6–61.9
Internal offal[a]	30.1	4.23	22.9–37.5	25.0	1.14	24.9–27.0	26.4	1.04	18.7–33.7
External offal[a]	14.9	1.16	12.9–16.9	17.9	1.31	16.2–20.5	17.6	0.59	13.7–23.0

	IMMATURE FEMALE (n = 2)			YEARLING FEMALE (n = 5)			MATURE FEMALE (n = 11)		
	$\bar{x}$	$S_{\bar{x}}$	Range	$\bar{x}$	$S_{\bar{x}}$	Range	$\bar{x}$	$S_{\bar{x}}$	Range
Whole weight (lb)	78.0	3.50	74.5–81.5	100.7	3.83	91.0–112.0	110.8	2.25	100.0–124.0
Hog-dressed weight (lb)	53.7	3.75	50.0–57.5	71.1	2.91	63.0–78.0	73.2	2.21	62.5–84.5
Dressed weight (lb)	40.7	3.75	37.0–44.5	54.9	2.42	48.0–60.5	56.8	1.77	48.0–67.0
Carcass yield[a]	52.1	2.46	49.7–54.6	54.5	0.52	52.7–55.8	51.2	1.10	46.4–56.3
Internal offal[a]	31.2	1.70	29.5–32.9	29.4	0.62	27.3–30.8	33.9	1.41	26.8–39.6
External offal[a]	16.7	0.75	15.9–17.4	16.1	0.44	15.3–17.7	14.9	0.41	12.7–16.9

[a] Percentage of whole weight.

and Johnson (1951), Ledger and Smith (1964), and Blood et al. (1967), respectively.

Table 6 shows conversion factors that can be used to determine whole weights from partial carcass weights. Using the hog-dressed conversion factors 1.36 and 1.51 to calculate whole weights resulted in deviations of 4.0 ± 2.0 percent for males and 6.3 ± 1.7 percent for females. These figures represented actual deviations of 0.3 to 10.6 pounds for males, and 2.5 to 11.8 pounds for females. The use of dressed-weight conversion factors 1.78 and 1.95 produced mean deviations of 4.6 ± 1.8 percent and 6.2 ± 1.9 percent for mature males and females, respectively. The conversion factors for yearlings and immatures are less reliable because of small sample sizes. The mean deviations using hog-dressed conversion factors ranged from 1.5 to 7.0 percent for these submature animals, with each category having a large confidence interval. These partial-to-whole-weight conversion

factors are similar to those given by O'Gara (1970) for Montana pronghorns.

Whole weights can also be estimated using formulas derived from the regressions of whole weights on hog-dressed weights. Linear regression lines fitted to the whole and hog-dressed weights of 13 males and 16 females (Fig. 1) gave the equations: $y = 16.7496 + 1.1732x$ for yearling and mature males, and $y = 38.7119 + 0.9501x$ for corresponding females, with y representing whole weight and x representing hog-dressed weight. Whole weights for males and females estimated from the equations showed mean deviations from actual whole weights of 4.3 ± 1.4 percent and 4.7 ± 1.7 percent, respectively. Actual deviations ranged from 0.5 to 11.4 pounds for males, and 0 to 11.4 pounds for females. There is no significant difference between the deviations with the use of the conversion factors and the regression formulas.

Pronghorn carcass yields and internal and external offal percentages (Table 7) show little variation by sex and age. Yearling

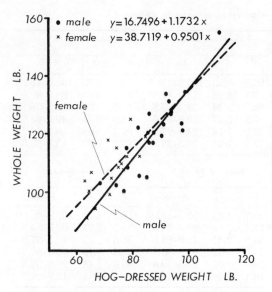

Fig. 1. Regression of whole weight on hog-dressed weight for 23 male and 16 female yearling and mature pronghorn antelopes.

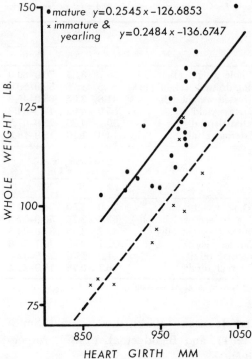

Fig. 2. Regression of whole weight on heart girth for 22 mature and 11 immature and yearling pronghorn antelopes.

and mature males have the highest proportion of external offal. The mean external offal for mature females was significantly lower than for yearlings and mature males.

The analysis of various body measurements showed that only whole weights and heart girths demonstrated a useful relationship. Correlation coefficients for all age groups of both sexes ranged from 0.68 to 1.00, and when tested for homogeneity (Steel and Torrie 1960:190–193), showed no differences. Therefore, in determining regression equations, the data were lumped by sex and age; additionally, they were combined by sexes into mature and submature categories.

The regression equation: $y = 0.3043x - 179.4817$, where y and x represent whole weight and heart girth, respectively, was computed using the lumped data for all pronghorns. The regression equations for mature males and females and immature and yearling males and females are: $y = 0.2545x - 126.6853$, and $y = 0.2484x -$

136.6747, respectively (Fig. 2). Prediction of whole weights using the lumped data equation gave a mean deviation of estimated from actual whole weights of 8.1 ± 1.9 percent. Mean deviations using the equations derived for the mature and submature categories are 5.8 ± 4.1 percent and 5.6 ± 2.4 percent, respectively.

Whole weights may vary as a result of condition, rumen fill, and water content of the viscera (Talbot and McCulloch 1965). Therefore, body weight estimates that are just as reliable as individual weighings taken when the animals are sacrificed, may be obtained by using (1) the equations for the regressions of whole weights on heart girths, (2) the equations for the regressions of whole weights on hog-dressed weights, and (3) the conversion factors for estimating whole weights from hog-dressed and dressed weights. These methods should be of practical value to the field technician.

LITERATURE CITED

ALLEE, W. C., A. E. EMERSON, O. PARK, T. PARK, AND K. P. SCHMIDT. 1949. Principles of animal ecology. W. B. Saunders Company, Philadelphia. 837pp.

ANDERSON, R. M. 1948. Methods of collecting and preserving vertebrate animals. Natl. Museum of Canada Bull. 69. 161pp.

BLOOD, D. A., AND A. L. LOVAAS. 1966. Measurements and weight relationships in Manitoba elk. J. Wildl. Mgmt. 30(1):135–140.

———, J. R. McGILLIS, AND A. L. LOVAAS. 1967. Weights and measurements of moose in Elk Island National Park, Alberta. Canadian Field-Naturalist 81(4):263–269.

BOWSER, W. E., T. W. PETERS, AND A. A. KJEARSGAARD. 1963. Soil survey of eastern portion of St. Mary and Milk Rivers Development Irrigation Project. Univ. of Alberta Soil Survey Rept. 22. 49pp.

BUCK, P. D. 1947. The biology of the antelope (*Antilocapra americana*) in Montana. M.S. Thesis, Montana State College. 70pp.

BUECHNER, H. K. 1950. Life history, ecology, and range use of the pronghorn antelope in Trans-Pecos Texas. Am. Midland Naturalist 43(2):257–354.

CANADA YEAR BOOK. 1969. Dominion Bureau of Statistics. Ottawa, Canada. 1329pp.

CLARKE, S. E., J. A. CAMPBELL, AND J. B. CAMPBELL. 1942. An ecological and grazing capacity study of the native grass pastures in southern Alberta, Saskatchewan and Manitoba. Canada Dept. Agr. Tech. Bull. 44. 31pp.

COUPLAND, R. T. 1950. Ecology of mixed prairie in Canada. Ecol. Monographs 20(4):271–315.

———. 1961. A reconsideration of grassland classification in the northern Great Plains of North America. J. Ecol. 49(1):135–167.

DOW, S. A., JR., AND P. L. WRIGHT. 1962. Changes in mandibular dentition associated with age in pronghorn antelope. J. Wildl. Mgmt. 26(1):1–18.

EDWARDS, W. C. 1958. A study of the reproductive potential and ovarian structures in the pronghorn antelope, *Antilocapra americana* (Ord.) in Wyoming. M.S. Thesis. Univ. of Wyoming. 63pp.

EINARSEN, A. S. 1948. The pronghorn antelope and its management. The Wildlife Management Institute, Washington, D. C. 238pp.

GOLENPAUL, D. 1969 (1970). Information please almanac atlas and yearbook. 24th ed. Simon and Schuster, New York. 1023pp.

HAMERSTROM, F. N., JR., AND F. L. CAMBURN.

1950. Weight relationships in the George Reserve deer herd. J. Mammal. 31(1):5–17.

HEPWORTH, B. 1965. Investigations of pronghorn antelope in Wyoming. Proc. Annual Antelope States Workshop 1:1–12.

HOOVER, R. L., C. E. TILL, AND S. OGILVIE. 1959. The antelope of Colorado. A research and management study. Colorado Dept. of Game and Fish Tech. Bull. 4. 110pp.

KELSALL, J. P. 1968. The migratory barren-ground caribou of Canada. Canada Dept. of Indian Affairs and Northern Development, Canadian Wildl. Serv. 340pp.

KOLENOSKY, G. B., AND R. S. MILLER. 1962. Growth of the lens of the pronghorn antelope. J. Wildl. Mgmt. 26(1):112–113.

LEDGER, H. P., AND N. S. SMITH. 1964. The carcass and body composition of the Uganda kob. J. Wildl. Mgmt. 28(4):827–839.

LONG, L. H. 1969 (1970). The world almanac and book of facts. Doubleday and Co., Inc. New York. 952pp.

MASON, E. 1952. Food habits and measurements of Hart Mountain antelope. J. Wildl. Mgmt. 16(3):387–389.

McKEAN, W. 1951. Sex, age, and physical characteristics of North Dakota antelope as obtained by field checking 1951. Project 7 R, North Dakota State Game and Fish Dept. 5pp. Mimeo.

McLEAN, D. D. 1944. The prong-horned antelope in California. California Fish and Game, 30(4):221–241.

MITCHELL, G. J. 1965. Natality, mortality and related phenomena in two populations of pronghorn antelope in Alberta, Canada. Ph.D. Thesis. Washington State Univ. 205pp.

O'GARA, B. W. 1970. Derivation of whole weights for the pronghorn. J. Wildl. Mgmt. 34(2):470–472.

QUIMBY, D. C., AND D. E. JOHNSON. 1951. Weights and measurements of Rocky Mountain elk. J. Wildl. Mgmt. 15(1):57–62.

SHAW, W. M. 1960. Notes on Idaho antelope management data. Proc. Interstate Antelope Conf.:92–99.

———. 1961. Miscellaneous data on Idaho antelope. Proc. Interstate Antelope Conf.:15–19.

SMOLIAK, S. 1956. Influence of climatic conditions on forage production of shortgrass rangeland. J. Range Mgmt. 9(2):89–91.

STEEL, R. G. D., AND J. H. TORRIE. 1960. Principles and procedures of statistics. McGraw-Hill Book Company, Inc., Toronto. 481pp.

TALBOT, L. M., AND J. S. G. McCULLOCH. 1965. Weight estimations for East African mammals from body measurements. J. Wildl. Mgmt. 29(1):84–89.

Received for publication April 10, 1970.

PRONGHORN ANTELOPE RANGE CHARACTERISTICS AND FOOD HABITS IN ALBERTA

GEORGE J. MITCHELL, Alberta Department of Lands and Forests, Edmonton[1]

SYLVESTER SMOLIAK, Research Station, Canada Department of Agriculture, Lethbridge, Alberta

Abstract: Range productivity, vegetation characteristics, and food habits of the pronghorn antelope (*Antilocapra americana*) were studied in the Pakowki and Newell areas, Alberta, from 1962 through 1965. Quantitative measurements of canopies, frequencies, constancies of taxa, and yields of plant categories showed that the Pakowki and Newell areas represented spear grass–western wheat grass/blue grama (*Stipa comata–Agropyron smithii/Bouteloua gracilis*), and spear grass/blue grama habitat types, respectively. Food habits were studied by analysis of 162 samples of rumen contents collected at monthly intervals in each month except December. The yearlong diet in the Newell area consisted of 51 percent forbs, 35 percent browse species, and 13 percent grasses and sedges. Antelopes in both areas had eaten 52 forbs, 12 browse species, an undetermined number of grasses and sedges, and a trace of lichens. The important food categories in the Newell area were browse species in summer, fall, and winter; forbs in all seasons; and grasses and sedges in spring. Cultivated grain was of minor importance. In the Pakowki area, browse species and grasses and sedges were the most important food categories in late fall and early winter. The five major food items, comprising 73 percent of the total diet in the Newell area, were silver sagebrush (*Artemisia cana*), pasture sagewort (*A. frigida*), grasses and sedges, ball cactus (*Mamillaria vivipara*), and western snowberry (*Symphoricarpos occidentalis*), in order of decreasing volume. These same species comprised 90 percent of the diet of antelopes in the Pakowki area in late fall and early winter. Comparisons between vegetation abundance and antelope food habits in two areas in 1964 indicated that both forbs and browse species are preferred foods, and that forbs, when available, are eaten in preference to grasses and sedges. Silver sagebrush and pasture sagewort are key antelope foods in the Newell area, comprising 82 percent of the winter diet, and over one-half the diet at all times except summer. Silver sagebrush, western snowberry, and graminaceous species are the key foods in the Pakowki area in fall and early winter. The role and importance of big sagebrush (*Artemisia tridentata*) in the diet of antelopes south of latitude 49° N is assumed by silver sagebrush and pasture sagewort in the diet of antelopes in Alberta.

The area occupied by the pronghorn antelope in North America has been considered to be divisible into two major regions on the basis of land productivity and on the factors that regulate antelope numbers (Buechner 1961). According to this classification, the steppe of southern Alberta is located in that region characterized by relatively moist conditions, high land productivity, and the regulation of antelope numbers by man. Published information on range productivity and antelope range use in Canada and adjacent states is limited. Dirschl (1963) reported on the major food plants eaten seasonally by antelopes on mixed prairie and fescue grasslands in Saskatchewan. Cole (1956:16–33), and Cole

and Wilkins (1958:8–25) described range and food habits of antelopes in Montana with reference to alfalfa (*Medicago sativa*) and winter wheat (*Triticum aestivum*) production, respectively. Bayless (1969) presented a detailed account of winter range, range use, and food habits of the pronghorn in central Montana. These Montana studies, those for California (Ferrel and Leach 1950), those for Oregon and Nevada (Mason 1952), and those for other regions report on the importance of big sagebrush in the diet of the pronghorn. The absence of this plant species on antelope ranges in Canada raises the question as to what species or combination of species supplants this important food item in the diet of pronghorns in Alberta.

Our study, conducted from 1962 through 1965 on two antelope ranges in southern

[1] Present address: Biology Department, University of Saskatchewan, Regina Campus, Regina.

Alberta, was designed to measure land productivity, vegetation characteristics, vegetation changes, and their influence on antelope diets.

We thank R. G. H. Cormack, Botany Department, University of Alberta, for his participation in 1962; and T. W. Peters, Pedologist, Canada Department of Agriculture Soil Survey, University of Alberta, for his soil analyses in 1964. Thanks are also extended to L. G. Sugden, Canadian Wildlife Service, for critically reviewing the manuscript. The laboratory analysis of food materials was supported in part by a grant from W. A. Riddell, former principal, University of Saskatchewan, Regina Campus; and by National Research Council Grant-in-Aid No. 3913.

STUDY AREAS

The Pakowki study area is located in extreme southeastern Alberta bordering the Province of Saskatchewan and the State of Montana (Fig. 1). It comprises about 624,000 acres of treeless rangeland, over 90 percent of which remains as large uncultivated blocks used for livestock grazing. Dryland farming is essentially limited to the western portion of the area. The physiography is characterized by undulating to strongly rolling upland plains, bottom lands, exposed shales, and steep, eroded coulees associated with the deeply entrenched Milk River and Lost River channels.

The geological formations consist of soft, light-colored shales and sandstones. The soils have been formed *in situ* from the weathering of country rock and subsequent reworking and mixing of materials. Many of the hilly areas are stony and gravelly, and are morainal formations. Upland soils range from Solodized Solonetzic to Orthic greyish-Brown Chernozems. The soil profile varies from a light loam to a clay loam

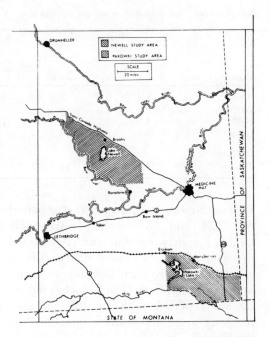

Fig. 1. The Pakowki and Newell study areas, southeastern Alberta.

and has a lime layer at a depth of about 10 inches.

The Newell study area in south-central Alberta is located between the Trans-Canada Highway and the Bow River (Fig. 1). Within this 663,000-acre block, tracts of native rangeland are interspersed with units of intensively irrigated farms. The characteristic physiographic features include undulating to rolling topography with local hilly areas, sand dunes, and a margin of coulees adjacent to the Bow River. The Orthic Brown Chernozem soils show a loamy sand profile with a lime layer at 20–30 inches.

The climate of southern Alberta is semiarid with low annual precipitation, high rates of evaporation, prolonged periods of drought, and great extremes in temperature between seasons. The mean annual precipitation at the Manyberries Range Station (Pakowki area) and Brooks Horticultural

Table 1. April, May, June, and annual precipitation totals (in inches) on two study areas, 1961–64.

	PAKOWKI AREA					NEWELL AREA				
YEAR	April	May	June	Annual	Departure from 30-year Mean (percent)	April	May	June	Annual	Departure from 30-year Mean (percent)
1961	0.5	1.4	0.6	8.5	−30	0.4	0.7	0.2	6.3	−53
1962	0.3	2.2	3.3	11.3	− 6	0.4	1.6	1.2	9.6	−30
1963	0.8	1.0	2.7	10.3	−15	0.1	0.7	5.0	14.3	+ 5
1964	1.0	1.6	2.3	15.1	+ 3	0.7	2.0	1.9	14.4	+ 7
1931–60 mean	1.0	1.3	2.5	12.1		0.8	1.6	2.3	13.6	

Station (Newell area) over a 30-year period was 12.1 and 13.6 inches, respectively (Table 1). Between 1961 and 1964 annual precipitation in both areas increased from less than to more than the 30-year mean. Snowfall varied from 17 to 75 inches during the study period, with the Pakowki area receiving a greater amount annually than the Newell area.

Mean temperatures are similar in both study areas. The mean average annual temperature is 40.2 F and 39.1 F in the Pakowki and Newell areas, respectively. Temperature extremes in the two areas between 1954 and 1964 were −45 F and 105 F, and −46 F and 100 F. The mean precipitation/evaporation ratio in the Pakowki area was 0.35 during the study period.

The level-to-hilly areas in southern Alberta support a mixed prairie vegetation (Coupland 1950). Shrubs are widely dispersed and relatively scarce except in depressions, coulee bottoms, and sand hills where favorable subsurface soil moisture conditions prevail. Trees are generally limited to river channel sites.

During spring, summer, and fall, antelopes are abundant on the upland prairie in both areas. Mean population densities for the Pakowki and Newell areas during the summers of 1962–64 were 2.35 and 3.87 antelopes per square mile, respectively (Mitchell 1965:65). Movements to river

breaks and hilly areas coincide with the period of active hunting in late October or early November. However, antelope use of the upland sites occurs throughout the winter when weather conditions are not too severe and snow depths and hardness do not impede the easy movement of animals. In some years large numbers of antelopes concentrate on several ranches in the southeast corner of the Pakowki study area. In severe winters the large concentrations of antelopes along the Milk River near Havre, Montana, contain animals from the Pakowki area.

METHODS AND MATERIALS

Measurements of Vegetation

The canopy-coverage method of vegetation analysis (Daubenmire 1959) was used in both study areas. On the basis of uniformity of soils, topography, and animal grazing history, six sampling sites were selected in each study area. A permanent 20-m transect line was established at each site. Forty 2- × 5-dm plots were studied on each transect each year from 1962 through 1964. Forage productivity was determined by hand-clipping a total of 125 $1m^2$ rectangular plots near the transect lines. Grasses and forbs were clipped at ground level, and the current year's growth of shrubs was removed. Clipped vegetation was separated into categories of grasses and sedges, forbs, and shrubs; these were later dried and weighed. Vegetation analyses and plot clippings were conducted each year when spear grass was headed. The constancy, or the mean percentage of occurrence of a species among the transects in a study area, was computed for each species from 1962 through 1964. Botanical nomenclature follows Budd and Best (1964) and Moss (1959).

Analyses of Rumen Samples

A collection of 162 rumen samples, representing every month of the year except December, was made between August 1962 and January 1965. Approximately 90 samples were contributed by hunters during the October and November hunting seasons between 1962 and 1964. The remaining samples were taken from antelopes collected for other studies. The 50 rumens obtained in the Pakowki area represent fall and early winter samples only. All other samples were obtained on and adjacent to the Newell study area.

Quart samples of rumen contents were preserved in a 10 percent solution of formalin in the field. In the laboratory each sample was thoroughly washed under tap water through a Canadian Sieve Series mesh (Mesh No. 3½), with a mesh size of 5.66 mm. According to Dirschl (1962), this mesh size is the most efficient for analysis of samples from an antelope's rumen. Food materials remaining on the mesh were examined and separated by species.

Food items were identified using a plant collection made at the time of range vegetation analysis, and by reference to herbarium sheets at the University of Saskatchewan, Regina Campus, as well as the Canada Department of Agriculture Research Stations at Lethbridge, Alberta, and Regina, Saskatchewan.

Table 2. Percentage of total canopy coverage furnished by each of the principal species (excluding *Selaginella densa* and lichens) in two study areas, 1962–64.

TAXA	PAKOWKI	NEWELL
Shrubs		
Artemisia cana	1.5	3.2
Other shrubs	tr[a]	tr
Total shrubs	2.3	3.2
Forbs		
Artemisia frigida	3.8	8.7
Other forbs	6.2	9.5
Total forbs	10.0	18.2
Total shrubs and forbs	12.3	21.4
Grasses		
Stipa comata	23.8	34.9
Agropyron smithii	20.8	tr
Bouteloua gracilis	7.0	17.5
Other grasses	21.5	19.0
Total grasses	73.1	72.2
Sedges		
Carex eleocharis	13.8	5.6
Other sedges	tr	tr
Total sedges	14.6	6.4
Total grasses and sedges	87.7	78.6

[a] Tr = trace, and indicates less than one percent.

All sorted food items were dried on a towel and placed in a graduated cylinder to determine volumes by water displacement. Food plants were grouped into four categories: browse plants, forbs, grasses and sedges, and unidentified materials. Mean seasonal percentage volumes of each food item (except grasses and sedges) and food category in the diet were computed by the aggregate percentage method (Martin et al. 1946). Grasses and sedges in rumen samples were not identified by species. Weighted mean annual values were determined by using seasonal mean percentage volumes and the number of months in each seasonal period. Frequency of occurrence expressed as a decimal value (frequency index) was computed by divid-

Table 3. Mean percentage canopy coverage, frequency and constancy of taxa in two study areas and habitat types, 1962–64.

TAXA	PAKOWKI AREA			NEWELL AREA		
	Coverage[a]	Frequency[b]	Constancy[c]	Coverage	Frequency	Constancy
Shrubs						
Artemisia cana	2	6	67	4	20	39
Eurotia lanata	1	12	67			
Forbs						
Artemisia frigida	5	47	100	11	53	100
Phlox hoodii	4	48	100	tr[d]	3	44
Erigeron caespitosus	2	20	72			
Sphaeralcea coccinea	1	30	100	tr	7	50
Lomatium foeniculaceum	1	7	11			
Chenopodium leptophyllum	tr	9	67	5	49	67
Lappula redowskii	tr	6	29	1	17	56
Chrysopsis villosa	tr	2	22	4	25	78
Lepidium densiflorum	tr	tr	5	1	20	61
Salsola kali	tr	tr	5	1	17	25
Grasses						
Stipa comata	31	78	100	44	82	100
Agropyron smithii	27	83	100	1	7	44
Koeleria cristata	18	90	100	4	27	58
Bouteloua gracilis	9	73	100	22	84	100
Calamagrostis montanensis	7	39	83	3	17	39
Poa secunda	3	26	83	13	36	89
Calamovilfa longifolia				4	9	33
Sedges						
Carex eleocharis	18	74	94	7	55	94
Carex filifolia	1	6	28	tr	4	55
Carex heliophila				1	4	17
Club Mosses						
Selaginella densa	23	84	100	12	69	100
Lichen	10	99	100	2	42	100

[a] Canopy coverage—mean percent of area covered by foliage.
[b] Frequency—mean percent occurrence among plots.
[c] Constancy—mean percent occurrence among sampling sites.
[d] Tr = trace, and indicates taxon present but having less than one percent canopy coverage or less than one percent frequency of occurrence. Only species having more than a trace of canopy coverage on at least one area are listed.

ing the number of occurrences of individual samples by the total number of samples obtained during a season (Anderson et al. 1965).

RESULTS

Vegetation Coverage

Vegetation analyses indicate that the two study areas represent two distinct types of grassland vegetation. The Pakowki area is characterized by a spear grass–western wheat grass/blue grama habitat type. The three dominants in this area contributed 52 percent, and all graminaceous species contributed 88 percent of the total vegetative cover (Table 2). Although June grass (*Koeleria cristata*) had a greater coverage (14 percent) than blue grama (7 percent), it was not considered to be dominant because of its dependency upon moisture in excess of that required by the dominant grasses (Coupland 1961). Furthermore, blue grama was somewhat under-represented inasmuch as the sampling was done each year prior to blue grama heading, and at a time when the phenologically earlier June grass was fully headed. The shrubs, silver sagebrush and winter fat (*Eurotia lanata*), and the forbs, pasture sagewort and moss phlox (*Phlox hoodii*), were the most abundant of 37 broad-leaved species recorded in the Pakowki area (Table 3).

The Newell area is characterized by a spear grass/blue grama habitat type in which the two graminaceous dominants contributed 52 percent, and all graminaceous taxa contributed 79 percent of the total vegetative cover (Table 2). Sandberg bluegrass (*Poa secunda*) contributed 10 percent to total canopy coverage, but it was not considered an important or dominant species because of dependency on early spring moisture and response to changes in climatic and grazing pressures. Because of their stature, abundance, and coverage, pasture sagewort and silver sagebrush were the most conspicuous of 30 broad-leaved plants recorded on the transects (Table 3).

Vegetation Yields

Forage yields in both areas declined between 1962 and 1963 and then increased markedly in 1964 (Table 4). Graminaceous as well as total forage production differed significantly ($P < 0.05$) between study areas each year. The Pakowki area showed the higher yields and received the greater amount of spring rainfall in 1962 and 1963. The Newell area produced the greater forage yield and received the greater amount of April–May rainfall in 1964.

Earlier studies (Clarke et al. 1947:25–27, Smoliak 1956) have shown a high correlation between spring and summer rainfall and forage production on mixed prairie grasslands in Alberta. In the present study,

Table 4. Percentage of canopy coverage and dry matter yields in pounds per acre of vegetation in three categories on two study areas, 1962–64.

Year	Vegetation Category[a]	Pakowki Area		Newell Area	
		Percent Canopy Coverage[b]	Dry Matter Yield	Percent Canopy Coverage	Dry Matter Yield
1962	Shrubs	3.0	9	4.5	26
	Forbs	20.6	237	26.6	187
	Grasses[c]	70.9	343	57.8	231
	Total		589		444
1963	Shrubs	3.2	—	4.8	12
	Forbs	16.7	82	12.1	108
	Grasses	116.8	394	80.8	176
	Total		476		296
1964	Shrubs	4.2	tr[d]	6.4	8
	Forbs	19.5	111	47.9	340
	Grasses	134.6	589	184.3	1,074
	Total		700		1,422

[a] *Selaginella densa* excluded from the tabulations.
[b] Canopy coverage values greater than 100 represent layering effects.
[c] Includes sedges.
[d] Tr = trace, and indicates less than one percent.

computed correlation coefficients ranging from 0.9154 to 0.9623 for canopy coverage and yields of forbs, and spring rainfall suggest a high correlation. However, because of the small sample size for each area ($n = 3$), these coefficients are not significant ($P > 0.05$).

Food Habits

It has been shown (Norris 1943) that differential digestibilities of food items consumed by domestic sheep placed limitations on the quantitative data obtained through rumen sample investigations. The extent of these limitations in interpretations of analyses of antelope rumen samples in this and other antelope studies is unknown. The possibility of such limitations is recognized.

Quantitative differences in antelope use of food items in vegetation categories by month facilitated differentiating four periods in which preferences in vegetation categories occurred: (1) spring (April–May)—forbs, grasses, and sedges; (2) sum-

Table 5. Late fall and early winter food items in 50 samples of rumen contents from pronghorn antelopes collected in the Pakowki study area, 1963–64. Sample size in parentheses.

| | SEASON | | | |
| | Late Fall (44) | | Early Winter (6) | |
FOOD ITEM	Mean Volume (percent)	Fre- quency Index	Mean Volume (percent)	Fre- quency Index
Browse				
Artemisia cana	55	1.00	26	1.00
Symphoricarpos occidentalis	9	0.39	22	0.33
Rosa sp.	1	0.18	tr[a]	0.17
Juniperus horizontalis	1	tr	3	0.33
Elaeagnus commutata	tr	tr	1	0.17
Salix sp.	tr	tr	1	0.17
Total	66		53	
Forbs				
Mamillaria vivipara	4	0.27	4	0.33
Antennaria sp.	3	0.32	2	0.67
Artemisia frigida	2	0.48	12	1.00
Haplopappus spinulosus	1	0.16		
Opuntia polyacantha	1	tr		
Polygonum neglectum	tr	0.11		
Hedysarum alpinum			1	0.17
Solanum triflorum			1	0.17
Achillea millefolium			tr	0.17
Gutierrezia diversifolia	tr	tr	tr	0.17
Haplopappus lanceolatus	tr	tr	tr	0.17
Lepidium densiflorum			tr	0.17
Phlox hoodii	tr	tr	tr	0.17
Potentilla gracilis			tr	0.17
Sphaeralcea coccinea			tr	0.17
Total	12		21	
Grasses and sedges	20	0.98	26	1.00
Unidentified components	1	0.23	tr	0.17

[a] Tr = trace, and indicates less than one percent volume or less than 0.1 percent frequency.

mer (June–August)—forbs and browse plants; (3) fall (September–October)—forbs and browse plants; and (4) winter (November–March)—forbs and browse plants. In addition, grasses and sedges were important items in the fall and early winter diet of antelopes in the Pakowki area.

In addition to grasses and sedges, 31 forbs and 8 browse species were recorded in the fall and early winter samples from the Pakowki area. Fourteen food items, which occurred in fall, in early winter, or in both, in mean volumes of one percent or more, and eight items, which occurred in trace amounts with a frequency of 10 percent or more, are listed in Table 5. Silver sagebrush, pasture sagewort, grasses and sedges, ball cactus, and western snowberry comprised 90 percent of the fall and early winter diet of pronghorns in the Pakowki area. These same items comprised 73 percent of the mean annual diet in the Newell area. Thirty-six identified food items that occurred seasonally in mean volumes of one

Table 6. Seasonal summary of food items in 112 samples of rumen contents from pronghorn antelopes collected in the Newell study area, 1962—65. Sample size in parentheses.

SEASON	Spring (6)		Summer (8)		Fall (55)		Winter (43)		ANNUAL (112)	
FOOD ITEM	Mean Volume (percent)	Fre-quency Index	Mean Volume (percent)	Fre-quency Index	Mean Volume (percent)	Fre-quency Index	Mean Volume (percent)	Fre-quency Index	Weighted Mean Volume (percent)	Fre-quency Index
Browse										
Artemisia cana	15	0.83	13	0.87	41	0.98	40	0.86	29	0.92
Salix sp.	3	0.50	2	0.62	1	0.13	tr[a]	tr	1	0.16
Elaeagnus commutata			9	0.12	1	tr	tr	tr	2	tr
Rosa sp.			1	0.37	tr	tr	tr	tr	tr	0.10
Crataegus chrysocarpa			tr	0.12					tr	tr
Symphoricarpos occi-dentalis					7	0.20	2	tr	2	0.13
Atriplex nuttallii					tr	tr	1	tr	tr	tr
Total	18		25		50		43		35	
Forbs										
Artemisia frigida	39	0.83	4	0.87	19	0.98	42	0.93	26	0.95
Mamillaria vivipara	7	0.50	tr	0.25	12	0.42	tr	tr	3	0.27
Potentilla gracilis	3	0.17							tr	tr
Antennaria sp.	2	0.50			1	0.11	1	0.12	1	0.12
Potentilla anserina	2	0.17	1	0.12					1	tr
Achillea millefolium	1	0.17	tr	0.12	tr	tr			tr	tr
Anemone patens	1	0.17							tr	tr
Descurainia sophia	1	0.17	1	0.37	tr	tr	tr	tr	1	tr
Taraxacum officinale	1	0.17			tr	tr			tr	tr
Phlox hoodii	tr	0.33	tr	0.12	tr	0.11	1	0.23	tr	0.17
Erysimum incon-spicuum	tr	0.17							tr	tr
Lepidium densi-florum	tr	0.17	1	0.25	1	0.16			tr	0.11
Potentilla sp.	tr	0.17			tr	tr	tr	tr	tr	tr
Solanum triflorum			11	0.25	tr	tr			3	tr
Polygonum neglectum			10	0.50	1	0.16	tr	tr	3	0.12
Tragopogon dubius			9	0.12	1	tr			2	tr
Gaura coccinea			5	0.12					1	tr
Hymenoxys richardsonii			5	0.12	tr	tr			1	tr
Chrysopsis villosa			3	0.50			tr	tr	1	tr
Achillea lanulosa			3	0.25			tr	tr	1	tr
Haplopappus lanceolatus			2	0.37	tr	tr	tr	tr	tr	tr
Melilotus officinalis			1	0.37	2	tr			1	tr
Arnica fulgens			1	0.12					tr	tr
Astragalus crassicarpus			1	0.12					tr	tr
Astragalus sp.			1	0.12					tr	tr
Cirsium arvense			1	0.12			tr	tr	tr	tr
Erigeron caespitosus			1	0.12					tr	tr
Oxytropis sp.			1	0.12					tr	tr
Gutierrezia diversifolia			tr	0.25	tr	tr			tr	tr
Polygonum sp.			tr	0.25	tr	tr	1	tr	tr	tr
Camelina sp.			tr	0.12					tr	tr
Androsace septen-trionalis							1	tr	tr	tr
Hedysarum alpinum							1	tr	tr	tr
Total	57		62		37		47		51	
Grasses and sedges	25	1.00	13	0.87	13	0.98	9	0.98	13	0.97
Unidentified com-ponents	tr	0.17	1	0.12	tr	tr	1	tr	tr	tr

[a] Tr = trace, and indicates less than one percent volume and less than 0.1 percent frequency.

Table 7. Percentage of canopy coverage and yields of vegetation categories in summer, and the fall diet of antelopes in two areas, 1964. Number of rumens sampled is in parentheses.

	PAKOWKI AREA (23)			NEWELL AREA (23)		
CATEGORY	Percent Canopy Coverage	Yield (lb/acre)	Diet (percent volume)	Percent Canopy Coverage	Yield (lb/acre)	Diet (percent volume)
Shrubs	4	tr[a]	57	6	8	57
Forbs	20	111	14	48	340	25
Grasses[b]	133	589	26	184	1,074	17

[a] Tr = trace, and indicates less than 1 lb/acre.
[b] Includes sedges.

percent or more, and five items that occurred in trace amounts with a frequency of at least 10 percent, are listed in Table 6.

In spring the important food items on the Newell area were pasture sagewort, grasses and sedges, silver sagebrush, ball cactus, willows (*Salix* sp.), and graceful cinquefoil (*Potentilla gracilis*), in order of importance (Table 6). Use of graminaceous items in the Newell area was greatest during spring, coinciding with the initiation of new grass growth in late March or early April. Pasture sagewort provided 39 percent of the spring diet.

The summer diet was characterized by a decreased use of grasses and sedges and an increased use of browse plants and forbs. Utilization of forbs was greatest during this season; the number of forb items consumed showed a marked increase over the spring period. Most of the utilization of forbs in summer was on wild tomato (*Solanum triflorum*), doorweed (*Polygonum aviculare*), goat's-beard (*Tragopogon dubius*), scarlet butterfly-weed (*Gaura coccinea*), Colorado rubber-plant (*Hymenoxys richardsonii*), golden aster (*Chrysopsis villosa*), and woolly yarrow (*Achillea lanulosa*). Silver sagebrush and silver-berry (*Elaeagnus commutata*) were also important food items.

Browse species, especially silver sagebrush and western snowberry, were the main food items during the fall. The use of forbs was lowest and the use of browse plants highest during this season, in both areas. Except for ball cactus, everlasting (*Antennaria* sp.), and pasture sagewort, most forbs were present in rumen samples in volumes of one percent or less. Graminaceous items comprised one-fifth of the fall diet in the Pakowki area.

The winter diet of antelopes in the Newell area consisted of approximately equal volumes of browse plants and forbs. Pasture sagewort and silver sagebrush comprised 82 percent of the total winter diet. Graminaceous material was present in least amounts during this season in antelopes from the Newell area, but it comprised 26 percent of the diet in the sample from the Pakowki area. The volumetric values for utilization of forbs in fall and winter in the Pakowki area were lower than those recorded at any season in the Newell area.

Forage Availability and Utilization

The relationship between abundance in forage categories in summer and percent volumes of forage categories in the fall diet of antelopes was assessed by comparing the 1964 vegetative coverage and yields with the fall food-habits data for both areas. Although the absolute abundance and the relative abundance, and therefore the availability of forage categories, in fall differ from those recorded in summer, the differences in these values between seasons for individual categories are assumed to be similar in both study areas.

In 1964 the canopy coverages and yields of shrubs, forbs, and grasses and sedges in the Newell area were greater than the corresponding values recorded in the Pakowki area (Table 7). The 1964 fall utilization of browse species by antelopes was similar in both areas, but Newell antelopes consumed relatively more forb and less graminaceous material than did antelopes at Pakowki. It appears that when forbs are available, they are eaten by antelopes in preference to grasses, even when graminaceous materials are abundant. The high consumption of grasses at Pakowki suggests that antelopes there used these food plants because of the relative scarcity of forbs at that time.

DISCUSSION

The highest densities of antelopes in Alberta during the study occurred in the Pakowki and Newell areas in vegetational communities replete with forbs and graminaceous species, but relatively wanting in shrub taxa except where suitable conditions of subsurface soil moisture prevailed. Thirty-four forbs, 3 shrubs, 6 grasses, and 2 sedges were recorded in plots in the Pakowki area; 27 forbs, 3 shrubs, 7 grasses, and 3 sedges were recorded in the Newell plots. Common to both areas were 17 forbs, 1 shrub, 6 grasses, 2 sedges, club-moss (*Selaginella densa*), and lichens. Forbs and browse plants contributed more to total cover at Newell than at Pakowki (21.4 vs 12.3 percent) over the 3-year period, but in 1963 when April–May rainfall in the Newell area was 67 percent below normal, shrub and forb cover was less than at Pakowki.

Annual variations in the presence and abundance of vegetative taxa reflected climatic conditions. The low canopy coverage values recorded in 1962 for graminaceous species resulted from extreme droughty conditions in 1961, and from a series of arid conditions since 1955 in the Newell area and moderately severe conditions since 1958 in the Pakowki area. The high values recorded in 1964 resulted from above-normal rainfall in April and May. However, growth of forbs in 1962 was substantial as a consequence of above-normal spring rainfall.

This study and the studies of Clarke et al. (1942:23), Clarke et al. (1947:26), Coupland (1961), and Smoliak (1965) have shown that forage yields on grazed rangeland in the Pakowki area during relatively wet years (1956, 1964) exceeded production during the relatively dry periods of 1931–47 and 1961–63. The dependency of vegetative growth, abundance, and species composition on annual and spring precipitation has been recorded for most antelope regions (Foree 1959, 1960). Measurements of changes in vegetative composition and yields in Wyoming (Severson et al. 1968: 18) and Utah (Beale and Smith 1970) have demonstrated a similar relationship between forage yields and precipitation.

Antelopes in Alberta consume a variety of plants comprising 52 forbs, 12 browse species, and an undetermined number of grasses and sedges. Most of these plant species occurred in volumes of less than one percent in the annual diet. Although all categories of vegetation were represented in the diet at all seasons, browse species were present in greatest volume in summer, fall, and winter; forbs in all seasons; and graminaceous species in spring in the Newell area. Grasses and sedges were much more important in the fall and early winter diet in the Pakowki area than in the Newell area.

The changes in forage utilization by season appear to be related to plant structure and changes in plant abundance and availability. However, the high nutritive content of grasses in April (Dirschl 1963) was probably a factor causing increased use of graminaceous plants in spring. Forbs were abundant and heavily utilized in summer, but in fall all forbs, except pasture sagewort, were minor items in the diet. The cured condition of forbs and the presence of snow in fall and winter reduce the availability of all forbs other than pasture sagewort. Pasture sagewort is almost always available because of its abundance and erect stature. The decrease in shrub utilization in winter is possibly related to the greater abundance, preference for, and availability of pasture sagewort at that time.

The predominance of forbs over browse plants in the spring and summer diets of Alberta antelopes corresponds to diet data presented for antelopes in most regions except Wyoming (Severson et al. 1968:21). The relatively greater importance of browse plants over forbs in the fall diet in Alberta conforms to that reported for all other regions except Texas (Buechner 1947). The equal importance of browse and forb material in the winter diet in the combined sample in this study differs markedly from the browse-predominating winter diets of antelopes in all other regions.

Forbs comprised the greatest portion of the yearlong diet (51 percent) in the Newell area, followed by browse species (35 percent), and grasses and sedges (13 percent). This forbs–browse relationship agrees with that reported for antelope diets in Texas (Buechner 1950) and Colorado (Hoover et al. 1959:58), but is in contrast to that reported for most antelope diet studies. This forbs–browse relationship also agrees closely with that reported for Montana (Cole 1956:27) when the Alberta data are adjusted to conform to Cole's method of classifying pasture sagewort and cactus as browse species.

The annual proportion of browse species

in the diet in Alberta was much smaller than that reported for antelope in Montana (Cole and Wilkins 1958:20), Colorado and South Dakota (Einarsen 1948:63–64), Oregon (Mason 1952, Yoakum 1958), Wyoming (Severson et al. 1968:21), and Utah (Beale and Smith 1970). The heavier utilization of browse species in these states may be related to the greater diversity of habitats and vegetation types (Foree 1959) and to the greater abundance and availability of shrubs, particularly big sagebrush (Deming 1963), in these regions.

Rangelands in southern Alberta demonstrated a high productivity during the favorable growing season of 1964. A comparison of the vegetation yields in Alberta, Wyoming, and Utah in years of high precipitation during the growing season shows that forage production in Alberta (700 lb/acre and 1,422 lb/acre) exceeded that reported by Severson et al. (1968:32) for Wyoming (493 lb/acre), and Beale and Smith (1970) for Utah (321 lb/acre); also that forb production in Alberta (111 lb/acre and 340 lb/acre in the Pakowki and Newell areas, respectively) was greater than that reported by Beale and Scotter (1968) and Beale and Smith (1970) for Utah ranges (43 lb/acre and 45 lb/acre, respectively).

Silver sagebrush and pasture sagewort are the key foods of antelopes in Alberta. The relatively high protein and fat contents of these species in summer, fall, and winter (Clarke and Tisdale 1945:23, Dirschl 1963) probably exceed the minimum requirements of antelopes.

It appears that the role and importance of *Artemisia tridentata* in the diet of antelopes south of latitude 49° N is assumed by *A. cana* and *A. frigida* in the annual diet of antelopes in Alberta, and by these species and *Symphoricarpos occidentalis* in the fall and early winter diet of antelopes in the Pakowki area. The minor importance of creeping juniper (*Juniperus horizontalis*) and the major importance of pasture sagewort in Alberta are in marked contrast to the data reported by Dirschl (1963) for Saskatchewan antelopes during the hunting season (October 11–November 3).

Management procedures for antelopes in Alberta must be based upon recognition of the importance of silver sagebrush and pasture sagewort. Silver sagebrush stands on upland sites should be maintained. Management programs should consider the availability of antelope key foods during severe winters and the seasonal demand placed on the range resources by both domestic and wild ruminants.

LITERATURE CITED

ANDERSON, A. E., W. A. SNYDER, AND G. W. BROWN. 1965. Stomach content analyses related to condition in mule deer, Guadalupe Mountains, New Mexico. J. Wildl. Mgmt. 29(2):352–366.

BAYLESS, S. R. 1969. Winter food habits, range use, and home range of antelope in Montana. J. Wildl. Mgmt. 33(3):538–551.

BEALE, D. M., AND G. W. SCOTTER. 1968. Seasonal forage use by pronghorn antelope in western Utah. Utah Sci. 29(1):3–6,16.

———, AND A. D. SMITH. 1970. Forage use, water consumption, and productivity of pronghorn antelope in western Utah. J. Wildl. Mgmt. 34(3):570–582.

BUDD, A. C., AND K. F. BEST. 1964. Wild plants of the Canadian prairies. Canada Dept. Agr. Publ. 983. 519pp.

BUECHNER, H. K. 1947. Range use of the pronghorned antelope in western Texas. Trans. N. Am. Wildl. Conf. 12:185–191.

———. 1950. Life history, ecology, and range use of the pronghorn antelope in Trans-Pecos Texas. Am. Midland Naturalist 43(2):257–354.

———. 1961. Regulation of numbers of pronghorn antelope in relation to land use. La Terre ct la Vie 2:266–285.

CLARKE, S. E., AND E. W. TISDALE. 1945. The chemical composition of native forage plants of southern Alberta and Saskatchewan in relation to grazing practices. Canada Dept. Agr. Tech. Bull. 54. 60pp.

———, J. A. CAMPBELL, AND J. B. CAMPBELL. 1942. An ecological and grazing capacity study of the native grass pastures in southern Alberta, Saskatchewan and Manitoba. Canada Dept. Agr. Tech. Bull. 44. 31pp.

———, E. W. TISDALE, AND N. A. SKOGLUND. 1947. The effects of climate and grazing practices on shortgrass prairie vegetation. Canada Dept. Agr. Tech. Bull. 46. 54pp.

COLE, G. F. 1956. The pronghorn antelope: its range use and food habits in central Montana with special reference to alfalfa. Montana Fish and Game Dept. and Montana State Coll. Agr. Expt. Sta. Tech. Bull. 516. 63pp.

———, AND B. T. WILKINS. 1958. The pronghorn antelope: its range use and food habits in central Montana with special reference to wheat. Montana Fish and Game Dept. Tech. Bull. 2. 39pp.

COUPLAND, R. T. 1950. Ecology of mixed prairie in Canada. Ecol. Monographs 20(4):271–315.

———. 1961. A reconsideration of grassland classification in the northern Great Plains of North America. J. Ecol. 49(1):135–167.

DAUBENMIRE, R. 1959. A canopy-coverage method of vegetational analysis. Northwest Sci. 33(1):43–64.

DEMING, O. V. 1963. Antelope and sagebrush. Trans. Interstate Antelope Conf.: 55–60.

DIRSCHL, H. J. 1962. Sieve mesh size related to analysis of antelope rumen contents. J. Wildl. Mgmt. 26(3):327–328.

———. 1963. Food habits of the pronghorn in Saskatchewan. J. Wildl. Mgmt. 27(1):81–93.

EINARSEN, A. S. 1948. The pronghorn antelope and its management. Wildlife Management Institute, Washington, D. C. 238pp.

FERREL, C. M., AND H. R. LEACH. 1950. Food habits of the prong-horn antelope of California. California Fish and Game 36(1):21–26.

FOREE, W. W. 1959. Antelope questionnaire conducted by Nevada Fish and Game Commission. Trans. Interstate Antelope Conf.: 65–75.

———. 1960. Nevada antelope studies progress report. Trans. Interstate Antelope Conf.: 58–82.

HOOVER, R. L., C. E. TILL, AND S. OGILVIE. 1959. The antelope of Colorado: a research and management study. Colorado Dept. Game and Fish Tech. Bull. 4. 110pp.

MARTIN, A. C., R. H. GENSCH, AND C. P. BROWN. 1946. Alternative methods in upland game-bird food analysis. J. Wildl. Mgmt. 10(1):8–12.

MASON, E. 1952. Food habits and measurements of Hart Mountain antelope. J. Wildl. Mgmt. 16(3):387–389.

MITCHELL, G. J. 1965. Natality, mortality and related phenomena in two populations of pronghorn antelope in Alberta, Canada. Ph. D. Thesis. Washington State Univ., Pullman. 205pp.

Moss, E. H. 1959. Flora of Alberta. University of Toronto Press. 546pp.

Norris, J. J. 1943. Botanical analyses of stomach contents as a method of determining forage consumption of range sheep. Ecology 24(2): 244–251.

Severson, K., M. May, and W. Hepworth. 1968. Food preferences, carrying capacities, and forage competition between antelope and domestic sheep in Wyoming's Red Desert. Univ. of Wyoming Agr. Expt. Sta. Sci. Monograph 10. 51pp.

Smoliak, S. 1956. Influence of climatic conditions on forage production of shortgrass rangeland. J. Range Mgmt. 9(2):89–91.

————. 1965. A comparison of ungrazed and lightly grazed *Stipa–Bouteloua* prairie in southeastern Alberta. Canadian J. Plant Sci. 45(3): 270–275.

Yoakum, J. 1958. Seasonal food habits of the Oregon pronghorn antelope. Trans. Interstate Antelope Conf.: 47–59.

Received for publication March 11, 1968.

THE VALIDITY OF THE WEAR-AGE TECHNIQUE FOR ALBERTA PRONGHORNS

M. LARRY KERWIN, Biology Department, University of Saskatchewan, Regina Campus, Regina

GEORGE J. MITCHELL, Biology Department, University of Saskatchewan, Regina Campus, Regina

Abstract: The incisor (Pil) teeth of 190 mature pronghorn antelopes (*Antilocapra americana*) collected between 1961 and 1964 in Alberta were histologically prepared and examined for the presence and number of cementum annulations. The ages of animals determined by this method were compared with those assigned previously on the basis of a wear-age technique. The percentage of agreement between these two methods ranged from 69.2 percent in the 3.5-year class, to 50.0 percent in the 7.5-year class. The overall agreement for all age-classes (2.5–8.5 years) was 60.9 percent. Of the animals misclassified using the wear-age technique, 68.1 percent were underaged. Examination of the cementum annuli of histologically prepared teeth provided a more reliable interpretation of age than the examination of teeth prepared by standard cutting and grinding techniques. For pronghorns in Alberta the wear-age technique is not a valid management tool.

The ability to determine the age structure of a population accurately, either by direct examination of living animals or from animals killed by hunters, is a necessary prerequisite for any study of the dynamics of that population. To meet this requirement, three age-classification techniques have been applied to pronghorns: (1) the sequence of tooth eruption and wear (Dow and Wright 1962); (2) the weight of the eye lens (Kolenosky and Miller 1962); and (3) the number of cementum annulations of incisor teeth (McCutchen 1966, 1969). These techniques have also been applied to other ungulates, but until recently there have been few reports comparing the accuracies of these methods. Our study evaluates the accuracy of the wear-age method used for Alberta pronghorns. In addition, the use of a histological technique in the preparation of the incisors is compared with the cutting and grinding method used previously for antelopes (McCutchen 1966, 1969).

We acknowledge the advice and assistance of R. Y. Zacharuk and H. E. Mann,

JWM 35(4): 744

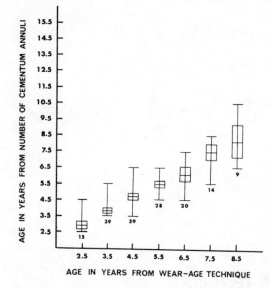

Fig. 1. A comparison of age determination in 184 mature Alberta pronghorn antelopes by the wear-age technique and by cementum annulations. Vertical lines represent range in years of individual antelopes in age-classes assigned on the basis of the wear-age technique, horizontal lines the computed mean values, and the columns the 95 percent confidence intervals. The number of specimens in the various age-classes based on the wear-age method are shown below each unit.

Biology Department, University of Saskatchewan, Regina Campus, who were instrumental in the development of the histological procedures used. The laboratory analysis was supported by National Research Council Grant-In-Aid No. A3913.

METHODS AND MATERIALS

The incisor teeth used in this study were extracted from 190 mandibles obtained by the junior author from mature pronghorn antelopes harvested in Alberta during the 1961–64 hunting seasons. The mandibles were previously assigned to age-classes on the basis of the wear-age techniques (Dow and Wright 1962) by Mitchell (1965:47) and four wildlife technicians. It is believed that the classification of the mandibles on this basis was as accurate as possible, since

the level of experience of the technicians was a lesser factor in erroneous classification than the basic method of aging by eruption and wear itself.

From each of the mandibles, the first incisor (Pil) was removed by placing the anterior, tooth-bearing portion of the mandible in boiling water for a period of about 45 minutes. This method is similar to the one Sergeant and Pimlott (1959) used for moose incisors. The method we used was found to be preferable to that employed by McCutchen (1966:6), who removed the incisors by splitting each mandible along its symphysis and chipping away the surrounding alveolar bone with a penknife. In our sample the mandibles were too dry and brittle to employ McCutchen's technique without scratching, chipping, or fracturing the incisors. Removal of incisors from freshly killed antelopes in the field could be accomplished using straight-beaked, upper anterior, tooth-extracting forceps (Keiss 1969).

The method most commonly used to expose root cementum is to cut relatively thick (100–200 microns) sections with a jeweller's or dentist's saw and by some mechanical means to grind these sections to the required thickness (Fisher and Mackenzie 1954, Frost 1958). Inasmuch as this approach has certain limitations in age determinations of pronghorns, we developed a histological technique similar to that reported by McEwan (1963) and Gilbert (1966).

Each tooth was decalcified in 30 percent formic acid for a period of about 72 hours with changes of solution every 12 hours. Decalcification was considered complete when the addition of 1 ml of sodium oxalate to 5 ml of the solution containing the tooth did not form a white precipitate (Humason 1967:27). After decalcification, standard

Table 1. Comparisons of specific ages of 184 pronghorns based on the wear-age and cementum annuli techniques.

AGE BY WEAR (YEARS)	SAMPLE SIZE	NUMBER CORRECT[a]	NUMBER INCORRECT	PERCENTAGE OF AGREEMENT	PERCENTAGE UNDERAGED[b]	PERCENTAGE OVERAGED[b]
2.5	15	9	6	60.0	40.0	0.0
3.5	39	27	12	69.2	30.8	0.0
4.5	59	34	25	57.6	33.9	8.5
5.5	28	19	9	67.9	14.3	17.9
6.5	20	11	9	55.0	10.0	35.0
7.5	14	7	7	50.0	28.6	21.4
8.5	9	5	4	55.6	11.1	33.3
Total	184	112	72			
Mean				60.9	26.6	12.5

[a] Correct signifies that animals were assigned to the same age-class by both techniques.
[b] Underaged signifies that the animals were actually older (by cementum) than indicated by the wear-age technique; overaged signifies the reverse.

histological procedures were used to dehydrate, clear, and infiltrate the tissues with paraffin. Each incisor was sectioned sagittally at 10 microns on a standard microtome. Sections were stained with Delafield's hematoxylin for 10 minutes and counterstained with eosin for 1 minute. After staining, a permanent coverslip was mounted on each slide.

Representative sections of each incisor were examined as many times as necessary to count accurately the number of cementum annulations present and assign each tooth to a specific age-class. Since all mandibles in the sample were from animals collected in late October and early November, approximately 5 months after the assumed mean birth date of June 1 (Mitchell 1967), all animals were aged to the nearest month, and the designations 2.5 years, 3.5 years, and similar age-classes were used. These designations approximate those used by McCutchen (1966, 1969) in Montana. Ages derived using this method were compared with the respective ages assigned by the wear-age technique, and the variation between the two techniques was assessed. Since previous research on known-age antelopes (McCutchen 1969)

confirmed the validity of the cementum annuli technique, the ages we assigned, using this method, were assumed to be the correct ages of the animals.

RESULTS

The graphic comparison of pronghorn ages estimated by the wear-age and cementum methods (Fig. 1) shows that animals placed in a specific age-class by the former method actually differed in age by as much as 5 years. In our sample, the animals grouped in the 9-year class by the wear-age method showed correct ages ranging from 8.5 to 15.5 years.

The percentage of agreement between these two techniques ranged from 69.2 percent in the 3.5-year class to 50.0 percent in the 7.5-year class (Table 1). The overall agreement for all age-classes (2.5–8.5 years) was 60.9 percent. The 9-year age-class was not included in the comparison, because animals older than 9 years cannot be differentiated by the wear-age technique. The agreement between the two methods was generally higher in the younger than in the older age-classes, but no strong linear relationship was found between age and technique. There was a

JWM 35(4): 746

tendency for animals to be underaged by the wear-age method more frequently in the younger age-classes (2.5–4.5 years) and overaged more frequently in the older age-classes (5.5–8.5 years). However, these data also lacked a strong linear relationship.

DISCUSSION AND CONCLUSIONS

McCutchen (1966:31) reported that "the overall percent agreement of the two techniques is low." With the use of his data, the overall agreement was calculated to be 51 percent. However, this figure is based on only those animals that were placed in specific age-classes by his cementum method and did not include approximately 35 percent of his sample in which age could be determined only to within 2 years. Thus, depending on the classification of the unused portion (23 animals) of his sample, McCutchen's overall agreement could range from 33.3 to 65.1 percent. The latter figure is approximately equivalent to the agreement found in our study. Only 1.5 percent (three incisors) of our sample could not be placed in specific age-classes. This suggests that the cutting of sagittal sections and the use of an histological technique allowed for a more exact interpretation of cementum annuli than did the cutting and grinding method and the examination of transverse root sections in the Montana study. Our results show closer agreement between the two techniques for Alberta antelopes than for the Montana animals on which the wear-age technique was based.

One well-recognized problem resulting from the use of the wear-age technique as a management tool is the reluctance of hunters to donate a mandible, especially if the animal is a male of trophy caliber. This reluctance can bias the results of the

sampling in favor of the younger age-classes. Removal of the first incisor in the field would leave the trophy head undamaged.

The apparent low accuracy of the wear-age technique may result in incorrect analysis and incorrect recommendations for management being made on the basis of age structures determined through the wear-age technique. Although the cementum annuli technique is more expensive and time-consuming than the wear-age technique, the improved accuracy that results justifies its use. For pronghorn antelopes in Alberta, the wear-age method is not a valid management tool. Use of an histological technique in the preparation of the teeth allows a better interpretation of the cementum than does a cutting and grinding procedure.

LITERATURE CITED

Dow, S. A., Jr., and P. L. Wright. 1962. Changes in mandibular dentition associated with age in pronghorn antelope. J. Wildl. Mgmt. 26(1):1–18.

Fisher, H. D., and B. A. Mackenzie. 1954. Rapid preparation of tooth sections for age determinations. J. Wildl. Mgmt. 18(4):535–537.

Frost, H. M. 1958. Preparation of thin undecalcified bone sections by rapid manual method. Stain Technol. 33(6):272–277.

Gilbert, F. F. 1966. Aging white-tailed deer by annuli in the cementum of the first incisor. J. Wildl. Mgmt. 30(1):200–202.

Humason, Gretchen L. 1967. Animal tissue techniques. 2nd ed. W. H. Freeman and Company, San Francisco and London. 569pp.

Keiss, R. E. 1969. Comparison of eruption-wear patterns and cementum annuli as age criteria in elk. J. Wildl. Mgmt. 33(1):175–180.

Kolenosky, G. B., and R. S. Miller. 1962. Growth of the lens of the pronghorn antelope. J. Wildl. Mgmt. 26(1):112–113.

McCutchen, H. E. 1966. Aging pronghorn antelope by the incisor cementum. M. S. Thesis. Univ. of Montana. 49pp.

———. 1969. Age determination of pronghorns by the incisor cementum. J. Wildl. Mgmt. 33(1):172–175.

McEwan, E. H. 1963. Seasonal annuli in the

cementum of the teeth of barren ground caribou. Canadian J. Zool. 41(1):111–113.

MITCHELL, G. J. 1965. Natality, mortality and related phenomena in two populations of pronghorn antelope in Alberta, Canada. Ph.D. Thesis. Washington State Univ. 205pp.

——. 1967. Minimum breeding age of female pronghorn antelope. J. Mammal. 48(3):489–490.

SERGEANT, D. E., AND D. H. PIMLOTT. 1959. Age determination in moose from sectioned incisor teeth. J. Wildl. Mgmt. 23(3):315–321.

Received for publication February 10, 1971.

170

A TELEMETRY SYSTEM TO DETERMINE BODY TEMPERATURE IN PRONGHORN ANTELOPE[1]

E. M. LONSDALE, Electrical Engineering Department, University of Wyoming, Laramie

BERNARD BRADACH, University of Wyoming, Laramie

E. TOM THORNE, Wyoming Game and Fish Research Laboratory, Laramie

Abstract: Radiotelemetry units were designed and used to transmit body temperatures from two pregnant pronghorn antelopes (*Antilocapra americana*) confined in a small pen. Normal body temperatures were established, after which the animals were experimentally inoculated with leptospirosis and a temperature record kept. It was found that the normal body temperatures for both animals was 38.5 C and that a rise of 3.0 C occurred in one doe at the onset of the disease and lasted 5 hours. The temperature then dropped to 39.5 C and remained at this level. The second doe did not become infected but showed a temperature rise of 1.7 C during fawning and a return to normal 4 hours later. Novel features of the telemetry system consist of the use of a keyed squegging oscillator, a flat package-arrangement for easier surgical implanting, and a noncritical circuit design employing inexpensive and readily available components.

Research has been undertaken at the Sybille Big Game Research Unit of the Wyoming Game and Fish Commission to study bovine leptospirosis in pronghorn antelope through artificial infection of captive animals. The current phase of the study called for sacrificing the animals at the time of peak infection in order to collect tissues for fluorescent antibody examinations. The particular animals under study were mature does weighing about 95 pounds each; they were approximately 6 months pregnant. The course of this disease is such that an infected adult antelope shows little visible sign of illness. It was felt that a rise in body temperature

would signal the onset of the disease, and at that time the animals were to be sacrificed. Direct measurements of body temperature, using a rectal thermometer, on a big game animal give almost meaningless results due to the rise in temperature from the stress and excitement of the animal being handled. Under such circumstances, a radiotelemetry system that allows remote determination of body temperature is ideally suited.

A long record of body temperature telemetry applied to both wild and domestic animals is available in the literature beginning with the pioneering work of Eklund and Charlton (1959) and continuing through the present time with a report of Downhower and Pauley (1970). Bligh and Harthoorn (1965) described a system, for use on large African mammals, which

[1] The study was supported in part by Federal Aid in Wildlife Restoration, Wyoming Project FW–3–R.

employed an implanted thermistor connected to an external transmitter and gave
accuracies to within 0.1 C. Fryer et al.
(1966) described a short-range miniature
unit, completely implantable, with an accuracy of 0.05 C. After reviewing the extensive literature on this topic, the authors
decided that none of the systems described
would fulfill the unique requirements of
this project and hence designed and built
their own apparatus.

Long-term (3 months) reliability was a
prime requirement since antelope are difficult to handle in captivity and it was
hoped that a repeat of the surgery, because
of apparatus failure, would not be necessary. Furthermore, a rise in body temperature of several degrees was anticipated with
the onset of the disease, and this made
precision measurements unnecessary. An
accuracy of 0.5 C was considered ample.
Also, the data were to be collected under
field conditions by personnel who assumed
the recording chores in addition to heavy
work loads. Consequently, a data-collecting
system as simple as was feasible was desired. Lastly, a limited equipment budget
was available, and this placed a premium
on minimum component design and the use
of an inexpensive receiver. This report describes the relatively simple telemetry system used.

The authors acknowledge the assistance
of M. Schrib and W. Marshall, who constructed the apparatus and of F. Blunt and
his assistants, who collected most of the
field data on temperature.

METHODS

A temperature telemetry unit was sur-
gically implanted in the flank of each
antelope. Prior to surgery, both antelopes
were tranquilized with 10 mg of acetyl-
promazine administered intravenously. One
of the antelopes was further restrained
chemically using 3.5 mg of M99 etorphine
administered intramuscularly by hand. Additional manual restraint was required for
both animals, and surgery was performed
with the animals standing. Local anesthesia
was produced using lidocaine hydrochloride
infiltration. Standard aseptic veterinary
surgical procedures were followed in implanting and anchoring the transmitters
between the external and internal abdominal oblique muscles. The package was
oriented flat between the muscle layers,
with its long axis perpendicular to the
spine. Total time for surgical implantation
of a package was approximately 30 minutes. The implanted packages did not appear to cause discomfort or to interfere
with the movements of the antelopes.
Within 3 weeks after surgery, hair had begun to re-cover the implantation sites.

After a 3-week period, it was assumed
that all effects of the surgery had subsided
and that a normal body temperature for
the animal in its accustomed surroundings
could be established. The two does were
then artificially infected with *Leptospira
pomona*. Urine and blood specimens were
taken three times weekly, and frequent
daily body temperatures, as determined by
the telemetry system, were recorded.

Five days after inoculation with live
leptospires, one of the does exhibited a temperature rise of 3 C over a 5-hour period
followed by a decline of 2 C over 2 hours
and a steady elevated reading of 1 C above
normal. This doe was sacrificed and a
necropsy performed as planned. The other
doe did not develop the disease and was
kept confined for several months. During
this time, she gave birth to a fawn. A
record of body temperatures was also kept
on this second animal during the entire
period, including parturition.

ELECTRONIC DESIGN

The sensing system devised was based on a circuit suggested by Mackay (1965: 216–217) but contained several novel features. The circuit diagram and the parts list of the transmitting unit are shown in Fig. 1.

The unit conveys temperature information by its pulse rate, which is approximately 160 pulses per minute at 38 C. It changes rate almost exactly 7.2 pulses per minute per degree C. This rate allows for an accuracy in the neighborhood of 0.14 C for a 1-minute count. Since an error of one or two counts per period is a constant chance occurrence per period, the use of a longer measurement period would assure greater accuracy.

The right-hand pair of PNP transistors constitute an astable multivibrator whose two states differ in period by approximately 20 to 1. Transistor Q_1 has a short *on* period that is independent of temperature; Q_2 has an *on* period that varies with the resistance of the temperature-sensing element R_5 (a thermistor). The result is a cycling rate that increases very nearly linearly with temperature, over the range of interest.

The unit is energized by four miniature silver oxide cells that, when discharged at a fractional milliampere drain, provide a terminal voltage that remains constant to within less than 100 mv over the usable life. This assures that the calibration will remain substantially unaffected by battery discharge for at least 3 months of operation.

Transistor Q_3, an NPN type, and its associated circuitry make up the radio-frequency portion of the circuit, transmitting a low-power pulsed signal in the commercial FM band. When *on*, the oscillator sends two or three short bursts of radio-frequency energy that sound to the ear like a single

Fig. 1. Circuit diagram and parts list for temperature telemetry transmitter. Transistors: Q_1 and Q_2, 2N3905; Q_3, 2N4996. Resistors all $1/8$ watt: R_1, 3.9 k; R_2 and R_4, 470 k; R_3, 100 k; R_5 1.0 M thermistor, Yellow Springs Instrument Co.; R_6, 47 k. Capacitors: C_1, 20 pfd; C_2 and C_4, 0.10 μfd electrolytic; C_3, 51 pfd ceramic; C_5, 2.2 μfd electrolytic; C_6, 120 pfd. Coil: one turn, $7/8$ inch in diameter, of No. 16 bare wire. Battery: E, series parallel connection of four type S76 cells.

click and are easy to count. Because the oscillator is self-excited and has considerable frequency modulation, it tunes broadly on the band and is easily located on the receiver. No federal licensing problem exists because the radiated power is safely below the maximum set for experimental telemetry by the Federal Communications Commission.

The radio-frequency circuit is a simple inexpensive type known as the squegging Hartley oscillator. It has been described by Lonsdale et al. (1964), and Lonsdale (1967). The squegging oscillator seems ideally suited for this particular telemetry application because of its noncritical design and because it is economical on battery drain (less than 10 microamperes average current when pulsed by the multivibrator). A further advantage of the squegging oscillator is that it shifts instantaneous frequency during each pulse. This property enhances the sensitivity of an FM receiver to this signal by making use of the discriminator's sensitivity frequency deviations.

All components except the batteries are mounted inside the one-turn resonant loop circuit. First, the radio frequency portion,

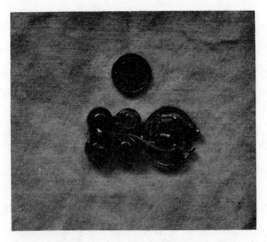

Fig. 2. Assembled unit before encapsulation. The coin indicates relative size.

transistor Q_3 and its associated components, was assembled in the plane of the loop. No critical problems of parts placement arose here other than the necessity of connecting the 51 pfd capacitor to the coil ends with minimum lead lengths. Next, the multivibrator portion was constructed in a plane directly over the oscillator. The resultant assembly was approximately 8 mm thick. The unit before encapsulation is shown in Fig. 2.

The encapsulation process consists of two steps: first, dipping the unit in molten paraffin once or twice to secure complete coverage of all components; and second, adding a final covering of polyester resin to assure mechanical rigidity.

The transmitter, after encapsulation, was approximately elliptical when viewed from the top, with a long axis of 7 cm and a short axis of 4.5 cm. The greatest thickness, measured through the center of the package, was 1.2 cm. A series of 12 small holes was drilled around the perimeter to provide tie points for sutures. The package weighed 25 grams.

Calibration was then accomplished by immersing the unit in a constant-temperature water bath and recording its pulsing rate at five different temperatures. No hysteresis effects were observed when the temperature was cycled either slowly or rapidly. A temperature indication response with a time constant of 4 minutes was typical. This relatively long response period was caused by the thermal insulation of the coatings surrounding the sensor, but it was considered to be inconsequential when establishing normal temperatures or looking for rises in temperature due to the onset of disease.

The component cost for the entire telemetry package is approximately $10.00, and a satisfactory receiver can be purchased for less than $25.00.

RESULTS AND DISCUSSION

The implanted units performed reliably in the animals for the duration of the experiment (over 2 months). The usable range was up to 50 yards. Final failure, as predicted, was caused by battery exhaustion.

An average body temperature of 38.5 C was recorded, with ambient temperatures varying between the extremes of 5 C and 22 C, and with an average of 10 C. Daily fluctuations of plus and minus 0.3 C in body temperature were common and occurred during feeding and in the course of the daily activities of the animals.

Even though the animals had been raised in captivity and were accustomed to the presence of the attendants, they exhibited a body temperature rise, over a period of 10 minutes, of as much as 2.0 C due to handling or to cleaning of the corral. During fawning, a rise of 1.7 C was noted, with a return to normal after 4 hours. This 2-month life seems somewhat short, based on mah cell ratings. However, 3 weeks of operating time was put on the cells during the test and calibration period. In addition, the current drain was pulsating, and this lowers the mah capacity of the cells somewhat.

Five days after inoculation, the diseased animal showed a 3.0 C rise in temperature over a 5-hour period followed by a drop of 2.0 C. The temperature then remained at this elevated level for 36 hours until the animal was sacrificed.

It was generally agreed by the persons involved in this project that the telemetry units performed satisfactorily and constituted a useful tool for determining body temperatures of closely confined big game animals. Surgical implantation was quickly and easily accomplished. The flat package-arrangement caused no discomfort or problems to the animals. No difficulties or failures with equipment were encountered. This is extremely important when the value of both the researcher's time and the big game animals that can be confined for research purposes are considered. The simplicity of the temperature-recording system was also important. The body temperature of both antelopes could be recorded by one worker in a period of about 5 minutes. Because the time required for temperature determination was short, numerous determinations for both animals could be made throughout each day. Just as this system

for telemetering body temperature was valuable in following the course of an artificial infection of leptospirosis in an antelope, it could be applied to many other diseases or physiological studies in other game animals.

LITERATURE CITED

BLIGH, J., AND A. M. HARTHOORN. 1965. Continuous radiotelemetric records of the deep body temperature of some unrestrained African mammals under near-natural conditions. J. Physiol. 176(1):145–162.

DOWNHOWER, J. F., AND J. D. PAULEY. 1970. Automated recordings of body temperature from free-ranging yellow-bellied marmots. J. Wildl. Mgmt. 34(3):639–641.

EKLUND, C. R., AND F. E. CHARLTON. 1959. Measuring the temperatures of incubating penguin eggs. Am. Scientist 47(1):80–86.

FRYER, T. B., G. J. DEBOO, AND C. M. WINGET. 1966. Miniature long-life temperature telemetry system. J. Appl. Physiol. 21(1):295–298.

LONSDALE, E. M. 1967. The use of radio frequency telemetry for tracking fresh water fish. Pages 47–52. *In* Proc. Natl. Telemetering Conf., San Francisco.

———, I. DUNMIRE, AND S. BROWN. 1964. A transistorized self pulsing oscillator for telemetry. Proc. Natl. Telemetering Conf., Los Angeles. Session 2(1).

MACKAY, R. S. 1965. Telemetering from within the body of animals and man: endoradiosondes. Pages 147–235. *In* C. A. Caceres [Editor], Biomedical telemetry. Academic Press, New York and London. 392pp.

Received for publication December 3, 1970.

MORTALITY OF PRONGHORN ANTELOPE FAWNS IN WESTERN UTAH[1]

DONALD M. BEALE, Utah State Division of Wildlife Resources, Salt Lake City 84116

ARTHUR D. SMITH, Department of Range Science, Utah State University, Logan 84322

Abstract: Over a period of 5 years 117 pronghorn antelope (*Antilocapra americana*) fawns 1–5 days of age were captured in a 4,000-hectare enclosure and fitted with radio transmitters to provide a means of relocating them to determine causes of mortality. Each fawn was located and observed daily until approximately 4 months of age or until death. Fawns with transmitters that functioned beyond this period were thereafter checked periodically. A total of 55 cases of fawn mortality were discovered during the study. Bobcats (*Lynx rufus*) accounted for 27 deaths; golden eagles (*Aquila chrysaetos*) one; and coyotes (*Canis latrans*) one. Two died from salmonellosis, three from pneumonia, four from starvation, and one from an esophageal injury. Five died from unknown causes and eleven were abandoned by does as a result of handling. The ages of fawns definitely killed by bobcats ranged from 3 to 104 days; one weighed 22 kg at the time of kill.

J. WILDL. MANAGE. 37(3):343–352

Although pronghorn antelope declined in Utah during the early 1900's as in other western states (Nelson 1925), herds in Utah failed to increase significantly following protection and improved range management as did those in other states, especially Wyoming and Montana (Yoakum 1968).

Udy (1953) studied the effects of predator control on pronghorn populations in Utah and found higher fawn survival on areas where intensive control measures were applied to coyotes than on areas with no control. He considered coyotes an important predator on pronghorn fawns and believed them to be partly responsible for low fawn crops among small herds, although he thought the basic and more important problem was poor range condition and competition with livestock. Arrington and Edwards (1951) studied the effects of predator control on pronghorn populations in Arizona and reported an increase in herd productivity where control was applied.

Similar concern for the role of coyotes in limiting pronghorn production was held in New Mexico (Larsen 1970), but no conclusive evidence that coyotes limited antelope populations was found. Independent studies of predator losses among pronghorn fawns in Oregon by Yoakum (1957) and Compton (1958) produced no firm evidence that predators limited pronghorns or that predator control measures had a salutary effect on production.

Earlier research (Beale and Smith 1970) had indicated good initial fawn production but high mortality during summer months, particularly July and August, on the desert ranges of western Utah. Fresh, undecomposed carcasses of dead fawns were seldom found, so that the cause of death could not be determined. Attempts were made in 1960 and 1963 to monitor fawns with telemetry but without success. Encouraged by the results of Tester et al. (1964) our efforts were renewed in 1967.

The objective of the study was to determine specific causes of summer mortality of fawns in a herd of pronghorns confined to a desert-shrub range in western Utah.

[1] A contribution from Utah Federal Aid Project W-105-R, and the Department of Range Science, Utah State University. Facilities were provided by the Intermountain Forest and Range Experiment Station, U.S. Forest Service.

We wish to express appreciation to many Division of Wildlife Resources Biologist and Conservation officers who took time from their own work and assisted us during the fawning season each year. Their help made possible the success of the project.

DESCRIPTION OF STUDY AREA

The study area is located 300 km west of Milford, Utah, on the Desert Experimental Range of the Intermountain Forest and Range Experiment Station, U.S. Forest Service. The study herd, which ranged in size from 33 to 75 head, was confined by a fence to a range of approximately 4,000 hectares (3.2 km wide and 11.3 km long). A division fence crossing the enclosure near midpoint enabled us to concentrate the herd in about half the area during fawning season to facilitate surveillance.

Habitat in the study area is typical of that in many intermountain valleys in western Utah. Elevations in the enclosure range from 1,600 m to 2,500 m above sea level. Rock ledges, impassable by pronghorns, served as a boundary on the northwest corner. The remainder is fenced. The chief topographical features consist of coalesced alluvial fans dissected by active and inactive flood drainage channels that extend from the mountains to the valley bottom. A few low hills and ridges extend outward from the mountain mass. The vegetation comprises various communities of the Northern Desert Shrub Formation.

Major shrub species present in the study area include shadscale (*Atriplex confertifolia*), winterfat (*Eurotia lanata*), little rabbitbrush (*Chrysothamnus stenophyllus*), black sagebrush (*Artemisia nova*), and bud sagebrush (*A. spinescens*). Desert almond (*Prunus fasciculata*) and big rabbitbrush (*Chrysothamnus nauseosus*) are present along drainages. The most abundant grasses were Indian ricegrass (*Oryzopsis hymenoides*), galleta (*Hilaria jamesii*), sand dropseed (*Sporobolus cryptandrus*), blue grama (*Bouteloua gracilis*), squirreltail (*Sitanion hystrix*), and needle-and-thread grass (*Stipa comata*). A sparse overstory of Utah juniper (*Juniperus osteosperma*) occurs on the higher alluvial fans above 1800 m elevation, particularly along the drainages. A large number of annual and perennial forbs occur but their abundance each year depends on spring and summer rainfall which is erratic.

MATERIALS AND METHODS

Radio Equipment

The transmitter circuit used was similar to the design used by Tester et al. (1964), although some modifications were made to minimize weight and increase longevity. The transmitter components were fitted into a printed circuit board which provided strength and made complete "potting" in plastic unnecessary. On-to-off ratios were reduced to minimize drain on the batteries and increase life of the transmitters.

The antenna-collar had a circumference of 36.8 cm which, from prior measurements, was known to be large enough to accommodate the neck of an adult. A band of soft elastic webbing 2.5 cm wide and 23 cm in circumference formed an inner collar which held the unit in place while the fawn was small (Fig. 1). The complete transmitting unit weighed approximately 140 grams.

The receivers were wired with crystals to permit reception on 22 transmitter frequencies which ranged from 50.000 through 50.210 MHz. Each receiver could be connected to a hand-held loop antenna or to stationary yagi antennas.

Seven stationary antennas, five on 15–20-m towers, and two on hills, were erected in the study area so as to provide coverage to any part of the study area from at least two receiving stations. Five of the antennas were 4-element units; one consisted of two 4-element units stacked horizontally; and one was a 6-element unit. All were 6-m designs with a maximum forward gain of 12.7 decibels for the 4-element units and 15 decibels for the 6-element unit. All antennas could be rotated manually through 360 degrees. A compass rosette at the base of each antenna corresponded to rosettes on maps of the study area from which azimuths could be read.

Instrumenting Fawns

Fawns were located by observing the does with spotting scopes from observation towers and other strategic points in early morning and evening hours. Whenever a doe was seen nursing fawns, it was kept under observation until the fawns bedded down. The observer kept the spotting scope focused on the site and directed a tagging crew to the location with a two-way radio. Once located, fawns were captured with a long-handled net, a radio was attached, and the fawn was released. Live weights of fawns were obtained in 1967 and 1971. Fawns were captured and marked with greatest ease when from 1 to 3 days of age. Older fawns were occasionally captured but this required great care in approaching the animal, for they often flushed at considerable distances. Fawns over 3 days of age could easily outrun a man.

To minimize abandonment by does, we used disposable plastic gloves when handling the fawns to reduce contamination by human scent. Radio transmitters were cleaned to remove human scent and placed in plastic bags containing sagebrush leaves prior to use to mask any foreign

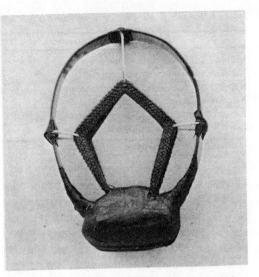

Fig. 1. Radio transmitter unit with a loop antenna 36.8 cm in circumference and elastic neck band.

odors. Nets were washed after each use and dried in the sun.

Determining Mortality

Once equipped with radios, the fawns were relocated and observed each day. Their approximate location was determined by triangulation from two or more stationary antennas. We then walked to each triangulation point carrying a receiver and hand-held directional-loop antenna until the fawn was sighted. Binoculars were used to advantage when the fawns were several weeks of age and flushed at greater distances. Daily location of each fawn was plotted on maps of the study area. When fawn carcasses were found, a field mortality report was filled out. If predation was indicated, evidence as to the kind of predator was sought including presence of hair, feathers, tracks, injury marks on the carcass, method and location of kill, and disposition of carcass. The carcass was weighed and an estimate was made of the weight of tissue removed by the predator to arrive

Table 1. Mortality of pronghorn antelope fawns at the Desert Experimental Range among marked and unmarked fawns.

	1967	1968	1969	1970	1971	Total
Number of fawns known born	20	19	29	34	49	151
Number of fawns instrumented	9	15	23	31	39	117
Number of successful instrumentations[a]	6	13	20	31	36	106
Number of fawns unmarked	11	4	6	3	10	34
Percent mortality of successfully marked fawns	66	46	25	32	53	42
Percent mortality of unmarked fawns	45	50	17	0	50	38

[a] Excluding those abandoned.

at total weight. Carcasses were left at the site to determine if the predator would return, in which case additional data regarding its activities were obtained. When predation was not indicated, the carcass was refrigerated and taken to the Diagnostic Laboratory, Utah State University, Logan.

RESULTS

Equipment Performance

Only minor equipment problems were encountered. The longevity of the radio transmitters, except for three that stopped operating soon after they were put on, ranged from 6 to over 24 months and averaged about 15 months.

Clear reception from the transmitters was obtained from distances of one-half mile to over seven miles depending on the type and location of the receiving antenna used and the terrain. The height of the receiving antenna above intervening terrain over which the signals traveled was of major importance in reception regardless of the kind of antenna used. When the line-of-sight path for radio signals was well above the ground surface throughout most of the distance to the receiver, even the small tuned-loop antenna gave clear signals from transmitters 5–10 km away. Weather conditions created some problems. When a thunderstorm was in progress in the immediate vicinity of the antennas, static

would obscure all but the strongest signals. Since summer storms are of short duration, these caused only temporary difficulties.

Marking Success

At the outset we were concerned about the effect transmitters might have on fawns; therefore, in 1967, the first year, we instrumented only one fawn of two pair of twins so that any difference in behavior might be observed. After hours of observation, we were convinced that the radio transmitters did not alter fawn behavior nor cause them discomfort. This conclusion is substantiated by the similarity in mortality of marked and unmarked fawns (Table 1).

A total of 117 of the 151 fawns born from 1967 through 1971 were captured and instrumented when 1–5 days of age (Table 1). Eleven of the 117 fawns marked were abandoned following marking. These fawns were observed attempting to nurse one or more times, but they were refused by their mothers and died within 2 or 3 days. In each instance the doe would approach her young as usual; but, when the fawn attempted to nurse, she would turn away, run off, or bunt the fawn. This type of behavior was repeated several times by the same animals in successive nursing periods. The reasons for rejection of marked fawns, whether due to strange odors or altered appearance of the fawn caused by

Table 2. Fates of 106 successfully instrumented pronghorn antelope fawns on the Desert Experimental Range.

	1967 n = 6	1968 n = 13	1969 n = 20	1970 n = 31	1971 n = 36	Total n = 106	Percent mortality n = 106
Predation							
Bobcat		5	4	3	15	27	25
Coyote	1					1	1
Eagle				1		1	1
Disease							
Pneumonia				2	1	3	3
Salmonellosis		1		1		2	2
Other							
Starvation				2	2	4	4
Injury					1	1	1
Unknown	3[a]	1		1		5	5
Total loss	4	6	5	10	19	44	42
Survived	2	7	15	21	17	62	58

[a] Two of these radio transmitters failed before death of the fawn but remains were found later.

the transmitter, are unknown; but we believe it is due to failure to identify the fawn as her own. The same behavior was observed when a fawn of known parenthood would attempt to nurse a doe that was not its mother. All does did not respond alike, however; some appeared much more tolerant than others even permitting nursing by fawns other than their own. Generally, the older does seemed most tolerant and were the least disturbed by our handling of fawns and the presence of radio transmitters.

In most cases we were able to locate dead fawns soon enough to establish the cause of death. The maximum time that elapsed between death and discovery of carcasses was seldom more than 24 hours and the time was usually less than this. Since the majority of the predator kills were made at night or in the early morning hours, not more than 12 hours had elapsed before a carcass was found. Two fawns appeared sick when flushed and were found dead less than 4 hours later. One fawn was found a few minutes after it was killed by a bobcat.

Predation

Of the 106 fawns successfully instrumented, 44 carcasses were retrieved (Table 2). Twenty-nine of these were killed by predators, 27 by bobcats, one by a coyote, and one by a golden eagle. During the study two uninstrumented fawn carcasses were discovered which had apparently been killed by bobcats.

Bobcats were by far the most significant cause of mortality among pronghorn fawns on the study area being responsible for 61 percent of the 44 losses among successfully instrumented fawns (Tables 2, 3). Predation occurred throughout the summer at ages of 3–104 days and up to 22 kg in weight. One fawn 230 days of age appeared to have been killed by a bobcat. Most kills occurred from late June through August. After fawns attained 20–23 kg in weight, it appeared they were much less susceptible to predation.

All fawns killed by bobcats except the very young had numerous tooth punctures on the neck just behind the head. Death apparently resulted from strangulation and

Table 3. Number of pronghorn antelope fawns of various ages and body weights killed by bobcats compared with other forms of mortality.

Age at death	Killed by bobcats	Other mortality
1–10	4	7
11–20	2	3
21–30	1	2
31–40	2	0
41–50	2	0
51–60	2	0
61–70	3	1
71–80	0	1
81–90	5	0
91–100	4	0
101+	2	3
Total	27	17

Fig. 2. An 89-day-old fawn weighing 22.3 kg killed by a bobcat and dragged into a wash and partially covered.

punctures in neck caused by the bobcats' canine teeth much as described by Young (1958). We had no opportunity to observe actual killing, but some interesting insights as to the hunting and stalking habits of bobcats are provided by Linsdale and Tomich (1953:358–375). Similar killing techniques are reported for the lynx (*Lynx canadensis*) on caribou calves in Newfoundland (Bergerud 1971).

Of the 27 bobcat kills, 18 took place near some type of dry wash or drainage channel. Four kills took place 100 m or more from a wash on wide alluvial fans or ridges. Five others were small fawns that had been carried, and the kill sites were not found. In every instance, fawn carcasses were either dragged or carried from the kill sites. Small fawns under about 7 kg were carried to cover such as a juniper tree or large desert almond bush and the only remains found were the legs, bits of skin, and skull fragments. Larger fawns were dragged from the kill site into or toward a wash. In one instance a carcass weighing 10 kg was dragged 85 m; 25–40 m was more common. In 14 instances attempts were made to cover the carcass with material at hand such as dead vegetation, gravel, sand, and hair

that became detached from the carcass during feeding. Usually, the head and hind quarters were the only parts covered. Frequently, efforts to cover the carcass left a fan-like pattern near the part of the carcass being covered (Fig. 2). Sometimes the carcass was covered, moved, and covered again the same night. Occasionally this was repeated a third time.

The parts of the carcass most often fed upon were the neck and hind quarters, particularly the anal area. Generally, tissue removed in one feeding was estimated at 1–1.5 kg. Seventy-five percent of the time the bobcat returned the following night to feed again and in a few instances returned a 3rd night. Usually carcasses were moved at each successive visit but efforts to cover it diminished.

Only one fawn was killed by a coyote (1967) although coyotes were frequently seen. This seems remarkable in view of the widely-held suspicion with which the coyote is regarded. For example, Yoakum (1967) lists a number of articles referring to coyote predation; only one to bobcats

(Compton 1958). Coyotes were found re- sponsible for many losses of white-tailed deer fawns in south Texas (Cook et al. 1971).

In 1970, a 12-day-old fawn weighing 6.1 kg was killed by a golden eagle. It was the largest and most active of a pair of twins. The carcass was found in a wash at 1600 hours within 4 hours of its death. Golden eagle feathers, wing marks and foot tracks in the sand, and talon punctures on the back and side of the fawn identi- fied the predator. About 1 kg of tissue had been eaten from the neck, chest, and leg.

The twin of the fawn killed by the golden eagle was much smaller and to all appear- ances was a week behind other fawns of the same age in growth. After the larger fawn was killed, the remaining twin seemed to gain rapidly, possibly as a result of greater milk supply.

In the above instances, as with most bob- cat kills, there was no apparent inclination for the predators to take weak individuals. This point was also made by Bruns (1969) regarding a study of predation on prong- horns in Canada.

Disease

Five instrumented fawns died of disease, three of pneumonia and two of salmonel- losis. All appeared to be healthy a day or two prior to death. Body weights obtained after death indicated that growth had been normal.

On the morning of 13 June 1969, a fawn was lethargic and appeared to have diar- rhea. Upon our return in the afternoon it was found dead. *Salmonella cubana* organ- isms were isolated by cultures from the internal organs and salmonellosis was diagnosed as the cause of death. This fawn was 27 days of age. In 1970, a second fawn died of salmonellosis when 13 days of age and *S. saka* organisms were identi-

fied. Of the three fawns which died of pneumonia, two were young, 9 and 22 days of age, and the third was 74 days of age. Weather conditions at the time these fawns died were warm and dry, so these deaths cannot be attributed to inclement weather.

Other Mortality Factors

Four fawns died of starvation. Exami- nation of these fawns revealed an empty digestive tract indicating they had not been nursing. They were not considered abandoned because no behavior we came to associate with abandonment was ob- served. Three of these were twins whose siblings were accepted. Possibly the does did not have adequate milk for both fawns, or they may have felt they had discharged their maternal obligations on caring for one.

Five fawns died from undetermined causes. Three of these could have been predator kills but the radios were damaged or stopped operating at the time of death or before, and when the carcasses were found later the specific cause could not be determined. One probably died from disease. Its stomach contained milk and it had not been killed by a predator, but no pathogenic organisms were isolated. One fawn was weak at birth and died a few hours after marking.

One fawn died when 137 days of age from an esophageal injury. A forked stick had punctured the esophagus and formed a partial block which restricted forage intake. Infection and absession of adjacent tissues were evident.

Bobcat Range

On 1 August 1971, a male bobcat was trapped when it returned to a fawn car- cass and instrumented with a radio. We were able to maintain almost daily con- tact with it through August and September.

During that period it spent about 40 percent of the time on the study area and about 60 percent on rangeland to the north and east. This bobcat would travel through the study area spending 1–3 days, move off the area to the north and east for several days, then return. Its range during this 2-month period encompassed an area of about 11 × 3 km. This agrees with the findings of Robinson and Grand (1958) who reported a mean recovery distance of 5.3 miles (8.5 km) for male bobcats. Evidence indicates this bobcat was responsible for three additional fawn deaths within the study area. A second bobcat was known to make at least one kill in the southwest part of the study area and about one-half mile from the route traveled by the bobcat which was instrumented.

The density of bobcats on the study area or adjacent range is not known. No predator control is exercised within the Experimental Range, but in successive winters from 1968–69 to 1971–72, 14, 12, 2, and 16 bobcats respectively, were taken by a private trapper along a trapline 9 miles long located about 3 miles east of the study area. In view of the range of the radio-equipped bobcat, this trapping removal could have influenced predation within the study area.

DISCUSSION

Bobcat predation was the most important cause of fawn losses in the study herd and was the greatest single decimating factor affecting net productivity of pronghorn. During two of the years, 1968 and 1971, 40 percent of the fawns instrumented were killed by bobcats. Other years, however, losses to bobcats were much lower, only 10 percent in 1970. Considering the differences in number of fawns and the wide fluctuation in losses from year to year, it is difficult to identify a norm and thus to extrapolate the results to free-ranging herds in surrounding areas. Counts to determine fawn to doe ratios among free-ranging herds during summer months have often indicated high fawn mortality. High mortality of fawns soon after birth might be expected with a species such as pronghorn antelope but loss of strong, healthy fawns 1–3 months of age seems much more alarming.

The significance of 42 percent mortality of fawns found in this study can best be analyzed by means of the ratio of fawns to does. Our data on fawn:doe ratios are not comparable to those reported elsewhere because our ratios are based on adult does only. In counts made on open range, yearling females are included along with mature does which widens the ratios. Over the 5-year period of this study, fall ratios were 91 fawns to 100 mature does. Since our overwintering yearling doe numbers are known, we can compute a fawn:doe ratio that is somewhat comparable to published data based on fall counts. When this is done the fawn:doe ratio over the 5 year period was 72:100 and ranged from a low of 52:100 in 1971 to a high of 1:1 in 1969. These ratios are biased downward by abandonment of instrumented fawns and by any death loss among yearlings. These are lower than ratios reported from Wyoming, 87:100 (Hepworth 1965) 100:100 (Hockley 1968), but the time of year when their counts were made were not specified. If one considers the downward bias in our own figures due to abandonment of marked fawns and the fact our yearling population may be overestimated, the differences are less imposing.

We considered the possibility that predation increased because pronghorns could not disperse when threatened by bobcats; however, we saw no evidence that does moved away from the scene of a kill. Often a doe was seen after one of its fawns was killed in the same area it had been previously. Another factor could possibly operate to intensify predation. The study herd had been confined in a fixed area for a period of 12 years in contrast to what takes place on the open range where pronghorn may frequent a locality for a year or two then disappear from it. In other localities numbers will simultaneously increase. Thus, the constant presence of pronghorn in one locality may have increased predation. This would seem possible if a bobcat is more likely to continue predation on a species such as pronghorn once it starts.

A possible relationship exists between bobcat predation on pronghorn and range conditions. Under good range conditions the distribution of black sagebrush is widespread and productive. Conversely, on ranges which in the past have received heavy use by livestock, black sagebrush has been reduced (Stewart et al. 1940) and is largely confined to drainages. Sagebrush is the most important food plant for pronghorn in Utah. When summer forage conditions were dry, pronghorn were found feeding in the washes where black sagebrush and other preferred browse species were most abundant. This may make them more vulnerable to predators. Moreover, Gashwiler et al. (1960) found that blacktailed jackrabbits were major food items of bobcats in western Utah and eastern Nevada. In our study area, jackrabbits were most abundant along washes and it is conceivable that bobcats would hunt these areas extensively. Thus, adverse weather and deteriorated range conditions may increase the opportunities for predation by increasing the likelihood of bobcat–pronghorn encounters. The fact that 63 percent of bobcat kills took place in or near washes tends to support this hypothesis.

In years of high summer precipitation, predation losses may be reduced. At such times succulent forbs are widely distributed and pronghorn do less foraging in washes thereby reducing the chance of bobcat–pronghorn contacts. This hypothesis is not well supported by our data. Losses were high in 1967 and 1968 when forb production was good, and low in 1969 and 1970 when forb growth was average or below average.

In 1970 and 1971, there were approximately equal numbers of radioed fawns. Three fawns were killed by bobcats in 1970 and only two bobcats were trapped the following winter; 15 fawns were killed by bobcats in 1971 and 16 bobcats were subsequently trapped. This suggests that predation may be related to bobcat densities, but it is not certain that high trap counts indicate high initial densities and low residual populations or both high initial and residual populations (Compton 1958). Moreover, other factors than densities determine trapping effort, and unless similar effort is expended, trapping records do not indicate actual populations.

We can only speculate whether a predator control program directed against bobcats would increase pronghorn productivity. Predator control efforts to date have been directed toward coyotes and may have had a minimal effect on bobcat populations. In fact, Robinson and Grand (1958) suggest that a reverse effect may result and that bobcats may move into coyote habitat when the latter is reduced in numbers. This response is supported by data compiled by The Advisory Committee on Predator Control (1972:54–56) and by Robinson (1961). At any rate predator control efforts would have to be tailored specifically for bobcats. Although, we do not know bobcat densities on the study area, evidence suggests that only a few bobcats were involved in predation upon fawns. If a few bobcats can inflict heavy losses on free ranging pronghorn herds, then probably nearly complete removal of bobcats would be required to significantly reduce predation.

Since bobcats appear to favor rough habitat, less predation might occur in open and flat terrain where the keen eyesight of pronghorn can be used to greater advantage and there is less opportunity for stalking. One management practice that offers possibilities for relieving pressure by bobcats is through placement of watering devices. By locating these in open areas and away from those preferred by bobcats, it may be possible to achieve separation in habitats used by the two species.

LITERATURE CITED

ADVISORY COMMITTEE ON PREDATOR CONTROL. 1972. Predator control—1971. Rep. to the Council on Environmental Quality and Dept. of the Inter. 207pp.

ARRINGTON, O. N., AND A. E. EDWARDS. 1951. Predator control as a factor in antelope management. Trans. N. Am. Wildl. Conf. 16: 179–193.

BEALE, D. M., AND A. D. SMITH. 1970. Forage use, water consumption, and productivity of pronghorn antelope in western Utah. J. Wildl. Manage. 34(3):570–582.

BERGERUD, A. T. 1971. The population dynamics of Newfoundland caribou. Wildl. Monogr. 25. 55pp.

BRUNS, E. H. 1969. Winter predation of golden eagles and coyotes on pronghorn antelopes. Can. Field Nat. 84(3):301–304.

COMPTON, H. O. 1958. The effects of predation on pronghorn antelope numbers in south central Oregon. M.S. Thesis, Oregon State University, Corvallis 71pp.

COOK, R. S., M. WHITE, D. O. TRAINER, AND W. C. GLAZENER. 1971. Mortality of young whitetailed deer fawns in South Texas. J. Wildl. Manage. 35(1):47–56.

GASHWILER, J. S., W. L. ROBINETTE, AND O. W. MORRIS. 1960. Foods of bobcats in Utah and eastern Nevada. J. Wildl. Manage. 24(2):226–229.

HEPWORTH, B. 1965. Pp. 1–12 *in* Investigations of pronghorn antelope in Wyoming. Proc. First Annu. Antelope States Workshop. Santa Fe, New Mexico.

HOCKLEY, M. 1968. Pp. 81–84 *in* Ten years of antelope management in the Gillette Area of Wyoming. Proc. Third Bienn. Antelope States Workshop. Casper, Wyoming.

LARSEN, P. 1970. A six-year study of antelope productivity and survival in southern New Mexico. Proc. Fourth Antelope States Workshop. Scottsbluff, Neb. 97–103.

LINSDALE, J. M., AND P. Q. TOMICH. 1953. A herd of mule deer—a record of observations made on the Hastings Natural History Reservation. University of California Press, Berkeley and Los Angeles. 567pp.

NELSON, E. W. 1925. Status of the pronghorned antelope, 1922–1924. U.S. Dept. Agric. Bull. 1346. 64pp.

ROBINSON, W. B. 1961. Population changes of carnivores in some coyote control areas. J. Mammal. 42(4):510–515.

————, AND E. F. GRAND. 1958. Comparative movements of bobcats and coyotes as disclosed by tagging. J. Wildl. Manage. 22(2): 117–122.

STEWART, G., W. P. COTTAM, AND S. S. HUTCHINGS. 1940. Influence of unrestricted grazing on northern salt desert plant associations in western Utah. J. Agric. Res. 60(5):289–316.

TESTER, J. R., D. W. WARNER, AND W. W. COCHRAN. 1964. A radio-tracking system for studying movements of deer. J. Wildl. Manage. 28(1):42–45.

UDY, J. R. 1953. Effects of predator control on antelope populations. Utah State Dept. Fish Game Publ. 5. 48pp.

YOAKUM, J. D. 1957. Factors affecting mortality of pronghorn antelope in Oregon. M.S. Thesis. Oregon State College, Corvallis. 112pp.

————. 1967. Literature of the American pronghorn antelope. U.S. Dept. Inter. 82pp.

————. 1968. Pp. 4–14 *in* A review of the distribution and abundance of American pronghorn antelope. Proc. Third Bien. Antelope States Workshop. Casper, Wyoming.

YOUNG, S. P. 1958. The bobcat of North America. The Stackpole Co. Harrisburg, Pa. 193pp.

Accepted 15 June 1973.

ENERGY METABOLISM OF PRONGHORN ANTELOPES[1]

D. E. WESLEY, Department of Fishery and Wildlife Biology, Colorado State University, Fort Collins 80521[2]

K. L. KNOX, Department of Animal Science, Colorado State University, Fort Collins 80521[3]

J. G. NAGY, Department of Fishery and Wildlife Biology, Colorado State University, Fort Collins 80521

Abstract: Energy metabolism trials conducted at 21 C temperature with pronghorns (*Antilocapra americana*) at four ages from 2 months to 18 months, indicated that 2-month-old animals showed higher energy intake, apparent digestible energy, metabolizable energy (*N*-corrected), energy retention, total, and fasting heat production than animals above 7.5 months of age. Mature animals at 21 C voluntarily consumed an average of 218 $kcal/kg^{0.75}$/day each and retained approximately 14 percent of this amount. Apparent digestible energy averaged 73 percent and metabolizable energy accounted for 69 percent of gross energy intake in metabolically mature animals. Total and fasting heat production averaged 119 and 76 $kcal/kg^{0.75}$/day, respectively.

Lower critical temperature for one animal on feed was found to exist between −12 C and −23 C. Lower critical temperature for fasting pronghorns under test conditions was determined to be near 0 C. Below this critical temperature, fasting heat production increased 1.7 $kcal/kg^{0.75}$/day for each degree Centigrade decrease in ambient temperature. With the exception of fasting heat production, no change in energy partitioning was noted in mature pronghorns when exposed to 21 C, 10 C, −1 C, and −12 C. Upon exposure to 32 C, young pronghorns showed a 9 percent increase in total heat production and a 6 percent increase in fasting heat production. Restricted activity increased total heat production by approximately 38 percent, while moderate activity increased heat production by 58 percent.

J. WILDL. MANAGE. 37(4):563–573

Carrying capacity of the pronghorn's range is dependent on many factors, which include the animal's food habits and his ability to utilize food resources to fulfill energy requirements. Although several studies of food habits of pronghorns have been conducted (Buechner 1950, Scarvie and Arney 1957, Hoover et al. 1959, Beale and Smith 1970), there is a paucity of information about his energetic capabilities. To provide information on energy partitioning in pronghorns, this study was undertaken. The pronghorn's intake was separated into food assimilated, which can be subdivided into biomass and respiration, and food eaten but not assimilated. Conventional methods of partitioning food energy were presented by Kleiber (1961), Blaxter (1962), Dougherty (1965), and Brody (1945) and apply equally well to wild and domestic animals. Data presented in this paper were gathered on a small number of antelopes held under specified conditions and are not intended for indiscriminate extrapolation to antelope in the wild.

Studies in animal energetics require cognizance of many factors that affect metabolism. Smaller animals, for example, have higher maintenance requirements per unit of weight than larger animals. Kleiber (1947) discussed the concept that fasting heat production (FHP), divided by the 0.75 power of body weight, was independent of body size. The power function, body weight in $kg^{0.75}$, has become known as the metabolic body size of homeotherms and is useful for comparative levels of food intake, maintenance requirements and production energy among animals of varying body weights. Under the conditions specified above, Kleiber (1961) reported that FHP's

[1] Financed under National Science Foundation Grants GB-7824, GB-13096, and GB-31862X2 as part of the U.S. International Biological Program, Grassland Biome Sub-program.

[2] Present address: Department of Wildlife and Fisheries, Mississippi State University, Mississippi State 39762.

[3] Present address: Department of Nutritional Sciences, University of Connecticut, Storrs 06268.

of adult homeotherms, from mice to elephants, average 70 kcal/kg$^{0.75}$/day. Several studies have shown that certain wild ruminants have FHP's above this suggested interspecies mean (Rogerson 1968; Silver et al. 1969, 1971; Brockway and Maloiy 1968). Fasting metabolic rate is measured as fasting heat production and is used as an estimate of net energy of maintenance (NEm).

One important factor affecting FHP and net energy of production (NEp) of ruminants is the age of the animal (Blaxter 1962:95). FHP per metabolic body size, which is a major part of maintenance cost, may decrease as much as 50 percent during the first 8 months or so of life but becomes relatively stable thereafter (Graham 1967, Ritzman and Colovos 1943). Efficiency of growth, in general, varies with age since the older the animal the greater the maintenance tax in comparison to the productive element (Brody 1945). On a constant energy intake, voluntary activity reduces the portion of total net energy available for production purposes and therefore, must be measured or controlled in order to estimate NEp.

In the interpretation of results from metabolic studies, there are discrepancies in whether sex differences should be considered. Graham (1968) found that Merino rams had a FHP approximately 20 percent higher than wethers and ewes. Nordan et al. (1970) showed similar results in black-tailed deer (*Odocoileus hemionus*). Hanus (1969), however, studied 10 sheep of both sexes and stated that sex differences in metabolic rate were not statistically significant. In a preliminary trial, Wesley et al. (1970) found no obvious sex differences in comparing 2 male with 2 female pronghorns. Since there was some question about the importance of sex on energetics of animals, only females were used in this study.

In an energy metabolism study of wild animals, particularly the FHP phase, training of the animals must also be considered in the interpretation of results. Graham (1968) showed that heat production of fasted sheep was 20 percent higher in untrained animals than it was 3 weeks later in the same habituated subjects. All antelopes in this project received similar training prior to and during all energy trials.

Like all homeothermic animals, pronghorns must maintain a relatively constant body temperature. Environmental temperature and other thermal conditions in the atmosphere, along with the amount of heat produced by the animal, determine the extent to which heat must be conserved or dissipated. Hormone response, shivering, metabolic alterations, and behavioral thermoregulation are important factors of such regulation and determine to some degree the energetic expense of animals exposed to inclement weather and extreme climates. Kleiber (1961:162) explained that theoretically all homeotherms have a thermoneutral range in which metabolic rate remains relatively constant. This temperature range was called the "zone of thermal comfort" by Maynard and Loosli (1969:378). As environmental temperature increases within the thermoneutral zone, excess heat is dissipated by physical and behavioral regulatory mechanisms. There is a point or short range of temperatures on either end of this zone, called the upper and lower critical temperatures, at which the animal can no longer maintain his homeothermy by physical means. As the environmental temperature increases above the upper critical temperature, body temperature and metabolic rate rise because cellular processes are uncontrolled. Theoretically, this functions as a fatal cycle since increased metabolism produces additional heat for the body to dissipate even though it is already beyond capacity. When the environmental temperature drops below the lower critical temperature, metabolic rate rises to produce heat to maintain body constancy. If the animal is fed at these low temperatures, the heat increment from this food consumption will be used as a part of the heat necessary for maintenance. If the temperature continues to drop, extra heat required for body heat maintenance exceeds the metabolic power of the animal and death ensues (Kleiber 1961). The initiation and rate of response of an animal to low temperatures is related to its thermal insulation (Kleiber 1961). It must be recognized that there are many factors in the dynamic animal system that prevent these theoretical energetics from being conventionally applied. Such factors as efficiency of heat dissipation (Taylor 1968), adaptations for fluctuating cellular temperatures (Schmidt-Nielsen 1964), and gross thermoregulatory behavior (Moen 1968) will alter the theoretical energetic response pattern described by Kleiber (1961) and Blaxter (1962).

METHODS

Design and Statistical Analysis

The experimental design was selected to show the effect of age, temperature, and limited activity on certain aspects of energy metabolism of pronghorns. Since only young animals were available at the onset of the trials, the influence of age on the various energy parameters was measured. For this analysis, 21 C was selected as a control temperature since preliminary trials showed this temperature to be in the pronghorn's thermoneutral zone. For studying age effect on energetics, the null hypothesis stated that age of the animals would have no effect on gross energy intake (GI), apparent digestible energy (DEapp), nitrogen-

corrected metabolizable energy (MEn), total heat production (THP), fasting heat production, and net energy of production. The antelopes were tested at 2 months, 7.5 months, and 12 months of age. Additional information was derived for THP and FHP when the animals were 18 months old. A one-way analysis of variance was conducted for each of the energy categories among the age groups and if significance ($P < 0.05$) occurred, a Duncan's New Multiple Range Test (DNMRT) was conducted to locate the differences.

The null hypothesis for studying the effects of temperature on energy metabolism stated that exposing pronghorns to temperatures of 5 equal decrements from 32 C to −12 C would not differentially affect energy utilization. For acquiring heat production values, the temperature range covered an additional trial at −23 C. Energy utilization, specifically, was determined by measuring energy intake, DEapp, MEn, THP, FHP, and NEp of the animals exposed to the various temperature treatments. A one-way analysis of variance was then conducted for each of these energy partitions among the range of temperatures. DNMRT was used to determine where the differences ($P < 0.05$) existed within each segment of partitioned food energy. These analyses were conducted separately for metabolically mature and immature antelopes. When only two groups or treatments were compared, such as in the immature antelope subcategory, the t-test was used to determine differences.

Since the animals were kept outside except during experimental periods, their coats developed and receded normally. The order of trials was selected to keep in phase with the hair coat of the animals and to simulate seasonal temperatures as closely as possible. The duration of the trials for de-

Table 1. Dry matter, percent protein, and gross energy content of diet fed to pronghorns during trials.

Ingredient	Dry matter	% protein	Gross energy (kcal/gram)
Mixed concentrate	88.8	17.4	4.07
rolled barley			
chopped corn			
rolled milo			
bran			
protein supplement			
molasses			
Leafy alfalfa	95.2	28.9	4.20
Milk[a]	17.5	36.0	5.42

[a] 26 liquid ounces of evaporated milk were made up to 1 gallon with whole cows milk.

termination of both age and temperature effects ranged from a minimum of 111 hours to a maximum of 170 hours.

Metabolism Measurement Procedures

Antelopes were placed in the animal holding room for an initial adjustment period of approximately 48 hours. This period was lengthened by 24 hours when the –12 C and –23 C trials were conducted. Prior to these trials, temperature was lowered in 10–15 degree decrements every 10–12 hours until the room was at maximum cooling capacity (usually near –3 C). Any additional drop in temperature that was required was accomplished with the refrigerated chambers. Metabolic chambers used during the trials were modified versions of the refrigerated chambers designed by the Department of Animal Science, University of Illinois. They were constructed to permit urine and fecal collection and could be sealed for respiratory measurement. Three one-way valves were installed in the rear of the chamber to allow adequate air flow. The first two trials involved small antelopes and required smaller chambers. To simulate natural photoperiods as closely as possible, lights were controlled by a timer to correspond with sunrise and sunset. Excretion collec-

tion and intake data were not begun for approximately 12 hours after the animals entered the metabolic chambers. Food and water were available ad libitum and their consumption was recorded twice daily during the trials. The diet consisted of a mixed concentrate and a small amount of leafy alfalfa (Table 1). During the trials on 2- and 3-month-old animals, this diet was supplemented with milk.

Feces and urine were collected each morning and afternoon. Feces were composited and dried at approximately 60 C. Urine was weighed at each collection and decanted into a composite bottle for each animal and later lypholized to provide dry matter data. During storage, urine was refrigerated and protected from ammonia loss by a covering of toluene. Nitrogen analysis was conducted on liquid samples. Nitrogen and energy analyses were conducted on dried feed and fecal samples. Gross energy of samples was determined by igniting a dried aliquot in a Parr oxygen bomb calorimeter and the micro-kjeldahl procedure was used in nitrogen determination.

Apparent digestible energy values (DEapp) were obtained by subtracting energy lost in the feces from total energy intake. Nitrogen corrected metabolizable energy values (MEn) were derived by subtracting urinary and methane energy losses from DEapp and correcting these values for nitrogen balance (Crampton and Harris 1969:70).

Indirect Calorimetry

For measurement of heat production, the respiratory exchange method was utilized (Crampton and Harris 1969:87). On at least two occasions during the phase of the trial in which the animals were receiving food, chambers were sealed with plexiglass

Table 2. Effect of age on energy utilization of female pronghorns exposed to 21 C.

Age class (months)	Wt (kg)	Kcal/kg$^{0.75}$/day			Percent of gross energy intake		
		Gross energy intake	Total heat production	Fasting heat production	Apparent digestible energy	Metabolizable energy (N-corrected)	Net energy for production
2	8.9	257 ± 13[a]	152 ± 2	117 ± 1	85 ± 1	79 ± 1	20 ± 2
7.5	26.1	181 ± 13	114 ± 6	73 ± 3	77 ± 1	72 ± 1	8 ± 3
12	26.8	223 ± 11	121 ± 1	75 ± 5	70 ± 3	65 ± 3	10 ± 5
18	37.8	221 ± 20	112 ± 7	80 ± 1			

[a] Mean ± $s_{\bar{x}}$.

and respiratory measurement made for a minimum of 5 hours. This procedure allowed each animal a minimum of 10 hours respiratory measurement for calculation of total heat production, which is the heat produced by an animal when fully fed. To acquire fasting heat production values, it was necessary to know what period of fasting produced the most reliable results. To supply this information, respiration was recorded for five animals at 24-hour increments during 72 hours of fasting. Data indicated that 48 hours of fasting produced reliable measurements of fasting heat production for metabolically mature pronghorn. In all subsequent trials, respiration was recorded for a minimum of 3 hours and 5 hours after 24 hours and 48 hours fasting, respectively. In all calculations of FHP, data from 48 hours fasting were used. Total and fasting heat production values were calculated from the caloric equation given by Crampton and Harris (1969:65). Total heat production in an animal is the sum of heat produced via activity, heat increment, and fasting metabolism. As was stated previously, fasting heat production is a quantitative estimate of fasting metabolism and was measured on quiescent, fasted animals. With activity thus negated, heat increment, which is the resultant heat from food consumption and metabolism, was derived as the difference in heat production between fed and fasted animals. Following

these calculations, energy retention (NEp) was estimated by subtracting energy losses in feces, urine, methane, and heat from the gross energy intake.

To ascertain the energetic demands of restricted activity, indirect calorimetry was recorded on several animals while they were standing but quiescent. Feeding trials on two pronghorns confined in 50- × 100-foot pens were also conducted to yield additional data on energetic costs of activity.

RESULTS AND DISCUSSION

Age Effect on Energy Metabolism

The effect of age on energy utilization of female pronghorns exposed to 21 C temperature is shown in Table 2. The 2-month-old pronghorn exposed to the control temperature of 21 C gave significantly higher values ($P < 0.05$) in all food energy categories measured than the other three age classes that were exposed to 21 C. Much of the difference in DEapp, MEn, NEp, and THP between the 2-month-age class and the other age classes may be accounted for by diet differences. The difference in the FHP values of the 2-month-old animals and the other age classes could not be related to diet and were of an obvious magnitude. Based on these data, any animals that were 2 or 3 months old during trials were classified as metabolically immature. Although differences were revealed between the 7.5-month-old animals and the 12-month-old

Table 3. Effect of temperature on energy utilization of metabolically mature and immature female pronghorns.

Metabolic status	Temperature (C)	Kcal/kg$^{0.75}$/day			Percent of gross energy intake		
		Gross intake	Total heat production	Fasting heat production	Apparent digestible energy	Metabolizable energy (N-corrected)	Net energy for production
Immature	21	257 ± 13[a]	152 ± 2	117 ± 1	85 ± 1	79 ± 1	20 ± 2
	32	291 ± 10	165 ± 6	124 ± 2	83 ± 1	78 ± 1	21 ± 3
Mature	21	201 ± 11	116 ± 3	77 ± 2	73 ± 2	68 ± 2	9 ± 2
	10	247 ± 16	125 ± 4	83 ± 4	74 ± 2	69 ± 2	18 ± 2
	− 1	198 ± 14	114 ± 10	73 ± 6	77 ± 2	71 ± 2	13 ± 1
	−12	233 ± 25	122 ± 7	96 ± 8	74 ± 2	69 ± 2	14 ± 6
	−23	278 ± 9	163 ± 47	108 ± 9			

[a] Mean ± $s_{\bar{x}}$.

animals in DEapp and MEn, these differences may be more related to reduced intake in the former group than to true age effect. THP and FHP were not different ($P < 0.05$) among the three latter groups and all observations for these age classes were combined and categorized as a mean for metabolically mature pronghorns exposed to 21 C. The mean FHP value derived was 76 kcal/kg$^{0.75}$/day with a standard error ($s_{\bar{x}}$) of 2.0. This value is approximately 20 percent lower than reported for most other mature wild ruminants. The apparent discrepancy may be due to a true species difference, differential training prior to metabolic trials, or to other unknown factors.

Before the pronghorn's energetic role in the short-grass ecosystem can be evaluated, a study of population dynamics must be conducted to determine age ratios and other factors that affect metabolism, biomass, and productivity. Per unit of body weight, pronghorns from birth to several months of age, place greater energetic demands on the ecosystem than at maturity. This increased demand by young animals is due primarily to higher heat production and growth rate (Maynard and Loosli 1969). The amount of energy stored per unit of body weight, however, becomes larger with age because of the lower water and higher fat content of the growth tissue.

Temperature Effect on Energy Metabolism

Data showing temperature effects on energy partitioning of pronghorns are recorded in Table 3. The effects of temperature on fasting metabolic rates of pronghorns are shown graphically in Fig. 1. To separate temperature and age effects on energy metabolism, trials conducted at 21 C served as controls. According to Student's t-test, the THP and FHP of animals exposed to 32 C were significantly higher ($P < 0.10$ and $P < 0.05$, respectively) than when these animals were exposed to 21 C. The FHP values for each animal measured at 32 C were corrected for age and plotted (Fig. 1). An upward trend in FHP's of animals exposed to 32 C indicated that the upper critical temperature of young pronghorns may be near this point, but no definite conclu-

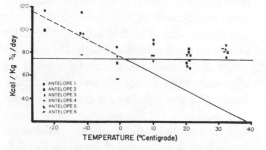

Fig. 1. Metabolic response of fasted female antelopes to various temperatures.

sions can be established from these data. Since pronghorns are not likely to be exposed in the wild to prolonged temperatures greater than 32 C, and because laboratory facilities prevented duplication of such factors as solar radiation, air movement, and animal behavior patterns (Moen 1968), no trials of higher temperatures were conducted.

According to DNMRT, no statistical differences existed in kcal intake and percents of DEapp, MEn, and NEp for the five temperature exposures conducted on mature pronghorns. This agrees with observations by Weichenthal (1967) who found that environmental temperatures had little effect on energy losses in steers via feces, urine, or methane although differences in intake affected them. The NEp values for all mature animal trials showed considerable variability, which probably reflected the variability in intake as well as experimental errors incurred. Since NEp was calculated by difference in energy expenditures and gross energy intake, both of these explanations are feasible.

One animal, which also had the lightest hair coat, showed an increased THP as temperatures were lowered to –23 C. This response accounted for the large $s_{\bar{x}}$ for the –23 C THP value and the subsequent increased food intake shown in Table 3. The animal which showed increased THP in response to –23 C produced no measurable methane at this temperature. This phenomenon was also noted by Soderquist (1967) who found a four-fold decrease in methane production when lambs were maintained at 0 C versus 21 C. From these observations, it seems evident that the lower critical temperature for this particular pronghorn on ad libitum intake under the test conditions was in the range between –12 C and –23 C. In extrapolating to wild

pronghorns, this conclusion should be accepted with caution. Kotb and Pfander (1964), for example, found that animals on a high concentrate diet showed less stress when exposed to cold. Atmospheric thermal conditions, behavior patterns and physiological response of wild pronghorns may also be different from those in this experiment.

Three of the four animals examined at –12 C showed a significant increase ($P < 0.05$) in FHP (Fig. 1, Table 3) when compared to the control temperature of 21 C. Upon exposure to –23 C, the FHP response was slightly, but not significantly, higher than at –12 C for two of the three animals that had shown response at –12 C. Kleiber (1961) maintains that the rate of FHP response of an animal to decreasing temperatures below critical temperature, represented by the dotted line in Fig. 1, is a function of insulation. Based on the theoretical assumption of Kleiber (1961) that heat production was zero when ambient temperature equals body temperature, this diagonal line was extrapolated to 39 C for the pronghorn. The horizontal line (Fig. 1) represents the average FHP in the thermoneutral zone of the experimental pronghorn. The animal with the lightest hair coat showed the highest FHP at –1 C, –12 C, and –23 C. This same animal showed the least response to 32 C exposure, possibly indicating better heat dissipation. Shivering was noted in two animals during fasting at –12 C and became more exaggerated under fed and fasted conditions in one of these animals during the –23 C trial. The data presented here indicate that the fasting, lower critical temperature of at least two of the female pronghorns in this study was near 0 C. Since only four antelopes were available for the –12 C and –1 C trials and only two for the –23 C trial, and since each animal responded differently to these temperatures, correlation for FHP response to decreasing ambient temperatures must be accepted with caution. The slope of the line that resulted from plotting FHP response with low ambient temperatures (Fig. 1) indicated that the fasting heat production for pronghorns increased approximately 1.7 kcal/kg$^{0.75}$/day for each degree (C) decrease in ambient temperature. During the 10 C, –1 C, –12 C, and –23 C trials, air was moved by a system of fans through refrigerated coils. Air velocity at several points in the chambers was measured by a portable recording anemometer and found to exceed 2.0 mph in only two places in each chamber. Since animals under cold stress avoided these areas and facilities were not available for making comparisons at various wind speeds, no conclusions were possible regarding wind effect.

Effect of Activity on Heat Production

During respiratory measurement, animals occasionally stood for short periods. Usually they would lie down before the chamber air became equilibrated with the increased respiratory demands. Under these circumstances, no estimate of energetic cost of standing could be made. On 12 occasions during the course of trials, however, the animals stood long enough for equilibration to occur. These 12 observations involved three metabolically mature animals. The energy cost of standing was calculated as the difference between heat production while lying and standing and averaged 45.7 ± 3.3 kcal/kg$^{0.75}$/day.

To supplement these data, the assumption was made that, under similar temperature, diet, and age conditions, a pronghorn would partition energy the same in semiconfinement as in metabolic chambers. Two of the pronghorns were placed in individual 50- ×

100-foot vegetation-free pens and given 3 days adjustment. Following the initial 3 days, food intake was recorded twice daily for each animal for 3 days. Intake increased 74 and 64 kcal/kg$^{0.75}$/day for the two animals, which represents increases of 36 and 29 percent, respectively, over the energy consumed while confined in the metabolic chambers. This expense can be contributed primarily to activity. Although there was some activity in the chambers, it should represent a small fraction of the total energy transformed.

Comparative Energetics

From the data presented in Table 3, the DEapp and MEn intake values for pronghorn exposed to 21 C were calculated to be 147 kcal/kg$^{0.75}$/day and 137 kcal/kg$^{0.75}$/day, respectively. These two values correspondingly represent 73 and 68 percent of the gross energy intake for the pronghorn and agree well with the DEapp and MEn values for mature, black-tailed deer (Nordan et al. 1970) and white-tailed (*Odocoileus virginiana*) deer does (Ullrey et al. 1970). The values for the DEapp and MEn for white-tailed does were 158 kcal/kg$^{0.75}$/day and 131 kcal/kg$^{0.75}$/day, respectively. Growing female black-tailed deer consumed approximately 194 kcal/kg$^{0.80}$ of digestible energy daily. Digestible and metabolizable energy values for cattle have been given to be approximately 70 and 60 percent of gross energy intake (Blaxter et al. 1966, Ritzman and Colovos 1943). Graham (1964) measured energy partitioning with sheep on low and high fiber diets and found digestible energy values to range from 62 percent of gross energy intake on high fiber diets to 76 percent on low fiber diets. Correspondingly, metabolizable energy values were 51 and 62 percent. In a study on the eland (*Taurotragus oryx*) and wildebeest

(*Connochaetes* sp.), Rogerson (1968) found the metabolizable energy values for both species to be approximately 59 percent of gross energy intake. Any comparison of the pronghorn's capacity to digest and metabolize food with the various wild and domestic species discussed above requires cognizance of the differences in diets used on the various studies. The relatively high metabolizable energy value of the pronghorn, however, can be accounted for by the loss of only 3–3.5 percent of gross energy intake in urine and a similar quantity via the methane route. These figures compare with a 4.5–5 percent urinary loss and a 7 percent loss via methane formation in the eland and wildebeest (Rogerson 1968) and in the sheep (Graham 1964). Maynard and Loosli (1969) stated that methane represents a loss of approximately 7 percent of gross energy intake in most domestic ruminants on concentrate feed.

Heat increment values are highly correlated with the diet of an animal and therefore, should be different for selective browsers such as deer and antelopes and nonselective grazers such as cattle. On the diet consumed by the antelopes in this study, however, heat increment represented 20–30 percent of gross energy intake, which was similar to values given for domestic ruminants (Maynard and Loosli 1969:376).

In a comparison of the relative energetics of wild and domestic animals, critical temperature must be considered. While sheep (Webster et al. 1969), white-tailed deer (Silver et al. 1969, 1971), and pronghorns have fasting lower critical temperatures near or below 0 C, cattle show increased FHP at temperatures of 16–20 C (Blaxter and Wainman 1961). For fed animals, these values dropped to approximately –20 to –30 C for sheep and pronghorns and to 6–8 C for cattle. Minimum weekly temperatures for a 4-month period of 1969 on the Pawnee National Grasslands averaged –10 C. There was a 3-day period in which the average minimum temperature dropped to –21 C. Although acclimatization will affect FHP values, and thus maintenance requirements, it is obvious that the reported cold temperatures influence energy uptake in cattle more often and to a greater extent than in sheep or pronghorns. This comparative liability for cattle would be increased by chilling winds. It seems certain, therefore, that pronghorns and sheep are better adapted to climatic conditions of the shortgrass ecosystem than cattle. When the environmental temperature is in the thermoneutral zone, the average FHP value for cattle (Blaxter and Wainman 1966) was higher than was found in this study for mature pronghorns. Kleiber's law (Kleiber 1961) states that the food consumption–FHP ratio, as well as the excess energy available for productive processes, is independent of species and body weight. Based on this principle, along with the data in this study, it seems that pronghorns are energetically more efficient than their domestic counterparts. This phenomenon would imply that carrying capacity of a given range would be greater for pronghorns than domestic ruminants if availability of the desired food plants was equal. Since pronghorns (Hoover 1971), however, are more selective in feeding than cattle (Free 1969), availability of desired plants may be more limiting in carrying capacity of pronghorn range than cattle or sheep range.

The average diet consumed by trained pronghorns on native vegetation at Colorado's Pawnee National Grasslands contained approximately 4.05 kcal/gram dry matter in winter and 4.3 kcal/gram dry matter in spring and summer (Hoover 1971).

After correcting for estimated seasonal changes in digestibility, it is reasonable to speculate that a 40 kg, unstressed pronghorn in winter would necessarily consume 900 grams dry matter/day for maintenance and growth. In spring and summer, this value would be approximately 805 grams. Both these values would be approximately 18 percent higher for animals 2 months of age if considered on the basis of metabolic body size, 32 percent higher for mature animals which were moderately active and variably increased by extremely cold temperatures. These calculations are based on energy data presented in this paper and are subject to many variables not examined here. It is possible to surmise from these figures that a complete study on energy metabolism capabilities of all species on a given range, along with an adequate estimation of population parameters, is necessary before conclusions can be drawn concerning carrying capacity of any habitat.

LITERATURE CITED

BEALE, D. M., AND A. D. SMITH. 1970. Forage use, water consumption, and productivity of pronghorn antelope in western Utah. J. Wildl. Manage. 34(3):570–582.

BLAXTER, K. L. 1962. The energy metabolism of ruminants. Charles C Thomas, Springfield, Ill. 329pp.

———, AND F. W. WAINMAN. 1961. Environmental temperature and the energy metabolism and heat emission of steers. J. Agric. Sci. 56: 81–90.

———, AND ———. 1966. The fasting metabolism of cattle. Br. J. Nutr. 20:103–111.

———, J. L. CLAPPERTON, AND F. W. WAINMAN. 1966. Utilization of the energy and protein on the same diet by cattle of different ages. J. Agric. Sci. 67:67–75.

BROCKWAY, J. M., AND G. M. O. MALOIY. 1968. Energy metabolism of the red deer. J. of Physiol. 194(1):22–24.

BRODY, S. 1945. Bioenergetics and growth. Reinhold Publishing Co., New York. 1023pp.

BUECHNER, H. K. 1950. Life history, ecology and range use of the pronghorn antelope in Trans-Pecos, Texas. Am. Midl. Nat. 43(3): 256–354.

CRAMPTON, E. W., AND L. E. HARRIS. 1969. Applied animal nutrition. W. H. Freeman and Co., San Francisco, Calif. 753pp.

DOUGHERTY, R. W., ed. 1965. Physiology of digestion in the ruminant. Butterworth Inc., Washington, D. C. 480pp.

FREE, J. C. 1969. Comparison of two methods for determining dry matter intake by large herbivores. M.S. Thesis. Colorado State Univ. 33pp.

GRAHAM, N. McC. 1964. Energetic efficiency of fattening sheep. I. Utilization of low fibre and high fibre mixtures. Aust. J. Agric. Res. 15(1):100–112.

———. 1967. The metabolic rate of fasting sheep in relation to total and lean body weight, and the estimation of maintenance requirements. Aust. J. Agric. Res. 18(1):127–136.

———. 1968. The metabolic rate of Merino rams bred for high or low wool production. Aust. J. Agric. Res. 19(5):821–824.

HANUS, K. 1969. Practical aspects of thermoregulation in sheep. Vet. Arch. 39:245–255.

HOOVER, J. P. 1971. Pronghorn antelope food habits on Pawnee National Grasslands. M.S. Thesis. Colorado State Univ. 285pp.

HOOVER, R. L., C. E. TILL, AND S. OGILVIE. 1959. The antelope of Colorado. Colorado Dept. Fish and Game, Tech. Bull. 4. 110pp.

KLEIBER, M. 1947. Body size and metabolic rate. Physiol. Rev. 27(4):511–541.

———. 1961. Fire of life: an introduction to animal energetics. John Wiley and Sons, New York. 454pp.

KOTB, A. R., AND W. H. PFANDER. 1964. Metabolism of sheep under cold and hot conditions. J. Anim. Sci. 23:1226 (abstr.).

MAYNARD, L. A., AND J. K. LOOSLI. 1969. Animal nutrition. McGraw-Hill Book Co., New York. 613pp.

MOEN, A. N. 1968. The critical thermal environment: A look at an old concept. Bioscience 18(11):1041–1043.

NORDAN, H. C., I. McT. COWAN, AND A. J. WOOD. 1970. The feed intake and heat production of the young black-tailed deer (*Odocoileus hemionus columbianus*). Can. J. Zool. 48(2): 275–282.

RITZMAN, E. G., AND N. F. COLOVOS. 1943. Physiological requirements and utilization of protein and energy by growing dairy cattle. Univ. New Hampshire Tech. Bull. 80. 59pp.

ROGERSON, A. 1968. Energy utilization by the eland and wildebeest. Pages 153–161 *in* M. A. Crawford, ed. Comparative nutrition of wild animals. Academic Press, New York. 429pp.

SCARVIE, O., AND J. ARNEY. 1957. Food habits of pronghorn antelope, *Antilocapra americana*, in October in northern Colorado. Colorado State Univ. 9pp.

SCHMIDT-NIELSEN, K. 1964. Desert animals: Physiological problems of heat and water. Clarendon Press, Inc. Oxford. 277pp.

SILVER, H., N. F. COLOVOS, J. B. HOLTER, AND H. H. HAYES. 1969. Fasting metabolism of white-tailed deer. J. Wildl. Manage. 33(3): 490–498.

———, J. B. HOLTER, N. F. COLOVOS, AND H. H. HAYES. 1971. Effect of falling temperature on heat production in fasting white-tailed deer. J. Wildl. Manage. 35(1):37–46.

SODERQUIST, H. G. 1967. Effects of environmental temperature on energy retention in fattening lambs. M.S. Thesis. Colorado State Univ. 60pp.

TAYLOR, C. R. 1968. The eland and the oryx. Sci. Amer. 220(1):88–95.

ULLREY, D. E., W. G. YOUATT, H. E. JOHNSON, L. D. FAY, B. L. SCHOEPKE, AND W. T. MAGEE. 1970. Digestible and metabolizable energy requirements for winter maintenance of Michigan white-tailed deer. J. Wildl. Manage. 34(4):863–869.

WEBSTER, A. J. F., A. M. HICKS, AND F. L. HAYS. 1969. Cold climate and cold temperature induced changes in the heat production and thermal insulation of sheep. Can. J. Physiol. Pharmacol. 47:553–562.

WEICHENTHAL, B. A. 1967. Temperature-energy trials with steers. Ph.D. Thesis. Colorado State Univ. 88pp.

WESLEY, D. E., K. L. KNOX, AND J. G. NAGY. 1970. Energy flux and water kinetics in young pronghorn antelope. J. Wildl. Manage. 34(4):908–912.

Accepted 15 August 1973.

NUTRITIONAL QUALITY OF SUMMER DIETS OF PRONGHORN ANTELOPES IN UTAH[1]

ARTHUR D. SMITH, Department of Range Science, Utah State University and Project Leader, Utah State Division of Wildlife Resources, Logan 84322

JOHN C. MALECHEK, Department of Range Science, Utah State University, Logan 84322

Abstract: Between 1 May and 30 September, 1969 and 1970, plants eaten by pronghorns (*Antilocapra americana*) on the Awapa Plateau and at the Desert Experimental Range in Utah were collected at tri-weekly intervals and subjected to chemical analysis for protein, phosphorus, and digestibility. Diets were determined by estimating percentage of utilization and quantity of vegetation available at locations where pronghorns were seen feeding. Crude protein values varied from 10 to 22 percent; digestibility coefficients were between 71 and 77 percent. Lowest levels of dietary crude protein were observed at the Desert Experimental Range, but the highest values were recorded there as well. Overall, there was little difference in digestibility of forage at the two locations, but differences that were found favored animals at the Desert Range location. Both protein content and digestibility declined more rapidly as the season advanced on the Awapa Plateau; at the Desert station, both nutritional parameters were erratic in response to the amount and timing of summer precipitation. There is nothing in the data to suggest nutritional constraints in the forage available to antelopes during summer at either location.

J. WILDL. MANAGE. 38(4):792–798

One of the reasons postulated for the present low productivity of pronghorns in many desert areas is that the vegetation now found on these ranges is deficient in one or more critical nutrients. This factor was cited by western game departments as a prime suspect for the failure of pronghorns to produce as well as their biological capacity seemed to indicate (Foree 1959).

Little is known of the nutritional qualities of forage used by pronghorns. The little information that is available comes from nutritional assessments for domestic livestock and, on the deserts of western Utah, these apply only to winter months. During the summer months, a wide variety of plants are available that are not present during the winter, and these have not been investigated as to chemical make-up or digestibility.

Feeding studies with captive pronghorns during winter indicated that the major items of the diet were big sagebrush (*Artemisia*

tridentata) and black sagebrush (*A. nova*) (Smith et al. 1965). Field observations confirm the importance of these species to pronghorns, especially during the winter period (Beale and Smith 1970). Both of these species are comparatively high in protein (Cook and Harris 1968). If we assume forage is ample and these plants are equally digestible to pronghorns as they are to sheep, there is probably adequate protein for growth and gestation during the winter period (National Research Council 1968).

Existing data do not permit similar extrapolations during the summer months. Weswig (1956) found no evidence of a vitamin A deficiency in the diet of pronghorns in Oregon. Dirschl (1963) ascertained the chemical composition of pronghorns' forage but included no forbs in his analyses. Review of the extensive bibliography compiled by Yoakum (1967) revealed no other information on chemical composition of forage used by pronghorns. In light of this lack of nutritional knowledge and its possible relationship to productivity, an exploratory study was designed to determine the nutri-

[1] A contribution of Pittman–Robertson Federal Aid in Wildlife Restoration, Utah Project W-105-R.

tional quality of forage used by pronghorns during the summer months at two locations to see if more intensive research was indicated.

STUDY AREAS

Triweekly plant collections were made during the summers of 1969 and 1970 at two locations in Utah where pronghorns are present: the Desert Experimental Range (administered by the Intermountain Forest and Range Experiment Station, U.S. Forest Service) in western Millard County and the Awapa Plateau in Wayne County. At the Desert Range, pronghorns were enclosed in an area which varies in elevation from 1600 to 1800 m. Mean annual precipitation from 1961 through 1973 was 17.4 cm; 18.9 cm and 15.7 cm were recorded in 1969 and 1970, respectively. The vegetation is characteristic of the salt-desert shrub community. The Awapa Plateau ranges in elevation from 2100 to 2400 m. There are two major vegetational types, one dominated by big sagebrush and one by black sagebrush. The latter is most extensive, but the big sagebrush type was most productive of forbs. No long-time precipitation records are available for the Awapa Plateau but 34.1 and 27.3 cm were recorded in 1969 and 1970, respectively.

PROCEDURES

Pronghorn bands were located during the early morning hours when animals were actively feeding and the sites of feeding activity were noted. Later in the day these sites were visited and an examination made of forage utilization. By tracking and observing evidence of forage removal, ocular estimates were made of the volume of forage removed and were weighted by plant abundance to obtain the composition in

percent of the diet for that location and time. The number of animals involved and the number of locations examined varied. Sometimes evidence indicated that a feeding site had been used for several days prior to the examination; at other times a single morning feeding was involved.

Samples of those plant species that had been eaten were collected from uneaten plants, freeze-dried, and stored in plastic bags for subsequent laboratory analysis. Observations and collections began about the first of May and ended in late September each year. Collections were made eight times on the Desert Experimental Range and seven times on the Awapa Plateau. Spring came to the Awapa Plateau later than at the Desert Range, and it was difficult to judge grazing use because the vegetation was poorly developed. We did, however, estimate diet in 1970. Approximately 300 plant samples representing 65 species were collected and analyzed individually for nitrogen, phosphorus, and ether extract (Association of Official Agricultural Chemists 1960).

Dry matter digestibility estimates were derived from analysis of composite samples. Each species made up the same percentage by weight as it did in the diet. These mixtures were then subjected to the fiber analysis scheme outlined by Van Soest (1963), Van Soest and Wine (1967), and Goering and Van Soest (1970). Through regression equations, this analytical procedure allows the prediction of the digestibility of forage dry matter and is based on relative concentrations of cell contents, cell walls, and lignin. The correction factor developed for sheep of −12.9 digestibility units due to additions of metabolic components to the fecal matter (Goering and Van Soest 1970) was applied to the data to yield estimates of apparent dry matter digestibility.

Table 1. Percentage composition of antelope diets on the Awapa Plateau at eight collection periods, 1 May to 20 September 1969 and 1970.

Forage species	Collection period[a]														
	1 (1970)	2 (1969)	2 (1970)	3 (1969)	3 (1970)	4 (1969)	4 (1970)	5 (1969)	5 (1970)	6 (1969)	6 (1970)	7 (1969)	7 (1970)	8 (1969)	8 (1970)
Browse															
Artemisia frigida	40		55				3		5				1		36
A. nova	2		5						5	17		7			
A. tridentata	15	85	11	12	6	1	5		1		2				4
Chrysothamnus spp.	5				11	24		37	30	7	25	13	50	27	8
Eriogonum microthecum	2				1	1				3	1	2			
Gutierrezia sarothrae				1					30	6		20			
Purshia tridentata					2	12		37		58	2	50		12	15
Rosa sp.				1											
Symphoricarpos sp.				10	2		5			1					
Tetradymia spp.			20	1	5	6	5							2	32
Total browse	64	85	91	25	27	44	18	74	71	92	30	92	51	41	95
Forbs															
Androsace septentrionalis													10		
Astragalus diversifolius						2									
Castilleja linariaefolia			1			12	6								
Chenopodium album										1	15			7	
Chaenactis douglasii	13		2	11		10	15	1	4				1	10	
Corydalis aurea											15				
Comandra pallida						10									
Cryptantha sp.			2								2			1	
Descurainia pinnata				11							4			16	
Eriogonum spp.				6	3		8			1	1	2	1		
Gilia aggregata				7				1							
Linum lewisii				7			20	6							
Lithospermum ruderale											2		1		
Lotus wrightii							2	5	5	5	4	8	5		
Lupinus caudatus					10										
Oenothera trichocalyx		2		4	40	4					25		40		1
Penstemon spp.			5	17	20	12	10	4			1		5		
Phacelia ivesiana	13	3	1						5						5
Salsola kali							10								
Senecio multilobata			1			2									
Sphaeralcea spp.				7			10		20					1	
Trifolium gymnocarpum		8	1												
Miscellaneous forbs		2	1			4	3	2							5
Lichens[b]	±10						2								
Total forbs	36	15	9	75	73	56	82	26	29	8	70	8	49	52	5
Grass														7	

[a] For approximate dates see Table 3.
[b] It is not certain the foliose lichen was eaten since the thallus is not attached and its removal leaves no evidence.

RESULTS AND DISCUSSION

Composition of Diets

On both areas, browse contributed most to the diet (Tables 1, 2). The only exceptions occurred on the Awapa Plateau in periods 3 and 4 for both 1969 and 1970, in period 6 in 1970, and period 8 in 1969, when forbs exceeded browse. Forbs did not exceed about one-third of the diet selected at the Desert Range at any collection date.

One cannot extrapolate seasonal trends in

Table 2. Percentage composition of antelope diets on the Desert Experimental Range at eight collection periods, 1 May to 25 September 1969 and 1970.

Forage species	1 1969	1 1970	2 1969	2 1970	3 1969	3 1970	4 1969	4 1970	5 1969	5 1970	6 1969	6 1970	7 1969	7 1970	8 1969	8 1970
Browse																
Artemisia nova	30	14	65	15	40	27	31	29	30	7	8	21	13		28	72
A. spinescens	35	40		25		1										
Atriplex canescens				2						5	1	4	7	5	2	
A. confertifolia							3	9	1	2	8	3			1	1
Brickellia oblongifolia				5	7	13	7	15	1	6		2	14		4	12
Chrysothamnus nauseosus						1							1	20		
Ephedra nevadensis								6					1			
Gutierrezia sarothrae		20		10		10	5		8	4	3	8	8	10	14	5
Prunus fasciculata	4		10	7	36	27	27	26	32	52	36	49	23	24	36	7
Salvia carnosa			1		1	1										
Tetradymia nuttallii				5					1							
Miscellaneous browse					2											
Total browse	69	74	76	69	86	80	73	85	73	76	56	87	67	59	85	97
Forbs																
Chenopodium album													1	1		
Cryptantha nana				4	1											
Enceliopsis nudicaulis	11		5	5	1	2	12	2	13	3				5		
Eriogonum ostlundi	10				4	1	6		9	5				1		
Euphorbia fendleri					1	1			1	1	1					
Halogeton glomeratus							1	11			1	1	1	5		
Hermidium alipes	1		2	15									1			
Oenothera caespitosa	1	1	1	5	1	2							1			
Salsola kali						1				4	4	4	12	28	1	3
Sphaeralcea grossulariaefolia	7	21	15	1	6	12	7	1	1	10	38	8	18	1	12	
Miscellaneous forbs	1	1	1	1		1	1	1	3					1	1	
Total forbs	31	23	24	31	12	20	27	15	27	24	44	13	33	41	15	3
Grass				3												

use from these data with any precision. Pronghorns move about a great deal, hence they select forage from among constantly differing mixes of plants. When the feeding site chanced to be within the big sagebrush type on the Awapa Plateau, a variety of forbs was available. If, on the other hand they were in the black sagebrush type, few forbs were available, and *Artemisia frigida* and other shrubs which were not present in the big sage type, were important food items. Continuous observations would be required to establish seasonal trends in plant selection and these would differ some- what each year as rainfall distribution differed.

Moisture Content of Forage

General observations had indicated that tender succulent vegetation was sought over less succulent material. Our data do not support the view that pronghorns select food plants primarily on the basis of their moisture content (Table 3). The forbs had more moisture than did browse, although, with few exceptions, forbs were less important in the diet. When percentage occurrence in the diet was plotted over percent-

Table 3. Percentage moisture in the diets of antelopes at eight periods by forage class.

Period	Approximate date	Awapa Plateau			Desert Experimental Range		
		Browse	Forbs	Diet	Browse	Forbs	Diet
1	1 May				69	71	70
2	20 May	58	75	60	64	72	67
3	12 June	66	75	74	60	65	61
4	2 July	60	71	71	50	81	55
5	22 July	66	70	67	52	63	55
6	15 Aug.	70	75	75	49	62	52
7	5 Sept.	59	67	61	57	70	63
8	25 Sept.	53	68	60	50	60	52

age moisture, no correlation was suggested. This indicates that moisture content alone does not determine plant palatability. It is possible that selection for moisture occurs within species, but this is impossible of determination, since only uneaten plants were available for analysis. It must be assumed that on any date and site all plants of a species are similar in moisture content.

Prairie mallow (*Sphaeralcea grossulariae-folia*) was taken less readily early in the season than it was later, when flower buds were well developed. This apparent preference for forbs when they reached the bud stage was frequently observed. Since no effort was made to determine daily moisture content, we are not certain that moisture content influenced the preference for the bud stage.

Protein Content of Forage

Crude protein percentages of individual species were multiplied by their estimated percentage in the diet to determine the level of dietary protein at each collection period (Table 4). The lowest protein content found was 10 percent and the highest 22 percent; both occurred at the Desert Experimental Range. The highest value was found in mid-August when two species, prairie mallow and desert peach (*Prunus*

Table 4. Percentage crude protein and phosphorus contents of diets of antelopes May through September at two locations in Utah.

Period	Approximate date	Desert Experimental Range				Awapa Plateau			
		Protein		Phosphorus		Protein		Phosphorus	
		1969	1970	1969	1970	1969	1970	1969	1970
1	1 May	20	21	0.31	0.28				
2	20 May	16	17	0.27	0.23	16	17	0.33	0.23
3	12 June	10	13	0.17	0.20	16	18	0.36	0.33
4	2 July	13	11	0.19	0.15	17	12	0.33	0.30
5	22 July	12	10	0.24	0.12	15	18	0.25	0.31
6	15 Aug.	22[a]	13	0.30	0.17	11	16	0.18	0.30
7	5 Sept.	16	13	0.22	0.20	13	13	0.19	0.27
8	25 Sept.	14	12	0.19	0.17	12	11	0.25	0.17
Mean		15	14	0.24	0.19	14	15	0.27	0.27

[a] Three-fourths of the diet was desert peach and prairie mallow (Table 2), both high in protein at this period.

fasciculata), which had responded to mid-summer rains and there was much new growth, were estimated to make up about three-fourths of the diet (Table 2).

In the early summer, which would coincide with late gestation and early lactation periods of pronghorns, crude protein levels on the Awapa Plateau remained at the higher levels for a longer period than at the Desert Range. This was particularly evident in 1969. Minimum requirements for protein were probably met at all periods studied and the data do not suggest that the forage available at the Desert Range was generally inferior in protein content to that on the Awapa Plateau.

Digestibility of Pronghorn Diets

In general, the levels of digestibility at both locations appeared to follow the patterns of forage development and maturity. At the Awapa Plateau, digestibility was high in late May and even higher in mid-June, followed by a general decline throughout the remainder of the summer as forage matured, although there was a late-summer rise in 1970.

On the Desert Range, peak levels of digestibility were observed approximately 6 weeks earlier in the spring than on the Awapa Plateau, probably from the earlier activation of plant growth in the desert environment. A gradual decline in digestibility was evident until late July when the trend again turned upward. This second period of relatively high digestibility levels (65–70 percent) that occurred in August is attributable to renewal of growth in response to late-summer precipitation, a common occurrence.

Season-long digestibility coefficients for both study areas (71 percent and 68 percent for the Desert Experimental Range and the Awapa Plateau, respectively) suggest that pronghorns were able to select a uniformly

Table 5. Digestibility coefficients (percent) for forage consumed by antelopes on the Awapa Plateau and Desert Experimental Range.

Period	Awapa Plateau			Desert Experimental Range		
	1969	1970	Mean	1969	1970	Mean
1				76	77	76.6
2	70	64	66.7	69	75	71.8
3	77	76	76.5	69	71	69.9
4	72	71	71.1	70	67	68.8
5	69	73	71.2	70	66	68.0
6	63	68	65.3	75	78	76.5
7	63	70	66.3	69	61	65.0
8	62	61	61.3	69	65	67.0
Mean	68	69	68.3	71	70	70.5

high quality diet throughout the summer and early fall (Table 5). Lowest values observed (late September) were within the range of 55–60 percent. These values compare favorably with estimates derived for good quality alfalfa, when using the same analytical scheme (Van Soest 1968).

Although the amounts of forage consumed is not known, there is no reason to suppose there was any shortage of forage. Utilization was in most cases light, so much so that it was difficult at times to discern use.

Phosphorus

Phosphorus levels in forage selected by pronghorns (Table 4) exhibited seasonal trends similar to the trends of dry matter digestibility and were undoubtedly related to phenological development of the major forage species. High levels on both study areas corresponded to periods of rapid spring plant growth, and in the case of the Desert Experimental Range, to late summer regrowth. These findings agree with the well-documented cycle of relatively high nutrient levels during periods of forage growth, followed by declines as the plant cell wall thickens and becomes lignified (Van Soest 1968).

Phosphorus requirements for pronghorns have not been established, but in view of recommendations for domestic sheep (National Research Council 1968), plant material selected by antelopes on both study areas appeared to contain adequate levels of phosphorus for growth, gestation, and lactation.

MANAGEMENT IMPLICATIONS

The findings are indicative rather than definitive. The ocular-estimation procedures followed were not sufficiently exhaustive to establish diets precisely. Furthermore, at some collection periods, only a few animals were present and for a single feeding period. At other periods, more than one herd and site were involved, and the data probably are representative of the diet of pronghorns at that time. Moreover, selection of samples by researchers has frequently been shown to understate forage quality. Despite these deficiencies, the data should provide an index to the nutritional quality of forage selected by pronghorn. At no time were they forced to accept forage considered substandard on the basis of nutritional standards for livestock.

Although the nutritional requirements of pronghorns are unknown, it is probable that if sufficient quantities of acceptable forage are available, there will not be a nutritional deficiency during the summer because of inadequate protein or dry matter digestibility, even in the arid desert valleys of the Great Basin. Since March to August precipitation during 1969 and 1970 was about average for the Desert Experimental Range

area, the forage should be adequate nutritionally except in extremely dry years.

LITERATURE CITED

ASSOCIATION OF OFFICIAL AGRICULTURAL CHEMISTS. 1960. Official methods of analysis. 9th ed. Association of Official Agricultural Chemists. Washington, D.C. 832pp.

BEALE, D. M., AND A. D. SMITH. 1970. Forage use, water consumption, and productivity of pronghorn antelope in western Utah. J. Wildl. Manage. 34(3):570–582.

COOK, C. W., AND L. E. HARRIS. 1968. Nutritive value of seasonal ranges. Utah State Univ. Agric. Exp. Stn. Bull. 472. 55pp.

DIRSCHL, H. J. 1963. Food habits of the pronghorn in Saskatchewan. J. Wildl. Manage. 27 (1):81–93.

FOREE, W. W. 1959. Antelope questionnaire. Trans. Int. Antelope Conf. 10:65–75.

GOERING, H. K., AND P. J. VAN SOEST. 1970. Forage fiber analyses. U.S. Dept. Agric. Res. Serv. Agric. Handb. 379. 20pp.

NATIONAL RESEARCH COUNCIL. 1968. Nutrient requirements of domestic animals: No. 5, Sheep. Natl. Acad. Sci. Publ. 1693. 64pp.

SMITH, A. D., D. M. BEALE, AND D. D. DOELL. 1965. Browse preferences of pronghorn antelope in southwestern Utah. Trans. N. Am. Wildl. Nat. Resour. Conf. 30:136–141.

VAN SOEST, P. J. 1963. Use of detergents in the analysis of fibrous feeds. 11. A rapid method for the determination of fiber and lignin. J. Assoc. Off. Agric. Chem. 46(5):829–835.

———. 1968. Structural and chemical characteristics which limit the nutritive value of forages. Pages 63–76 *in* C. M. Harrison, ed. Forage economics—quality. Am. Soc. Agron. Spec. Publ. 13. 144pp.

———, AND R. H. WINE. 1967. Use of detergents in the analysis of fibrous feeds: IV. Determination of plant cell-wall constituents. J. Assoc. Off. Anal. Chem. 50(1):50–55.

WESWIG, P. H. 1956. Vitamin A storage. Oregon State Game Comm. Bull. 11(12):7.

YOAKUM, J. 1967. Literature of the American pronghorn antelope. U.S. Dept. Inter. Unnumbered Bull. 82pp.

Accepted 16 June 1974.

REARING AND TRAINING PRONGHORNS FOR ECOLOGICAL STUDIES[1]

CHARLES C. SCHWARTZ, Department of Fishery and Wildlife Biology, Colorado State University, Fort Collins 80523

JULIUS G. NAGY, Department of Fishery and Wildlife Biology, Colorado State University, Fort Collins 80523

STEPHEN M. KERR, Department of Fishery and Wildlife Biology, Colorado State University, Fort Collins 80523[2]

Abstract: Pronghorn (*Antilocapra americana*) fawns were successfully hand-reared and trained for both laboratory and field studies in nutrition. Fawns were captured 1 to 3 days after birth, placed in an outdoor rearing facility, and bottle-fed a formula of 1 part evaporated milk and 4 parts homogenized milk. Dietary disorder and bacterial infection resulting in diarrhea, and bone and joint ailments were major problems encountered in rearing fawns. Seventy-four percent of 32 fawns reared were successfully trained for field and laboratory studies.

J. WILDL. MANAGE. 40(3):464–468

Use of tame ungulates to study food habits under controlled conditions has increased in the past decade. As cited by Reichert (1972), investigators have used red deer (*Cervus elaphus*), caribou (*Rangifer tarandus*), white-tailed deer (*Odocoileus virginianus*), and mule deer (*O. hemionus*) for such purposes. Tame pronghorns have been used successfully for both field (Hoover 1971, Schwartz and Nagy 1973) and laboratory (Wesley et al. 1969, 1970, 1973) studies of nutrition, and in field studies of behavior (Ellis and Travis 1975). This report describes techniques used in rearing and training 35 pronghorn fawns captured in the wild.

We acknowledge K. Miller for assistance with care and training of pronghorns, R. Souther for maintenance of animals, and D. Wesley and J. Hoover for suggestions throughout the study. J. Ellis, L. Menges, and O. C. Wallmo reviewed the manuscript.

METHODS

Capturing, Handling, and Feeding

Over a period of 7 years, 35 pronghorn fawns were captured on native range approximately 40 km NNW of Fort Collins, Colorado. Fawns were captured during early June at estimated or known ages of 1 to 3 days. Fawns were located, with the aid of a spotting scope or binoculars, by observing wild does from concealment on a topographical vantage point. Does that had fawns generally stopped grazing during mid-morning to nurse their young. After feeding, fawns would lie down, and this position was fixed by the observers. After several fawns were located, a capture team, equipped with a two-way radio and long-handled hoop nets, proceeded toward located fawns. One member of the team approached the fawn from the rear and dropped the net over it. Pronghorn fawns, when very young, remained motionless until the net was dropped.

Captured fawns were transported to Colorado State University for rearing and training. Each fawn was given a 0.5-cc injection of vitamin ADE, its navel was swabbed with tincture of iodine to reduce possibility of infection, and an identification collar was placed around the neck. They were retained in a 12.2- × 9.2- × 1.8-m woven wire enclosure, which contained a shelter. To minimize the possibility of disease and/or its

[1] This paper reports on work supported in part by National Science Foundation Grants GB-7824, GB-13096, GB-31862X, GB-31862X2, GB-41233X, and BMS73-02027 A02 to the Grassland Biome, U.S. International Biological Program, for "Analysis of Structure, Function, and Utilization of Grassland Ecosystems."

[2] Present address: College of Veterinary Medicine, Colorado State University, Fort Collins 80523.

spread, we cleaned and disinfected the holding pen each year before new fawns were captured. The pen was cleaned of droppings at least once each day, and personnel entering the holding area stepped into a footbath of povidone-iodine disinfectant to reduce the possibility of contamination. At 4 weeks of age fawns were moved to a 30.5-m² enclosure where they could exercise. Because of problems encountered in 1968 with *Clostridium perfringens* (Nagy et al. 1969), all fawns received preventative injections of antitoxin type B, C, and D starting at 1 month of age.

Bottle feeding started shortly after fawns arrived at the holding pen. Milk was fed from 300-ml capacity plastic baby bottles with the nipple hole enlarged to ensure adequate flow of milk. All feeding utensils were sterilized in boiling water prior to each feeding. Milk formula was heated to approximately 38 C for feeding.

To persuade young pronghorns to drink milk from a bottle required persistence. A few animals took the nipple readily, but for most the nipple had to be forced into the mouth. Feeding was stimulated by squeezing milk from the bottle into the animal's mouth. While doing this, we placed one hand over the animal's muzzle and gently exerted pressure on the jaws to simulate sucking. When the fawn tasted the milk, normal feeding usually followed. By the end of 2 weeks, feeding was routine.

We tried different milk additives (condensed milk, cream, Similac® [Ross Laboratories, Columbus, Ohio 43216]) but had best results with a mixture of one part evaporated canned milk and four parts homogenized milk. In addition to this standard milk formula we also fed each fawn first-day colostrum from dairy cows for the first 8 days (Table 1). Although antibodies of colostrum were probably beneficial to nursing fawns for the first 1 or 2 days, co-

Table 1. Daily feeding schedule and amount of milk formula bottle-fed to pronghorn fawns from day of capture to weaning (formula was 1 part evaporated canned milk and 4 parts homogenized milk).

Day	Dairy cow colostrum (ml)	Milk formula (ml)	No. feedings/day
1	45.0	45	4
3	30.0	60	4
5	15.0	75	4
7	7.5	82.5	4
9		105	4
10		120	4
13		135	4
20		150	4
23		165	4
24		180	3
43		240	2
75		300	2
100		360	2

lostrum in the diet gradually was reduced to eliminate an abrupt change in the diet. Fawns were fed milk until they were 100 to 120 days old and weaned. In addition to the milk formula, leaves of alfalfa hay, mixed concentrate (Wesley et al. 1973), and block salt were available ad libitum. Observations indicated that fawns consumed small quantities of soil, so a bucket of soil was also available at all times.

To prevent constipation, we used a method described by Youngson (1970) to stimulate defecation: the buttocks and area around the anus were gently sponged with a warm moist cloth after each feeding until the animals were 1 week of age. After the first week, this was done at least once per day until the animals were 4 weeks old or defecating normally.

Training

Training of pronghorn fawns started immediately following their capture. As did Reichert (1972), we found "tender loving care" an essential element throughout the training period. For the first few weeks after capture, trainers spent most of their time gaining the confidence of the fawns.

This was accomplished by repeated contact with each animal during feeding periods. In preparation for foraging studies an intensive training program started when fawns were approximately 2 weeks old. We initially tried to use a harness similar to that used on deer (Healy 1967, Neff 1974, Reichert 1972) to lead fawns. It became evident that pronghorns would not accept restraint in any form, so use of the harness was discontinued and fawns were trained to follow their handler.

A twin-axle horse trailer was modified to transport fawns to the study area. Sides and top were covered to obscure the fawns' view and a Plexiglas window was placed in the front so the trainer could observe them from outside. The trailer was parked so fawns could enter it from inside the holding area. Fawns were given a few days to investigate and adjust to the trailer after which they were enticed into it for feeding. As soon as they were accustomed to entering and feeding in the trailer, the gate was closed during feeding; milk was not fed to the fawns unless they entered the trailer. All other food items (concentrate, hay, and water) were placed in the trailer. Short trips in the trailer were started when fawns were 4 weeks of age and were repeated several times each day with distance per trip gradually increased.

At 4 to 6 weeks of age, fawns were transported to a large pasture and released for the first time. They were allowed to move freely while the trainer walked with them. After a period of 0.5–1.0 hour they were led back in the trailer for bottle feeding. This procedure was repeated every other day until fawns were 4 months old, at which time it was repeated at least once a week until fawns were transported to the study area.

Fawns were conditioned to accept metabolic chambers and holding rooms similar to the way we trained them to accept the horse trailer. Starting at 2 to 3 weeks of age individuals were alternated between the metabolic cages and the horse trailer every other day so they became accustomed to both.

RESULTS AND DISCUSSION

Capturing, Handling, and Feeding

The technique used to locate and capture pronghorn fawns was quite successful, because over 90 percent of all fawns located were captured. The 2-way radios and spotting scope made it possible to direct a capture team to within 20 m of a concealed fawn. Fawns as far away as 3.2 km were located and captured successfully.

Each fawn had an individual personality, and acceptance to feeding and handling varied. Tractability did not seem to be related to sex or age at time of capture, and some animals were untamable and untrainable. Pronghorns are highly excitable, and a great deal of patience was required to work with them. All activity around the animals was conducted in a slow and quiet manner, and any change in an established routine usually resulted in a setback of the training program. They responded best on a voluntary basis, and rarely accepted restraint or physical force.

Training

Of 32 (91 percent) fawns that survived to weaning, 26 (74 percent) were usable in ecological studies. Extremely flighty animals were not used for field studies of food habits, but were used for field behavior studies. Only the calmest of the group were used for metabolic studies in the laboratory. Six animals remained too wild for any use.

Early in the study (1969–70) when the fawns were approximately 3 months old, an attempt was made to find a "reward food"

JWM 40(3): 467

Table 2. Cause of death for 29 hand-reared pronghorns.

Cause of death	No. animals	Age at death (yr)
Disease	10	
Digestive disorder (*Clostridium perfringens*)	1	0.3
Digestive disorder (*Escherichia coli*)	1	0.3
Leptospirosis sp.	1	1.0
Pneumonia and/or pulmonary edema	2	0.5, 3.9
Joint infection (*Staphylococcus* sp.)	1	0.2
Salmonella sp.	1	1.6
Lumpy jaw (*Actinomyces bovis*)	3	3.1, 4.0(2)[a]
Poaching or predation	5	
Gun shot	2	3.0, 3.1
Coyotes	3	0.5, 0.7, 2.4
Accidents	5	
Injured and/or fractured neck	4	0.5, 1.4(3)
Fractured femur	1	1.0
Other	9	
Postpartum complications	1	2.0
Plant toxicity (*Senecio tridenticulatus*)	1	2.9
Drug overdose (M-99)	1	unknown
Unknown	6	3.8, 4.7, unknown(4)
Total	29	

[a] Number of animals in parentheses.

that would be associated with the trainer to take the place of milk when fawns were weaned. Various sweets, vegetables, fruits, and tobacco were offered to the fawns with little success. The normal concentrate diet was most effective as a bait to entice them onto a trailer or into the corrals. Concentrate was not effective as a "reward food" when animals received it ad libitum.

Sickness and Losses

Dietary upset and bacterial infections resulting in diarrhea were the most common sicknesses encountered. Death of one fawn (Table 2) was attributed to *Clostridium perfringens* organisms (Nagy et al. 1969). Preventative measures were discussed earlier. *Escherichia coli* also was isolated from pronghorn feces in 1968. No fawns succumbed to this organism in that year, although it caused high mortality in mule deer fawns raised at the same facility

(Kramer et al. 1971). In 1970 one pronghorn fawn died with *E. coli*.

Early detection of diarrhea depends upon recognition of a change in the character of the feces. Experience during the first 2 years revealed that "normal feces" were soft and pasty, changing from white to yellow to yellowish orange in the first few weeks of life. Green pellets began to form at about 3 weeks of age, coinciding with intake of hay and grain. Mucous was produced periodically up to 6 weeks with no indication of morbidity.

When loose or watery feces were encountered, the presumably infected animal was isolated from the group to prevent possible spread of infection to pen mates. Initially, fawns with diarrhea were treated with 200 mg/kg of sulfamethagine orally at each feeding. We changed to 100 mg/kg of sulfaquinoxaline orally after it was learned that sulfamethagine was contraindicated in young animals because the drug crystallized in the urine and kidneys. Both drugs appeared effective for control of diarrhea in the few instances they were used. One animal, however, died of suspected digestive disorder even though it was treated with sulfamethagine periodically for 3 weeks.

Dietary upset, diarrhea, and bone and joint problems contributed most to reduced vigor of young animals. Mortality resulted from assorted causes (Table 2). Two of three animals lost to coyote (*Canis latrans*) predation were ailing from sickness or injury. An additional animal died of suspected plant toxicity caused by *Senecio tridenticulatus*. Its rumen was packed with this plant. Kingsbury (1964:425) stated that several species in the genus *Senecio* have proven poisonous to livestock and that toxic alkaloids have been isolated from other species. Necropsy indicated diffuse hepatic degeneration.

Pronghorns were maintained successfully in captivity and used in ecological studies up to 4.7 years. Eleven of 25 fawns (44 percent) with known death dates survived to 2 years of age and 9 (36 percent) lived at least 3 years. No animal to date has lived for 5 years. Our current herd has reproduced successfully and is being maintained on natural range.

LITERATURE CITED

ELLIS, J. E., AND M. TRAVIS. 1975. Comparative aspects of foraging behaviour of pronghorn antelope and cattle. J. Appl. Ecol. 12(2):411–420.

HEALY, W. M. 1967. Forage preferences of captive deer while free ranging in the Allegheny National Forest. M.S. Thesis. Pennsylvania State Univ., University Park. 93pp.

HOOVER, J. P. 1971. Food habits of pronghorn antelope on Pawnee National Grasslands, 1970. M.S. Thesis. Colorado State Univ., Ft. Collins. 285pp.

KINGSBURY, J. M. 1964. Poisonous plants of the United States and Canada. Prentice-Hall, Inc., Englewood Cliffs, N.J. 626pp.

KRAMER, T. T., J. G. NAGY, AND T. A. BARBER. 1971. Diarrhea in captive mule deer fawns attributed to *Escherichia coli*. J. Wildl. Manage. 35(2):205–209.

NAGY, J. G., T. A. BARBER, AND A. E. McCHESNEY. 1969. *Clostridium perfringens* enterotoxemia in hand-reared antelope. J. Wildl. Manage. 33(4):1032–1033.

NEFF, D. J. 1974. Forage preferences of tame trained mule deer on the Beaver Creek Watersheds. Arizona Game and Fish Dept. Spec. Rep. 4. 61pp.

REICHERT, D. W. 1972. Rearing and training deer for food habits studies. U.S. For. Serv., Rocky Mtn. For. Range Exp. Stn. Res. Note RM-208. 7pp.

SCHWARTZ, C. C., AND J. G. NAGY. 1973. Pronghorn food habits studies, 1970–1972. US/IBP Grassland Biome Tech. Rep. 231. Colorado State Univ., Ft. Collins. 32pp.

WESLEY, D. E., K. L. KNOX, AND J. G. NAGY. 1969. Water kinetics in pronghorn antelope. Proc. Western Sec. Am. Soc. Anim. Sci. 20:79–82.

———, ———, AND ———. 1970. Energy flux and water kinetics in young pronghorn antelope. J. Wildl. Manage. 34(4):908–912.

———, ———, AND ———. 1973. Energy metabolism of pronghorn antelopes. J. Wildl. Manage. 37(4):563–573.

YOUNGSON, R. W. 1970. Rearing red deer calves in captivity. J. Wildl. Manage. 34(2):467–470.

Accepted 12 February 1976.

PRONGHORN DIETS RELATIVE TO FORAGE AVAILABILITY IN NORTHEASTERN COLORADO[1]

CHARLES C. SCHWARTZ, Department of Fishery and Wildlife Biology, Colorado State University, Fort Collins 80523
JULIUS G. NAGY, Department of Fishery and Wildlife Biology, Colorado State University, Fort Collins 80523

Abstract: Studies were conducted to determine the botanical composition of the diet of tame pronghorns (*Antilocapra americana*) on a grama-buffalo grass (*Bouteloua-Buchloe*) prairie under light and heavy cattle grazing regimes. Results indicated that pronghorns consume a wide variety of plant species when available. The diet was composed of 44, 54, and 2 (light use treatment) and 52, 43, and 5 (heavy use treatment) percent grass, forbs, and shrubs, respectively. Comparisons of foods eaten by tame and wild pronghorns indicated some differences in forage preferences, but only fringed sagewort (*Artemisia frigida*) occurred at a significantly (*P* < 0.05) different frequency. Comparisons of forage preferences of three wild herds of pronghorns also indicated differences in plant species. A comparison of foods eaten by four ungulates grazing together showed that pronghorn diets were less similar to bison (*Bison bison*) and cattle diets than to domestic sheep diets.

J. WILDL. MANAGE. 40(3):469–478

Foods eaten by the pronghorn throughout its current range have been studied and reviewed by many investigators (Beale and Smith 1970, O'Gara and Greer 1970, Mitchell and Smoliak 1971, Taylor 1972, Sundstrom et al. 1973). In other studies workers have examined the extent of competition between domestic livestock and pronghorns (Buechner 1947, Severson and May 1967, Campbell 1970). Data collected by Hoover et al. (1959), Hoover (1966), and Hoover (1971) related information on foods of pronghorns on the shortgrass prairie and competition between pronghorns and domestic livestock.

Yoakum (1972) reviewed historical and current (as of 1964) distribution of pronghorns in North America. His findings showed that the pronghorn was historically an animal of the prairie grasslands and was closely associated with the bison. Yoakum (1972:173) further stated that "with the advance of white man's agriculture civilization, the herds of high density buffalo [sic] and antelope were extirpated from the majority of the grassland plains. It, therefore, appears that the majority of the vast prairie lands which produced millions of antelope in pristine times, are now so intensively farmed that antelope no longer inhabit them, and antelope today exist only in peripheral ranges which historically produced low density populations."

Bison and pronghorns do not coexist on vast areas of the shortgrass prairie today, so opportunities to study their food habits in close association are limited. Part of the Grassland Biome (IBP) analysis of the shortgrass prairie ecosystem involved determining the forage habits of four grassland herbivores (cattle, sheep, bison, and pronghorns) under two grazing regimes. The four ungulates shared common pastures, so differences in their food habits were attributed to the animals rather than to the environment. The purpose of our study was to determine in detail the botanical composition of the diets of tame pronghorns relative to forage availability through the year and to compare these feeding habits with those of wild pronghorns. We also make comparisons to diets of cattle, sheep, and bison reported by other investigators (Peden et al. 1974, Peden 1972) during this study.

[1] This paper reports on work supported in part by National Science Foundation Grants GB-13096, GB-31862X, and BMS73-02027 A02 to the Grassland Biome, U.S. International Biological Program, for "Analysis of Structure, Function, and Utilization of Grassland Ecosystems."

We acknowledge K. Miller and S. Kerr for their assistance with pronghorn care and training and R. Souther for maintenance of animals at the Pawnee Site. J. Hoover aided with study design. M. Travis assisted throughout the study with data collection. We also thank the many members of the IBP Grassland Laboratory who aided in various phases of data collection and analysis: C. Dickinson for plant biomass estimates, S. Woodmansee for fecal analyses, D. Swift for computer programming, M. Campion for statistical analysis, and J. Ellis and L. Menges for manuscript review.

METHODS

Study Area and Treatments

The study area was the Pawnee Site in NE Colorado. The Site, on the USDA Agricultural Research Service Central Plains Experimental Range, is 40 km S of Cheyenne, Wyoming, and 19 km NE of Nunn, Colorado. Vegetation was dominated by blue grama (*Bouteloua gracilis*) and buffalo grass (*Buchloe dactyloides*) and was described by Klipple and Costello (1960) and Jameson (1969).

This study was carried out in 2 pastures, 1 heavily grazed by cattle (3 animal units/ 12.1 ha/month) and the other lightly grazed (1 animal unit/12.1 ha/month). Cattle grazed the pastures between the months of May and October. Grazing treatments were established in May 1970. The heavily grazed pasture was 11.3 ha in area and the lightly grazed pasture was 21.9 ha. Each pasture was fenced with "sheep tight" woven wire and opened to a corral and holding pens (Jameson 1969).

Observations of Grazing

Tame, trained pronghorns (Schwartz et al. 1976) were used to determine the relative seasonal use of plant species. Six sampling periods were chosen to measure botanical composition of pronghorn diets. Periods were chosen to include all seasons; sampling was intensified during the plant growing season to enable changes in plant preference to be related to changes in plant phenology. Dates sampled were 20–28 March, 28 April–5 May, 25 June–5 July, 14–21 August, and 23–28 October 1971, and 15, 16, 22, and 23 January 1972.

During the sample periods, four pronghorns (one adult female, two juvenile females, and one juvenile male) were studied by two observers morning and afternoon on alternate days in each treatment. Morning *trials* began around 0800 and afternoon trials between 1430 and 1600. Observations were started near 1430 during winter and spring and 1600 during the summer. A grazing trial lasted 90 minutes during which each observer followed a separate animal for 45 minutes. During the afternoon trial, the observation sequence was reversed so that each observer checked each animal each day. Animals were held in a corral at night and released into the appropriate pasture each day. After the afternoon sampling period, animals were led back to the corral. To test if this had an effect on forage preferences, we divided six pronghorns into two treatments. Three animals in group 1 had free access to natural forage at all times; three animals in group 2 had access to forage between 0800 and 1700 MST but were enclosed in a corral at night. Results indicated no significant ($P > 0.05$) differences in species preference between groups 1 and 2 (Schwartz and Nagy 1973:22–24).

During each trial the observer, equipped with a portable tape recorder, recorded the date, treatment, animal, and the following data as the trial progressed: number of bites (Wallmo et al. 1972) by plant species, parts of plants, and phenological stage of the plant. Unusual behavioral activities and nonplant items consumed were noted. The observation distance was less than 3 m. Comparable samples were collected by hand of plant species comprising at least 2.5 percent of total bites counted for each treatment and season from plants closely resembling those eaten. These samples were used to convert bites counted to dry weight.

Estimates of Vegetation Biomass

To estimate biomass of plant species present on both grazing treatments, we used a method based on the technique of weight estimates (Uresk 1971). Biomass estimates were taken from 100 fixed 0.5-m^2 quadrats in each treatment and are presented here for plant species that comprised at least 3 percent of the total bites counted in at least 1 treatment for at least 1 season. All other species were lumped and included in the subtotals. Plains prickly pear (*Opuntia polyacantha*) was not included in these data. Biomass was estimated within 1 week of all grazing periods sampled except during March when no estimates were made.

Analyses of Fecal Samples

Diets of tame and wild pronghorns were compared according to relative frequency of plant remains in feces. Identification of each plant by microscopic technique (Baumgartner and Martin 1939, Dusi 1949) was based on characteristics of epidermal tissues (Davis 1959, Croker 1959). For each *fecal sample*, 20 slides with 20 fields per slide were analyzed. Feces were collected from tame pronghorns during dietary studies and composited for each animal each sample period (fecal sample). Feces were collected from wild pronghorns less than 1.6 km from the study area no later than 1 week after dietary studies, except for the period 25 June to 5 July. This herd could not be located during the June–July

sample period, so feces were collected from a wild herd 30 km away. Data were analyzed with a three-way factorial analysis of variance (animal type × plant species × season) with one observation per cell. Differences were determined in the animal type × plant species interaction with a studentized range test (Q) (Snedecor and Cochran 1967:272–273).

Diet similarity among three wild herds was compared after the August sampling period. Herd A was located 16 km east and 2.8 km south of the study area, herd B 1.6 km north of the study area, and herd C 6.5 km east of the study area. Feces were composited for each herd to provide a fecal sample for laboratory analysis. Only one sample was analyzed per herd, so no measure of animal variation was available.

Similarity Indices

Horn's R_o index of similarity (Horn 1966) was used to compare the overall similarity of diet composition vectors for tame pronghorns to cattle, sheep, and bison diets measured in the same pastures by Peden et al. (1974). An R_o value of 1 implies identical composition vectors, a value of 0 a complete lack of similarity. Horn (1966:419) indicated that these indices (R_o) are "intended to serve as empirical measures and should not be interpreted as estimates of statistical parameters of the population from which the samples are drawn, or as 'test' for heterogeneity." Plant group classifications into warm or cool season for pronghorn diets were by Sims and Singh (1972). Scarlet globemallow (*Sphaeralcea coccinea*) was classified as a warm season forb in our paper to conform to data of Peden et al. (1974) for comparisons. It has been reclassified, however, as a cool season plant (Williams and Markley 1973).

Table 1. Consumption (percentage of total bites eaten) and abundance (kg/ha) of the major forage species eaten by 4 tame pronghorns on a lightly grazed pasture at the Pawnee Site, March 1971–January 1972.

Taxa[a]	Sampling period and no. days sampled						Annual summary
	Mar(3)	Apr–May(4)	Jun–Jul(4)	Aug(4)	Oct(2)	Jan(2)	
Agropyron smithii	6	6(10)[b]	tr(10)	2(6)	2(4)	1(3)	3
Bouteloua gracilis	10	tr(302)	10(596)	11(366)	14(222)	38(217)	13
Bromus tectorum	51	16(tr)[c]	tr(4)	tr(2)	52(2)	18(2)	24
Carex spp.	tr[c]	4(13)	tr(18)	tr(24)	tr(9)	3(1)	1
Chrysopsis villosa	3	2(tr)	tr(tr)	tr(tr)	tr(tr)	1(tr)	1
Cymopterus acaulis	1	11(1)	2(tr)				3
Eriogonum effusum	1	tr(7)	tr(28)	2(12)	1(tr)	3(17)	1
Leucocrinum montanum		10(tr)	tr(tr)				2
Plantago patagonica	3	tr(1)	12(3)	tr(1)	(tr)	tr(tr)	2
Salsola kali	3	tr(tr)	3(tr)	7(tr)	tr(1)	tr(1)	2
Sphaeralcea coccinea	6	17(6)	19(35)	55(15)	29(5)	19(2)	25
Thelesperma filifolium	1	10(tr)	30(4)	5(3)	tr(1)	1(1)	7
Vulpia octoflora	1	4(1)	(20)	(2)	tr(1)	tr(2)	1
Total bites	12,255	26,707	18,426	19,813	15,037	9,222	64,903[d]

[a] Includes only taxa with values of at least 3% of the total bites eaten on at least 1 sampling date.
[b] 6% of 26,707 bites for Apr–May (10 kg/ha available).
[c] tr indicates less than 0.5% usage; (tr) indicates less than 1 kg biomass.
[d] Sampling sizes were unequal; percent annual usage is based on a 2-day weighted mean for each period.

RESULTS AND DISCUSSION

Observations of Grazing and Estimates of Biomass

During this study we counted 203,725 bites of forage eaten by 4 pronghorns of at least 87 plant species, including 18 grasses and sedges, 64 forbs, 4 shrubs, and 1 lichen. At least 22 grasses and sedges, 81 forbs, 4 shrubs, and 1 lichen occurred on the diet pastures. Of the 87 species eaten, only 26 (6 grasses and sedges, 17 forbs, 3 shrubs) contributed at least 3 percent of the total bites in either treatment in any season (Tables 1, 2).

The standing crop of oven-dry herbage (excluding *Opuntia* spp.) varied from a low of 520 kg/ha in January to a high of 1,130 kg/ha in June–July for the lightly grazed pasture (Tables 1, 2). Likewise, forage varied from a low of 190 kg/ha in January to a high of 1,340 kg/ha in June–July for the heavily grazed pasture. Grasses and sedges made up the major percentage of the biomass (65–78) for both treatments through-out the year, except for October and January in the heavily grazed pasture when shrubs were dominant (Table 3). Forbs were always the least abundant of the 3 forage classes and never made up more than 13 percent of the total plant biomass at any time. Although estimates of biomass for individual plant species varied between the two treatments, almost all plant species occurred in both treatments.

The percent composition of the diet changed by sampling period for three major classes (grasses, forbs, shrubs) in the diet (Table 3). Forbs made up 51 to 87 percent of the bites during the growing season (April, June, August) when they were abundant, whereas grasses and sedges made up 64 to 79 percent of the bites during the dormant season (March, October, January). Shrubs were eaten in small quantities but never made up more than 15 percent of the bites in any sampling period.

Differences in diet due to forage availability (treatment) were also apparent. Grasses and sedges were dominant in both

Table 2. Consumption (percentage of total bites eaten) and abundance (kg/ha) of the major forage species eaten by 4 tame pronghorns on a heavily grazed pasture at the Pawnee Site, March 1971–January 1972.

Taxa[a]	Sampling period and no. days sampled						Annual summary
	Mar(3)	Apr–May(4)	Jun–Jul(4)	Aug(4)	Oct(2)	Jan(2)	
Agropyron smithii	29	18(12)[b]	1(16)	2(9)	14(6)	5(6)	12
Artemisia frigida	10	tr(3)	tr(85)	tr(62)	3(38)	4(26)	2
Astragalus pectinatus	4	tr(tr)[c]	tr(1)	tr(2)			tr
Bahia oppositifolia	3	tr(tr)	tr(tr)	1(tr)	1(1)	1(tr)	1
Bouteloua gracilis	13	tr(188)	17(647)	14(268)	31(tr)	57(tr)	21
Carex spp.	22	28(19)	tr(42)	3(13)	34(8)	7(7)	18
Chrysothamnus nauseosus	2	tr(39)	(tr)	tr(13)	1(26)	5(21)	1
Descurainia pinnata		3(tr)	tr(tr)				1
Eriogonum effusum	3	1(tr)	5(25)	8(10)	10(5)	14(3)	7
Gutierrezia sarothrae	3	tr(12)	tr(146)	tr(58)	2(78)	1(76)	1
Iva axillaris		tr(tr)	2(2)	3(1)	(tr)		1
Lepidium densiflorum	tr	8 (tr)	5(11)	tr(1)	(1)	tr(1)	3
Leucocrinum montanum		4(1)	tr(tr)				1
Lomatium orientale	tr	3(tr)	(tr)				1
Sophora sericea	tr		1(6)	13(tr)	tr(tr)	(1)	2
Sphaeralcea coccinea	1	17(tr)	39(23)	44(4)	1(2)	tr(1)	16
Total bites	10,176	30,427	17,624	19,540	15,518	8,980	65,078[d]

[a] Includes only taxa with values of at least 3% of the total bites eaten on at least 1 sampling date.
[b] 18% of 30,427 bites for Apr–May (12 kg/ha available).
[c] tr indicates less than 0.5% usage; (tr) indicates less than 1 kg biomass.
[d] Sampling sizes were unequal; percent annual usage is based on a 2-day weighted mean for each period.

Table 3. Use of 3 major forage classes expressed as a percentage of total bites eaten by 4 tame pronghorns and herbage availability on a lightly and heavily grazed pasture at the Pawnee Site, March 1971 to January 1972.

Sampling date and grazing treatment	Grass and grass-like plants			Forbs			Shrubs		
	% total bites	Available herbage (kg/ha)	% total herbage	% total bites	Available herbage (kg/ha)	% total herbage	% total bites	Available herbage (kg/ha)	% total herbage
Mar									
Light	70			27			3		
Heavy	67			18			15		
Apr–May									
Light	32	385	65	67	28	5	tr[a]	180	30
Heavy	48	255	78	51	19	6	1	52	16
Jun–Jul									
Light	13	841	75	87	118	10	tr	169	15
Heavy	19	1,016	76	80	96	7	1	231	17
Aug									
Light	14	560	75	86	50	7	tr	141	19
Heavy	19	373	69	79	31	6	tr	133	25
Oct									
Light	68	411	72	31	77	13	tr	86	15
Heavy	79	92	38	14	12	5	7	141	58
Jan									
Light	64	360	69	32	27	5	4	132	26
Heavy	72	69	32	17	7	4	11	122	64
Annual summary									
Light	44			54			2		
Heavy	52			43			5		

[a] tr indicates less than 0.5% usage.

treatments during the dormant season, but species composition varied. Cheatgrass (*Bromus tectorum*) appeared to be a preferred species during early stages of growth when available. Cheatgrass was rare in the heavy use treatment, so the consumption of blue grama, western wheatgrass (*Agropyron smithii*), and two species of carex (*Carex eleocharis, C. heliophila*) increased. The number of forbs eaten during the dormant season varied by treatment and was higher for the lightly grazed pasture. This was particularly true for scarlet globemallow, a preferred species that was not abundant in the heavily grazed pasture. Although forbs were dominant dietary items in both treatments during the growing season, species composition varied. Scarlet globemallow was consumed in large quantities in both pastures. Greenthread (*Thelesperma filifolium*) was also an important forb but did not occur in large quantities in the heavily grazed pasture. Silky sophora (*Sophora sericea*) was eaten in the heavily grazed pasture, but little was consumed in the lightly grazed pasture, although it occurred in both treatments. The percentage of the total diet comprised of shrubs was greatest in the heavily grazed pasture during the dormant season. This probably was related to the lack of available forbs in that treatment during that time. Shrub consumption declined when forbs became available during the growing season.

Although Hoover et al. (1959:57–58) found variation (0–97 percent) in the percentage composition of browse (shrubs) in stomach samples from pronghorns in Colorado, the average amount of shrubs was much higher during fall (72 percent) and winter (54 percent) than was consumed by our pronghorns during these seasons. Likewise, they found a much lower percentage composition of grasses during fall (1 percent) and winter (5 percent). Data collected by Hoover (1971:140), who used tame pronghorns on the Pawnee Site, also showed a high occurrence of shrubs (47 percent) and grasses (31 percent) during winter.

This high occurrence of shrubs in the diets of pronghorns found by other investigators and its low occurrence in our study may be due to differences in forage availability. The major portion of plant biomass available to our pronghorns was grasses and sedges. The exception occurred in October and January in the heavily grazed treatment; this also corresponded to the time of highest shrub usage by our animals.

Hoover et al. (1959:54) classified wild buckwheat species (*Eriogonum* sp.) as browse, but we classified them as forbs. If we included false buckwheat (*Eriogonum effusum*) in our shrub category, the amount of shrubs in the diet increased to as high as 25 percent. Additional data presented by Hoover et al. (1959:63) showed shrubs to make up only 0 to 14 percent of the diet from November to April for pronghorns consuming winter wheat. Cheatgrass, which made up a large portion of the diet for our pronghorns during March and October, had growth characteristics similar to wheat during the period it was eaten. Both plants were green and relatively high in moisture. This, however, did not explain the high occurrence of grass in our pronghorn diets on the heavily grazed treatment.

Grazing treatments referred to in this study were maintained since May 1970. In such a short period major successional changes were unlikely. Consequently, the differences in treatments reflected mainly the influence in the removal of the current year's growth by the herbivores rather than a more permanent change in the phytosociological condition (Peden 1972:92). This may explain some of the discrepancies between our results and those of other investi-

Table 4. Percent relative densities of plant species found in fecal samples of tame and wild pronghorn herds by microtechnique on the shortgrass prairie.

Taxa	Mar		May		Jun		Aug		Oct	
	Tame	Wild	Tame	Wild	Tame	Wild	Tame	Wild	Tame	Wild
Grasses and sedges										
Agropyron sm:thii	16.5	0.3	5.6		0.5		6.3		25.4	0.7
Bouteloua gracilis	26.0	1.3	6.3	22.1	9.9	0.9	5.3	0.6	21.5	1.9
Bromus tectorum	11.5		13.5	2.0	9.1	3.8			0.2	
Carex heliophila	3.4		13.4	8.4	0.7	1.4	0.2	0.3	5.5	1.0
Forbs										
Astragalus spp.	0.8				0.2	1.1	1.6	8.2		
Erigeron bellidiastrum							1.8	8.7		
E. divergens			0.1		3.9	19.5				
Plantago patagonica	0.2		0.1		4.9	0.1	0.2			
Sphaeralcea coccinea	14.6	0.2	52.9	2.0	57.8	31.8	74.3	36.6	37.5	58.1
Shrub										
Artemisia frigida	4.4	95.1		64.2	7.1	35.5	7.8	38.0	7.5	32.1

gators, because continued overgrazing by cattle tends to reduce the available biomass of grasses in relation to shrubs.

Analyses of Fecal Samples

Analyses of feces with the microtechnique indicated considerable variation between diets of tame and wild pronghorns throughout the sampling period (Table 4). Analysis of variance indicated a significant ($P < 0.05$) difference in the percent relative density of fringed sagewort in fecal samples from tame and wild pronghorns. Those from tame pronghorns contained a higher percent relative density of scarlet globemallow for all seasons except October.

Comparisons among the three wild herds during August revealed marked variations in plant remains in fecal samples (Table 5). The percentage relative density of fringed sagewort ranged from 0 in 2 herds to 38 in 1 herd. Scarlet globemallow was the only species consumed in large quantities by all three herds. It also was consumed in large quantities by the tame pronghorns.

Available information indicates that the forage choices of tame pronghorns are similar to those of wild pronghorns (Wallmo and Neff 1970, Buechner 1950). The degree of similarity has not been established.

These data suggested that there was some variation in foods eaten by tame and wild pronghorns and among different herds of wild pronghorns. Forage preferences and plant consumption appeared to be related more closely to plant species availability and their relationship to other plants in the environment rather than to the animals themselves. Although the exact degree of similarity between tame and wild prong-

Table 5. Percent relative densities of plant species in fecal samples of 3 wild pronghorn herds on the shortgrass prairie, August 1971, as determined by microtechnique.

Taxa	Herd A	Herd B	Herd C
Grasses and sedges			
Agropyron smithii	1		2
Bouteloua grac:lis	1	1	1
Carex heliophila	tr[a]	tr	2
Forbs			
Astragalus sp.		8	5
Erigeron bellidiastrum		9	45
Kochia scoparia	3	2	tr
Alfalfa	61		
Sphaeralcea coccinea	23	37	42
Shrub			
Artemisia frigida		38	

[a] Less than 0.5%.

Table 6. Percent dry matter of plant groups in diets of pronghorns, bison, cattle, and sheep on a lightly and a heavily grazed pasture on the shortgrass prairie.[a]

Plant group	Lightly grazed pasture					Heavily grazed pasture				
	Mar	May	Jun	Aug	Oct	Mar	May	Jun	Aug	Oct
Pronghorns										
Warm season grass	17		9	8	21	30		10	11	35
Cool season grass	65	37			50	50	43		2	44
Warm season forbs	17	41	75	92	29	4	42	88	81	16
Cool season forbs	1	22	16			5	15	2	6	
Shrubs						11				5
Bison										
Warm season grass	70	44	78	88	82	56	18	80	93	78
Cool season grass	28	54	15	7	17	21	80	12	7	9
Warm season forbs		1	7	5	1		1	8	1	1
Cool season forbs		1	1							1
Shrubs						21				12
Cattle										
Warm season grass	32	12	24	65	58	35	3	22	41	21
Cool season grass	44	67	46	8	28	9	94	18	12	9
Warm season forbs	4	2	22	27	9	7	1	31	4	22
Cool season forbs		1	7			2	1	16	1	
Shrubs	21	15	1		5	46	1	13	42	47
Sheep										
Warm season grass	33	13	22	28	38	3	8	23	64	26
Cool season grass	7	50	19	4	31	1	81	4	6	34
Warm season forbs	4	8	38	68	28	1	4	69	24	18
Cool season forbs		1	14					3	1	
Shrubs	57	27	3		2	95	6	1	5	22

[a] Data for bison, cattle, and sheep are from Peden et al. (1974:492). Data for pronghorns were derived by converting information in Tables 1 and 2 to dry weight estimates determined from hand collected samples.

horns was not established in this study, forage commonly eaten by tame pronghorns was assumed to be important forage for wild pronghorns on the range studied.

Similarity Indices

We used Horn's R_o index of similarity to compare the percent dry weight of tame pronghorn diets (Table 6) determined by the handplucked estimates to diets collected through esophageal fistulas of bison, cattle, and sheep (Peden et al. 1974). The R_o index suggested (Fig. 1) that our pronghorn diets were more similar to diets of sheep than to those of cattle and bison for both treatments, except for the March sampling period when sheep diets were composed predominately of shrubs. Pronghorn diets were also more similar to diets of cattle than to those of bison. With the exception of March, sheep diets resembled diets of cattle and bison more closely than did diets of tame pronghorns.

The greatest differences between the diets of our pronghorns and those of bison and cattle occurred during the plant growing season when the pronghorns grazed more discriminantly and the number of species making up the diet was greatest. These findings were in agreement with data presented by Rice et al. (1971) for cattle and pronghorn diets on the Pawnee Site. Our data suggested that pronghorns compete less intensively for food with bison and cattle than with sheep. Thus, pronghorns with either bison or cattle under common grazing may be separated ecologically according to the theories of Bell (1971), which suggest that small and large ruminants will not compete for food resources.

JWM 40(3): 477

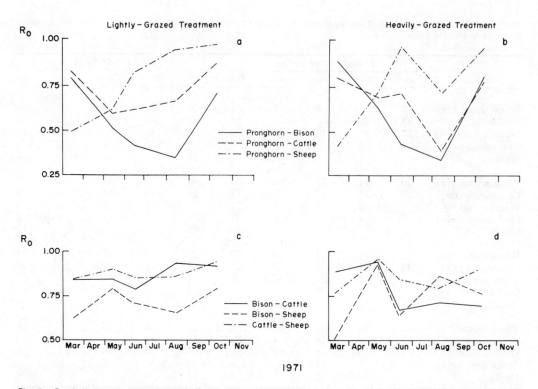

Fig. 1. R_o similarity estimates relating (*a,b*) pronghorn diets to bison, cattle, and sheep diets and (*c,d*) bison, cattle, and sheep diets to each other for both lightly grazed and heavily grazed treatments, respectively. R_o values 1 and 0 imply complete similarity and complete dissimilarity, respectively. Comparisons between cattle, bison, and sheep are from Peden (1972:59).

On this basis, we were not similiar to find that pronghorns were more similiar to sheep than either cattle or bison.

CONCLUSIONS

We feel that the tame pronghorns provided reliable data on the forage preferences of wild pronghorns. The bite count method was well suited and accurate for pronghorns, because they selected each bite carefully and took only one plant species with each bite. Many factors influenced forage selection and composition of plant species in the diet of the animals in this study at a given time and location. These included individual animal variation in plant preference, plant abundance and availability, and the association of a plant species with others.

Of significance was the fact that tame pronghorns did not compete with bison, the species with which they have coexisted historically on the shortgrass prairie. Likewise, our pronghorns did not compete with cattle, the species with which they coexist today. It is important to the range or wildlife manager to note that grasses were important in the diet of our pronghorns in this area where shrubs were not abundant. Diets of pronghorns vary considerably throughout their range, and management considerations should include plant abundance and availability.

LITERATURE CITED

BAUMGARTNER, L. L., AND A. C. MARTIN. 1939. Plant histology as an aid in squirrel food-habit studies. J. Wildl. Manage. 3(3):266–268.

BEALE, D. M., AND A. D. SMITH. 1970. Forage

use, water consumption, and productivity of pronghorn antelope in western Utah. J. Wildl. Manage. 34(3):570–582.

BELL, R. H. V. 1971. A grazing ecosystem in the Serengeti. Sci. Am. 225(1):86–93.

BUECHNER, H. K. 1947. Range use of pronghorned antelope in western Texas. Trans. N. Am. Wildl. Conf. 12:185–192.

———. 1950. Life history, ecology, and range use of the pronghorn antelope in Trans-Pecos Texas. Am. Midl. Nat. 43(2):257–354.

CAMPBELL, R. B. 1970. Pronghorn, sheep and cattle range relationships in Carter County, Montana. M.S. Thesis. Montana State Univ., Bozeman. 87pp.

CROKER, B. H. 1959. A method of estimating the botanical composition of the diet of sheep. N.Z. J. Agric. Res. 2(1):72–85.

DAVIS, I. 1959. The use of epidermal characteristics for the identification of grasses in the leafy stage. J. Br. Grassland Soc. 14(1):7–16.

DUSI, J. L. 1949. Methods for the determination of food habits by plant microtechniques and histology and their application to cottontail rabbit food habits. J. Wildl. Manage. 13(3):295–298.

HOOVER, J. P. 1971. Food habits of pronghorn antelope on Pawnee National Grasslands, 1970. M.S. Thesis. Colorado State Univ., Ft. Collins. 285pp.

HOOVER, R. L. 1966. Antelope food habits and range relationships in Colorado. Proc. Antelope States Workshop 2:75–85.

———, C. E. TILL, AND S. OGILVIE. 1959. The antelope of Colorado. Colorado Dept. Fish Game Tech. Bull. 4. 110pp.

HORN, H. S. 1966. Measurement of overlap in comparative ecological studies. Am. Nat. 100 (914):419–424.

JAMESON, D. A. 1969. General description of the Pawnee Site. US/IBP Grassland Biome Tech. Rep. 1. Colorado State Univ., Ft. Collins. 32pp.

KLIPPLE, G. E., AND D. F. COSTELLO. 1960. Vegetation and cattle responses to different intensities of grazing on shortgrass ranges of the central Great Plains. U.S. Dept. Agric. Tech. Bull. 1216. 82pp.

MITCHELL, G. J., AND S. SMOLIAK. 1971. Pronghorn antelope range characteristics and food habits in Alberta. J. Wildl. Manage. 35(2):238–250.

O'GARA, B. W., AND K. R. GREER. 1970. Food habits in relation to physical condition in two populations of pronghorn. Proc. Antelope States Workshop 4:131–139.

PEDEN, D. G. 1972. The trophic relations of *Bison bison* to the shortgrass plains. Ph.D. Thesis. Colorado State Univ., Ft. Collins. 134pp.

———, G. M. VAN DYNE, R. W. RICE, AND R. M.

HANSEN. 1974. The trophic ecology of *Bison bison* L. on shortgrass plains. J. Appl. Ecol. 11(2):489–497.

RICE, R. W., J. G. NAGY, AND D. G. PEDEN. 1971. Functional interaction of large herbivores on grasslands. Pages 241–266 *in* N. R. French, ed. Preliminary analysis of structure and function in grasslands. Colorado State Univ. Range Sci. Dept. Sci. Ser. 10.

SCHWARTZ, C. C., AND J. G. NAGY. 1973. Pronghorn food habits studies, 1970–1972. US/IBP Grassland Biome Tech. Rep. 231. Colorado State Univ., Ft. Collins. 32pp.

———, ———, AND S. M. KERR. 1976. Rearing and training pronghorns for ecological studies. J. Wildl. Manage. 40(3):464–468.

SEVERSON, K. E., AND M. MAY. 1967. Food preferences of antelope and domestic sheep in Wyoming's Red Desert. J. Range Manage. 20(1):21–25.

SIMS, P., AND J. SINGH. 1972. Herbage dynamics and net primary production in certain ungrazed and grazed grasslands in North America. Pages 59–124 *in* N. R. French, ed. Preliminary analysis of structure and function in grasslands. Colorado State Univ. Range Sci. Dept. Sci. Ser. 10.

SNEDECOR, G. W., AND W. G. COCHRAN. 1967. Statistical methods. 6th ed. Iowa State University Press, Ames. 593pp.

SUNDSTROM, C., W. G. HEPWORTH, AND K. L. DIEM. 1973. Abundance, distribution and food habits of the pronghorn. Wyoming Fish Game Comm. Bull. 12. 61pp.

TAYLOR, E. 1972. Food habits and feeding behavior of pronghorn antelope in the Red Desert of Wyoming. Proc. Antelope States Workshop 5:211–219.

URESK, D. W. 1971. Dynamics of blue grama within a shortgrass ecosystem. Ph.D. Thesis. Colorado State Univ., Ft. Collins. 52pp.

WALLMO, O. C., AND D. J. NEFF. 1970. Direct observations of tamed deer to measure their consumption of natural forage. Pages 105–110 *in* Range and wildlife habitat evaluation—a research symposium. U.S. Dept. Agric., For. Serv. Misc. Publ. 1147.

———, W. L. REGELIN, AND D. W. REICHERT. 1972. Forage use by mule deer relative to logging in Colorado. J. Wildl. Manage. 36(4):1025–1033.

WILLIAMS, G. J., III, AND J. L. MARKLEY. 1973. The photosynthetic pathway type of North American shortgrass prairie species and some ecological implications. Photosynthetica 7(3):262–270.

YOAKUM, J. 1972. Antelope-vegetation relationships. Proc. Antelope States Workshop 5:171–177.

Accepted 11 March 1976.

PRONGHORN DIETARY QUALITY RELATIVE TO FORAGE AVAILABILITY AND OTHER RUMINANTS IN COLORADO[1,2]

CHARLES C. SCHWARTZ, Department of Fishery and Wildlife Biology, Colorado State University, Fort Collins 80523

JULIUS G. NAGY, Department of Fishery and Wildlife Biology, Colorado State University, Fort Collins 80523

RICHARD W. RICE, Department of Animal Science, University of Wyoming, Laramie 82070[3]

Abstract: Plants eaten by tame pronghorns (*Antilocapra americana*) on the shortgrass prairie under light and heavy cattle grazing regimes were analyzed for crude protein, gross energy, ash, phosphorus, cell-wall constituents (CWC), acid-detergent fiber (ADF), lignin, and dry matter digestion in vitro. Pronghorn maintained similar diet quality on lightly and heavily grazed pastures. Crude protein content of the diet varied seasonally from 7 to 21 percent, but was adequate for maintenance. Gross energy values of foods eaten did not vary greatly throughout the year. Percentage of phosphorus in the diet varied from 0.43 in April to 0.09 in January. Dietary phosphorus was inadequate during August and January in both pastures, and March and October in the heavily grazed pasture. Fiber content of the diet including CWC, ADF, and lignin varied seasonally and was lowest when plants were young and actively growing. Dry matter digestion (DMD) coefficients indicated that quality of the diet was highest in spring and lowest during winter. Comparison of dietary protein, fiber, and digestion of dry matter indicated that pronghorn selected a diet higher in quality than sheep, followed by cattle and bison (*Bison bison*).

J. WILDL. MANAGE. 41(2):161–168

There is little documentation of nutritional qualities of pronghorn forage despite several studies of botanical composition of diets (Sundstrom et al. 1973). Dirschl (1963) determined protein content of six major plant species eaten by pronghorns in Saskatchewan, while Smith and Malechek (1974) ascertained nutritional quality of summer diets in Utah. Barrett (1974) determined importance, utilization, and quality of *Artemisia cana* on pronghorn winter ranges in Alberta.

Part of the Grassland Biome (IBP) analysis of the shortgrass prairie involved determination of foraging habits and nutritional quality of diets of four grassland herbivores (cattle, sheep, bison, and pronghorn) under different grazing regimes.

[1] This paper reports on work supported in part by National Science Foundation Grants GB-13096, GB-31862X, BMS73-02027 A02, and DEB73-02027 A03 to the Grassland Biome, U.S. International Biological Program for "Analysis of Structure, Function, and Utilization of Grassland Ecosystems."

[2] From a thesis submitted to the Graduate Faculty of Colorado State University in partial fulfillment of the requirements for the degree of Ph.D.

[3] Present address: Animal Science Department, University of Arizona, Tucson 85700.

Schwartz and Nagy (1976) discussed botanical composition of pronghorn diets. The present study investigated chemical composition of the same pronghorn diets. Comparisons between the chemical composition of diets of cattle and bison (Peden 1972, Peden et al. 1974) and sheep on the same area at the same time were also presented.

We thank K. Miller, R. Souther, and S. Kerr for pronghorn care and training. M. Travis assisted with data collection and analysis. We thank the USDA Agricultural Research Service for use of data collected at CPER. We thank D. Swift and M. Campion for computer programming and statistical analysis, U. Bokhari and D. Bigelow for chemical analysis, and J. Ellis, L. Menges, O. C. Wallmo, R. Bruce Gill, G. M. Van Dyne, and G. Donart for manuscript review.

METHODS

Investigations took place on the Pawnee Site on the Central Plains Experimental Range (administered by the USDA Agricultural Research Service) in northeastern Colorado. The study area, grazing treatments, sampling dates, and methods used to determine botanical composition of the diet were discussed by Schwartz and Nagy (1976). Hand-picked samples intended to duplicate observations of tame pronghorn provided estimates of mean bite-weight, and therefore dry matter composition of the diet by plant species (Schwartz and Nagy 1976:Tables 1 and 2). Only species comprising more than 3 percent of bites in a sample period were included. Chemical composition of diets was determined by summing weighted estimates of percent dry weight of each plant species in diets times percent of each chemical constituent for that species. Chemical estimates represented between 66 and 95 percent of total diets for both treatments for all seasons.

Plant samples analyzed were hand-plucked from locations on the study area where pronghorn grazed during sampling. Only materials resembling those eaten by tame animals were collected. These were sealed in plastic bags and weighed shortly after collection. Percent dry matter was determined on samples dried at 55 C for 48 hours.

Crude protein (Kjeldahl N × 6.25), gross energy, ash, and phosphorus were determined by procedures in A.O.A.C. (1965). Cell-wall constituents (CWC), acid-detergent fiber (ADF), and acid-detergent lignin were determined by procedures outlined by Van Soest and Wine (1967), Van Soest (1963), and Goering and Van Soest (1970). (Nutrient analyses were performed by the Analytical Chemistry Facility at the Natural Resource Ecology Laboratory, Colorado State University, Fort Collins, Colorado 80523.)

Digestion of dry matter (DMD) was determined in vitro using a modification of techniques described by Tilley and Terry (1963) and Pearson (1970). Substrate was ground in a Wiley mill to pass through a 0.5-mm screen. Inoculum of rumen fluid was prepared by adding one part of strained rumen fluid to four parts of prewarmed (38.5 C) standard buffer solution (McDougall 1948:Table 11) saturated with CO_2. Inocula were obtained from two adult male pronghorns shot on native range during the hunting season. The rumen fluid was mixed together to decrease animal variation. Triplicate fermentation tubes were used for each sample.

In vitro DMD was determined for March through August for pronghorn diets. Since pronghorn rumen inocula were collected in September, DMD coefficients for pronghorn diets for October and January were estimated. The predictive equation was derived using a stepwise multiple regression where DMD (Y) was estimated using the following variables: CWC, ADF, lignin, and lignin/ADF. The best equation to predict DMD was obtained using the three variables of CWC, ADF, and lignin. The lignin/ADF ratio (Goering and Van Soest 1970) did not contribute to the overall equation. The appropriate model was:

$$DMD = 97.8 - 0.55 \, CWC - 0.20 \, ADF - 1.98 \, \text{lignin}.$$

The relationship was significant ($P < 0.0001$) and accounted for 81 percent of the variation in DMD.

We also calculated DMD coefficients using the technique of Goering and Van Soest (1970) and statistically correlated these results to our DMD coefficients. Although the correlation was significant ($P < 0.01$), the regression equation accounted for only 32.7 percent of variation in our in vitro DMD (Y) coefficients using the Goering and Van Soest method (X). Predicted values for DMD using the Goering-Van Soest method were 14 percent higher than our DMD coefficients in vitro.

Pronghorn dietary quality was compared to data for bison and cattle (Peden 1972:

Table 1. Percentage dry matter, chemical constituents, and digestible dry matter of tame pronghorn diets recorded at a light and heavy cattle grazed pasture on the Pawnee Site, March–October 1971 and January 1972.

Date and Treatment	Dry matter of diet[a] (%)	Chemical constituents								Dry matter digested in vitro[c] (%)
		Dry matter (%)	Gross energy[b] (kcal/g)	Crude protein N × 6.25[c]	Ash[c] (%)	Phosphorus[c] (%)	CWC[c, d] (%)	ADF[c, d] (%)	Lignin (%)	
March										
Light	82	58	4.6	10.4	17.3	0.224	50.3	38.9	4.4	48
Heavy	87	80	4.6	10.0	9.1	0.118	62.7	42.5	6.1	39
April–May										
Light	78	28	4.6	19.2	12.5	0.427	34.6	26.3	2.8	68
Heavy	81	35	4.6	21.4	13.7	0.368	46.9	29.4	2.5	65
June–July										
Light	74	43	4.4	10.2	8.6	0.241	40.5	33.8	4.9	52
Heavy	66	43	4.5	13.9	8.5	0.207	45.1	40.8	5.6	63
August										
Light	78	50	4.5	8.9	11.1	0.124	41.2	30.3	3.6	59
Heavy	85	52	4.6	8.5	10.6	0.121	42.4	31.3	5.7	55
October										
Light	95	50	4.8	8.7	15.3	0.241	51.8	38.8	5.0	52
Heavy	94	66	4.8	8.7	8.2	0.171	64.1	40.2	7.5	40
January										
Light	81	85	4.7	7.3	14.5	0.123	63.0	44.0	7.2	40
Heavy	92	85	4.9	7.3	7.6	0.088	66.4	44.3	9.5	34

[a] Percent of the total diet composed of species listed by Schwartz (1977:App. C and D). Chemical constituents of diet were based on listed species only.
[b] Expressed on an organic matter basis.
[c] Expressed on a dry weight basis.
[d] CWC = cell-wall constituents, ADF = acid detergent fiber.

69–70) collected on the Pawnee Site. Pronghorn, cattle, and bison were sampled simultaneously during all seasons except winter. Here, we compared December 1970 cattle and bison data to January 1972 pronghorn data. We determined chemical composition of sheep diets using two to eight esophageally fistulated animals. At least five samples were composited by weight for each animal each date. Sampling dates and chemical analyses were the same as for pronghorn; digestion of dry matter was not determined.

RESULTS AND DISCUSSION

Protein Content of Forage

Crude protein of compounded diets (Table 1) varied between treatments and seasons, with lowest and highest levels in January (7.3 percent) and April (21.4 percent) respectively; both occurred in the heavily grazed diet pasture. Low crude protein levels occurred in August, October, and January while high levels occurred in March, April, and June during the period of active plant growth.

Crude protein content of the diet did not vary more than 3.7 percent between treatments in any season. This difference occurred during April and May when crude protein in preferred plants was abundant. Pronghorn maintained comparable crude protein levels in their diet irrespective of forage availability, which varied from 519 to 198 kg per ha for the lightly and heavily grazed pastures, respectively during January when forage was least abundant (Schwartz and Nagy 1976:Table 3).

Smith and Malechek (1974) examined crude protein content of pronghorn diets during summer on two desert ranges in Utah. Crude protein contents of estimated diets varied from 10 to 22 percent, and they concluded that minimum requirements for protein were probably met at all periods studied.

Dietz (1965) stated that if crude protein levels in deer (*Odocoileus* spp.) forage fell below 6 to 7 percent, rumen function was impaired. Deer fed diets containing 7 percent protein developed slower, were in poorer breeding condition, and had lower fawn survival than deer fed more protein (Murphy and Coates 1966). A diet of 12.7 percent protein was not sufficient for maximum gains in male white-tailed deer (*Odocoileus virginianus*), but it was adequate for female fawns (Ullrey et al. 1967). French et al. (1955) suggested that dietary levels of protein for white-tailed deer should be 13 to 16 percent for growth and 6 to 7 percent for maintenance.

If protein requirements for pronghorn were similar to deer, then the crude protein content in the diet of pronghorn was adequate for maintenance throughout the year in both treatments. Levels for growth were not consistently achieved and a diet containing more than 12 percent protein only occurred in April and June, and in April in the heavily and lightly grazed treatments, respectively.

Estimates of dietary protein probably represented minimum dietary levels for two reasons. Firstly, hand-plucked samples probably do not represent actual chemical intake. Rao et al. (1973) and Bredon et al. (1967) demonstrated that crude protein content of forage samples collected from esophageally fistulated cattle was higher than hand-clipped samples from the same

area. Therefore nutritive quality of our hand-plucked samples was probably below that of the forage consumed by the pronghorn. Secondly, dietary estimates were compiled using only plant species comprising 3 percent or more of total bites. This amount of forage represented between 66 to 95 percent of the total bites taken (Table 1). Estimates were closest to 100 percent during fall, winter, and spring when the diet contained few plant species; this corresponded to the time of year when forage quality was critical. Estimates were far from 100 percent during the plant growing season when the diet contained a wide variety of forage; this corresponded to the time when quality of the diet was highest.

Comparisons between protein content of pronghorn diets to those of cattle, bison (Peden et al. 1974:Table 3), and sheep indicated pronghorn and sheep selected diets higher in crude protein during all seasons and in both treatments (Fig. 1). This selectivity agrees with Bell (1971) who stated that in general, small ruminants require more protein per unit weight per day than large ruminants. Protein estimates for bison, cattle, and sheep diets may be high because of salivary nitrogen contamination. Scales (1972:139–140) found a significantly ($P <$ 0.05) higher crude protein content of blue grama and crested wheatgrass extrusa samples than corresponding hand-fed herbage samples. Therefore, actual differences may be greater than those presented here.

Gross Energy and Phosphorus

According to Sullivan (1962), an accurate representation of the amount of energy available to animals would be expressed by the gross energy on an organic matter basis. Gross energy expressed as a percentage of the total organic matter did not vary greatly (4.4–4.9 kcal/g) between treatments or seasons for calculated diets (Table 1).

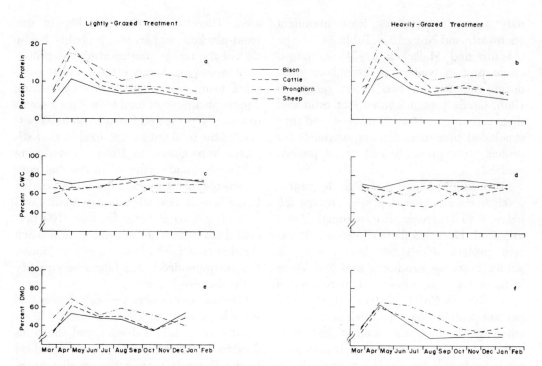

Fig. 1. Comparisons between the percent protein (a, b), cell-wall constituents (CWC) (c, d), and digestion of dry matter (DMD) (e, f) for diets of bison, cattle, pronghorn and sheep from lightly grazed and heavily grazed treatments, respectively. Data for bison and cattle are from Peden (1972:69–70, Tables 7 and 8).

Average concentration of phosphorus in the diet (Table 1) was greater in the lightly grazed pasture for all seasons except August when it was nearly equal to that in the heavily grazed pasture. We have no explanation for this if, indeed, it represents a real difference. Percentage of phosphorus in the diet by season varied from a high of 0.43 in April to a low of 0.09 in January. This would be expected from normal leaching.

Phosphorus requirements for cattle varied from 0.20 percent for finishing rations to 0.15 percent for other rations (NAS-NRC 1963). Requirements for sheep varied between 0.28 percent for lactating ewes to 0.20 for yearling lambs and ewes (NAS-NRC 1964). Phosphorus requirements of wild ungulates appear to equal or exceed those of domestic livestock (Magruder et al. 1957, Ullrey et al. 1975).

Phosphorus requirements for pronghorn were probably similar to those of domestic sheep. If pronghorn require between 0.20 and 0.28 percent phosphorus in the diet, the level was not attained in August and January in both pastures, nor in March and October in the heavily grazed pasture.

Fiber Content of Forage

The Van Soest (1965:835) method of fiber analysis partitioned the dry matter portion of forage into a fibrous part (CWC) and a soluble part (cell contents). Studies of forage and feces from in vivo digestion trials showed the soluble part to be nearly completely digestible (98 percent) and not affected by lignification in any way. Digestibility of the insoluble part was partial and varied according to the lignin content of the fiber fraction. Within the CWC the following fractions were distinguished: ADF which very nearly equaled the sum of lignin and cellulose, and an acid soluble fraction, which represented hemicellulose and fiber-bound protein. He further indicated that cell solubles were positively correlated with dietary quality while a negative association existed for dietary quality and CWC and ADF. Lignin was generally negatively associated with dietary assimilation, but the association varied among different forage species.

Fiber content of pronghorn diets varied little between grazing treatments (Table 1). All three fractions of fiber (CWC, ADF, and lignin) were greatest in October, January, and March and lowest in April, June, and August, a reflection of the principle that the ratio of fiber to cell contents of a plant increases as the plant matures. In all seasons, the CWC fraction for pronghorn diets was higher in the heavily grazed treatments.

Comparisons between percent CWC content (organic matter basis) of pronghorn diets to those of cattle, bison (Peden 1972: 69–70), and sheep diets (Fig. 1) indicated pronghorn generally were the most selective grazers during the growing season. They consumed a diet lower in cell wall contents. Bison were the least selective herbivore, followed by cattle and then by sheep. Sheep were more selective during winter sampling periods. These trends support Bell (1971:6) who concluded small ruminants had a higher nutrient requirement per unit weight than large ruminants while the reverse situation held for total maintenance requirements. As a consequence, small ruminants were more selective than larger ruminants.

Digestibility of Pronghorn Diets

In general, the level of DMD was proportional to protein content of the diet and was inversely related to dietary fiber levels

(Table 1). These findings agree with the generalization that plants are highest in nutrients during periods of growth, followed by nutrient decline as the plant cell wall thickens and becomes lignified (Van Soest 1968). Differences in digestion coefficients in relation to grazing treatment were not great; pronghorn were able to select a diet which was highly digestible regardless of forage availability. The DMD was highest during April and May and declined from June–July through January and March. Digestion increased slightly during August in the lightly grazed pasture.

Smith and Malechek (1974) estimated digestibility of pronghorn diets collected on two desert ranges in Utah during the growing season using the regression formula outlined by Goering and Van Soest (1970). Their results indicated diet digestibility varied from 61 to 79 percent and averaged between 68 and 71 percent on two ranges. As discussed earlier, calculated DMD coefficients using this technique and our data were 14 percent higher than DMD coefficients determined in vitro. If technique difference was considered, then our DMD coefficients during the plant growing season were similar to those of Smith and Malechek (1974).

Comparisons between DMD for diets of bison, cattle, and pronghorn (Fig. 1) indicated diets selected by pronghorn were more digestible in all seasons except January. Cattle diets were more digestible than bison diets during most seasons. Rice et al. (1974) compared dietary quality of bison, cattle, and sheep in 1972 on the same study and found that diet quality and in vitro DMD of sheep were higher than cattle, and cattle higher than bison. In general, sheep diets were about 2 percent higher in DMD than cattle and 6 percent higher than bison. In our study, pronghorn diets were about 6 percent higher in DMD than cattle diets and 9 percent higher than bison diets. By inference, therefore, pronghorn diets were about 4 percent higher than sheep diets in DMD. From this, it appeared that pronghorn selected a more digestible diet than sheep, followed by cattle and then by bison.

CONCLUSIONS

Although the bite count, hand-plucked estimates of pronghorn diets were not absolute, they provided valuable information used to compare diet quality to other herbivores. Esophageal fistulation no doubt provided a more accurate estimation of total dietary quality since *all* food items consumed made up the sample. However, as indicated by Schwartz et al. (1976) pronghorn were highly excitable animals and unsuited for excessive handling required of fistulated herbivores.

Our findings indicated that pronghorn and sheep were more selective grazers than bison and cattle and consumed a diet higher in crude protein and lower in fiber. Pronghorn were the most selective of the four herbivores while bison were least selective. This fact parallels findings of Schwartz and Nagy (1976) who indicated pronghorn were least competitive with bison when botanical composition of diets of bison, cattle, and sheep were compared. This botanical and chemical dietary divergence between bison and pronghorn may indicate evolutionary interspecific niche separation and dietary selection strategies between large and small ruminants. It can partially explain the coexistence of large herds of bison and pronghorn (Watt 1968:Table 4.3, page 70) on the pristine prairies of North America. It also suggests, as does empirical experience, that antelope can coexist on rangelands more successfully with cattle than with sheep.

LITERATURE CITED

A.O.A.C. 1965. Official methods of analysis. 10th ed. Association of Official Agricultural Chemists, Washington D.C. 957pp.

BARRETT, M. W. 1974. Importance, utilization, and quality of *Artemisia cana* on pronghorn winter ranges in Alberta. Antelope States Workshop Proc. 6:26–56.

BELL, R. H. V. 1971. A grazing ecosystem in the Serengeti. Sci. Am. 225(1):86–93.

BREDON, R. M., D. T. TORELL, AND B. MARSHALL. 1967. Measurement of selective grazing of tropical pastures using esophagal fistulated steers. J. Range Manage. 20(5):317–320.

DIETZ, D. R. 1965. Deer nutrition research in range management. Trans. N. Am. Wildl. Nat. Resourc. Conf. 30:274–285.

DIRSCHL, H. J. 1963. Food habits of the pronghorn in Saskatchewan. J. Wildl. Manage. 27(1):81–93.

FRENCH, C. E., L. C. McEWEN, AND N. D. MAGRUDER. 1955. Nutritional requirements of white-tailed deer for growth and antler development. Pa. Agric. Exp. Sta. Bull. 600. 50pp.

GOERING, H. K., AND P. J. VAN SOEST. 1970. Forage fiber analysis. U.S. Dep. Agric. Handbook No. 379.

MAGRUDER, N. D., C. E. FRENCH, L. C. McEWEN, AND R. W. SWIFT. 1957. Nutritional requirements of white-tailed deer for growth and antler development. II. Pennsylvania State Univ. Agric. Exp. Sta. Bull. 628, University Park. 21pp.

McDOUGALL, E. I. 1948. Studies on ruminant saliva. 1. The composition and output of sheep's saliva. Biochem. J. 43(1):99–109.

MURPHY, D. A., AND J. A. COATES. 1966. Effects of dietary protein on deer. Trans. N. Am. Wildl. Nat. Resourc. Conf. 31:129–139.

NATIONAL ACADEMY OF SCIENCES-NATIONAL RESEARCH COUNCIL. 1963. Nutrient requirements of domestic animals. No. 4. Nutrient requirements of beef cattle. 3rd Rev. Ed. Natl. Acad. Sci.-Natl. Res. Counc. Publ. 1137, Washington, D.C. 30pp.

NATIONAL ACADEMY OF SCIENCES-NATIONAL RESEARCH COUNCIL. 1964. Nutrient requirements of domestic animals. No. 5. Nutrient requirements of sheep. 3rd Rev. Ed. Natl. Acad. Sci.-Natl. Res. Counc. Publ. 1193, Washington, D.C. 40pp.

PEARSON, H. A. 1970. Digestibility trials: In vitro techniques. Pages 85–92 *in* Range and wildlife habitat evaluation—a research symposium. U.S. Dep. Agric., Forest Serv., Misc. Publ. 1147.

PEDEN, D. G. 1972. The trophic relations of *Bison bison* to the shortgrass prairie. Ph.D.

Thesis. Colorado State Univ., Fort Collins. 134pp.

———, G. M. VAN DYNE, R. W. RICE, AND R. M. HANSEN. 1974. The trophic ecology of *Bison bison* L. on shortgrass plains. J. Appl. Ecol. 11:489–498.

RAO, R. M., L. H. HARBERS, AND E. F. SMITH. 1973. Seasonal change in nutritive value of bluestem pastures. J. Range Manage. 26(6): 419–422.

RICE, R. W., R. E. DEAN, AND J. E. ELLIS. 1974. Bison, cattle and sheep dietary quality and food intake. Proc. Western Sect. Am. Soc. Anim. Sci. 25:194–197.

SCALES, G. M. 1972. Nutritive value and consumption of sandhill range forage by grazing cattle. Ph.D. Thesis. Colorado State Univ., Fort Collins. 259pp.

SCHWARTZ, C. C. 1977. Pronghorn grazing strategies on the shortgrass prairie, Colorado. Ph.D. Thesis. Colorado State Univ., Fort Collins. 113pp.

———, AND J. G. NAGY. 1976. Pronghorn diets relative to forage availability in northeastern Colorado. J. Wildl. Manage. 40(3):469–478.

———, ———, AND S. M. KERR. 1976. Rearing and training pronghorn for ecological studies. J. Wildl. Manage. 40(3):464–468.

SMITH, A. D., AND J. C. MALECHEK. 1974. Nutritional quality of summer diets of pronghorn antelopes in Utah. J. Wildl. Manage. 38(4): 792–798.

SULLIVAN, J. T. 1962. Evaluation of forage crops by chemical analysis: A critique. Agron. J. 54(6):511–515.

SUNDSTROM, C., W. G. HEPWORTH, AND K. L. DIEM. 1973. Abundance, distribution and food habits of the pronghorn. Bull. No. 12.

Wyoming Fish and Game Commission, Cheyenne. 61pp.

TILLEY, J. M. A., AND R. A. TERRY. 1963. A two-stage technique for the *in vitro* digestion of forage crops. J. Br. Grassl. Soc. 18(2):104–111.

ULLREY, D. E., W. G. YOUATT, H. E. JOHNSON, L. D. FAY, AND B. L. BRADLEY. 1967. Protein requirement of white-tailed deer fawns. J. Wildl. Manage. 31(4):679–685.

———, ———, ———, A. B. COWAN, L. D. FAY, R. L. COVERT, W. T. MAGEE, AND K. K. KEAHEY. 1975. Phosphorus requirements of weaned white-tailed deer fawns. J. Wildl. Manage. 39(3):590–595.

VAN SOEST, P. J. 1963. Use of detergents in the analysis of fibrous feeds. II. A rapid method for the determination of fiber and lignin. J. Assoc. Off. Anal. Chem. 46(5):829–835.

———. 1965. Symposium on factors influencing the voluntary intake of herbage by ruminants: Voluntary intake in relation to chemical composition and digestibility. J. Anim. Sci. 24(3): 834–843.

———. 1968. Structural and chemical characteristics which limit the nutritive value of forages. Pages 63–76 *in* C. M. Harrison ed. Forage economics-quality. Am. Soc. Agron. Spec. Publ. 13.

———, AND R. H. WINE. 1967. Use of detergents in the analysis of fibrous feeds. IV. Determination of plant cell-wall constituents. J. Assoc. Off. Anal. Chem. 50(1):50–55.

WATT, K. E. F. 1968. Ecology and resource management. McGraw-Hill, Inc., New York. 450pp.

Received 6 April 1976.
Accepted 19 January 1977.

WINTER BEHAVIOR OF PRONGHORNS IN RELATION TO HABITAT[1]

ELDON H. BRUNS, Department of Biology, University of Calgary, Calgary, Alberta T2N 1N4.[2]

Abstract: The winter behavior of pronghorn antelopes (*Antilocapra americana*) was studied from 6 January to 12 April 1969 in southeastern Alberta and northern Montana. January, climatically an exceptionally severe month in the study area, saw a pronounced movement of pronghorns southward. The mean herd size was 39.8 ± 11.5 head. Herds did not mix, nor move more than a few km from local sites during February and March; a distinct disbanding process was noted after 25 March. Fences and roads limited day to day movements. Herd composition counts for 6 herds (221 head) indicated a low fawn proportion (41 fawns to 100 does). The male to female fawn ratio of 42 to 100 indicated poor production or survival of male fawns. Pronghorns were adept at pawing away snow cover to reach their food. They spent 6.2 to 11.5 percent of their feeding time pawing. Interactions at feeding craters and bedding sites indicated a social heirarchy with male adults at the top, followed by female adults, and fawns. Pronghorns selected microhabitats with more favorable conditions than the average for the area as a whole, these being: 63 percent lower wind velocities, 24 percent less snow, and 87 percent softer snow. The daytime activity pattern began with a feeding period shortly after sunrise. Resting animals oriented the longitudinal axis of the body so that their anterior portions were downwind when chill factors were extreme; they also curled their heads alongside the body more often at lower chill factors.

J. WILDL. MANAGE. 41(3):560–571

Few efforts have been made to determine how wild ungulates have adapted their behavior to winter conditions. Pruitt (1959) has shown that snow influences much of the behavior of caribou (*Rangifer arcticus*). Henshaw (1968) confirmed much of this with supporting data for Alaskan caribou. In Quebec, DesMeules (1964, paper presented at N.E. Wildl. Conf., Hartford, Conn.) learned that moose (*Alces alces*) capitalize on the insulating properties of loose fluffy snow when selecting bedding sites. They also travel under large conifers where the snow is less deep. Verme (1968) was able to demonstrate that temperature and wind were the major climatic factors causing heat loss in white-tailed deer (*Odocoileus virginianus*) in normal habitat. Moen (1968) concluded that behavior of animals may easily turn a negative heat exchange into a positive one. The objective of this research was to determine the winter behavioral adaptations of pronghorn antelopes.

I am indebted to V. Geist for his support, valuable suggestions, and criticisms. Gratitude is also expressed to my wife, E. Scheinberg and D. R. Flook for their assistance.

STUDY AREA

In 1968–69, ground and aerial observations indicated that at least 300 pronghorns were wintering on a 2500 km² area in southeastern Alberta and northern Montana. The animals were concentrated on small localized ranges and did not utilize more than an estimated 7.5 percent of the available area.

The study area has a semi-arid climate with hot summers and cold winters, the daily mean temperature being +20 C for July and −11.1 C for January (Department of Transport 1968*a*:5). The winds are strong for a large inland region, the monthly means being 19–26 km/h. The average precipitation is 30.3 cm annually (Department of Transport 1968*b*:38), most of which occurs

[1] Financed by a National Research Council Grant to V. Geist.

[2] Present address: Alberta Fish and Wildlife Division, 304 Professional Building, Red Deer, Alberta T4N 1X5.

Table 1. Climate records from Onefour, Alberta.

Climatic elements	1931–60[a]				1969[b]		
	Year	Jan.	Feb.	Mar.	Jan.	Feb.	Mar.
Temperature							
Mean daily maximum (C)	11.0	− 6.1	− 4.6	1.1	−23.2	−10.0	− 2.2
Mean daily minimum (C)	− 2.2	−12.8	−16.1	−10.0	−29.3	−16.1	−11.7
Maximum (C)	40.6	16.1	19.4	22.8	−14.4	− 0.6	10.0
Minimum (C)	−42.7	−42.7	−42.7	−35.6	−38.9	−25.0	−24.4
Snowfall (cm)	93.3	15.5	15.0	18.0	61.2	20.4	4.0
Number of days with measurable snow	28	6	5	5	12	7	4

[a] Means are from Department of Transport (1968a,b).
[b] Data for temperature from this study and for snowfall from the Department of Agriculture (personal communication).

during the spring and summer (Clarke and Tisdale 1945:10). From Table 1, it can be seen that the weather in the first 3 months of 1969 was exceptionally severe in the study area.

The topography is typically glaciated. Wide areas of flat to gently undulating till plains dissected by coulees and gullies predominate (Westgate 1968:15). The most outstanding features are the deeply entrenched Lost River and Milk River canyons and Spring Ridge (887 m).

The soils of the area are mainly in the Chernozemic Order of the Brown Soil Group (Clarke and Tisdale 1945:11). They have developed under arid conditions and hence are low in organic matter, nitrogen, and available phosphorus and potassium (Clarke and Tisdale 1945:11).

The major vegetation community of the study area is the blue grama–western wheat grass (*Bouteloua gracilis–Agropyron smithii*) faciation (Coupland 1961:153). Another principal climax community is the spear grass (*Stipa comata*)–blue grama–western wheat grass faciation, which occurs in areas of deeper till deposits (Coupland 1961:155). Hoary sage (*Artemisia cana*) is common on dry exposed hillsides and in sheltered coulees (Cormack 1967:351). In many drainages, particularly along

the Milk River, it may grow to heights of 120 cm or more. The same areas may support balsam poplar (*Populus balsamifera*) and peach-leaved willow (*Salix amygdaloides*) (Cormack, typed report, Alberta Dept. of Lands and Forests 1954). Several species of dock (*Rumex* spp.) are common in nearly all of the wetter or marshy places in the area and may be important in the diets of some pronghorn herds. Flood irrigation and dryland farming are undertaken locally.

MATERIALS AND METHODS

Field observations began on 8 January 1969 and terminated on 12 April 1969. The weather data from the Canadian Department of Agriculture Range Experimental Farm at Onefour, Alberta were the standard of reference for the study area. These records included wind velocity and direction, temperature, daily precipitation, hours of sunlight, and relative humidity. With the exception of precipitation, all data were collected with continuous recording instruments. Corresponding data were collected from areas occupied by the herd under study, using calibrated hand instruments at a height of 70 cm above the ground. They were read every half hour when behavioral observations were recorded.

Comparative data for the depth, density, and hardness of snow were collected. One set of measurements was taken where topography, vegetative density, and composition appeared similar to the area occupied by the herd. This was the *preferred* set. Frequent checks were made to confirm the assumption that preferred sets did have similar characteristics to the areas actually occupied. Another set was taken at a location which appeared to have normal exposure to winds and average vegetative cover. This was called the *area* set. If it was not snowing, blowing, or melting, the same sets were used throughout a given observation period. New sets were taken when the herd moved to different locations. The instruments used for measuring hardness and density were Chatillon pressure gauges; one had a range of 0 to 1,000 g, the other 0 to 10 kg. Pressure plates of 10 to 100 cm² were designed to replace the standard 1 cm² plate supplied. These plates made the gauges much more suitable for soft snow. A 500 cm³ snow cutter was designed for use with the gauges so they could also be used to weigh the samples for determination of density.

Pronghorn herds were readily identified by number, composition and recognizable individuals. The locations of all herds were plotted on 1:250,000 scale topographical maps.

Observations of instantaneous behavior (taken at 0.5 hour intervals) were based on the percentage of individuals engaged in a specified activity. Ten classes were used: (1) feeding upwind, (2) feeding downwind, (3) lying head up, (4) lying head down, (5) walking upwind, (6) walking downwind, (7) running upwind, (8) running downwind, (9) fighting, and (10) standing.

Other behavioral data were obtained more casually. These included play, orientation of resting animals with respect to the direction of wind and sun and the amounts of time spent feeding, pawing, and the rate of pawing (during 10-minute periods) for adults and fawns of both sexes. Social interactions observed included butting, pawing, and hooking during interactions at bedding sites and feeding craters.

The classes of continuous activity for individuals were as follows: (1) lying down, whether sleeping or ruminating; (2) standing, including time spent ruminating; (3) feeding time, including time spent walking from one feeding spot to another if that took less than 1 minute. (The time spent pawing feeding craters is also included in this category. Therefore, the time spent actually ingesting food, as was measured in the feeding times based on 10-minute intervals, was much less than recorded here.); (4) walking, when an animal spent more than 1 minute walking; and (5) running.

Hoary sage leaves and stems were air dried and sent to the Agricultural Soil and Feed Testing Laboratory at Edmonton, Alberta. A standard chemical analysis determined percentages of moisture, protein, Ca, P, and crude fiber.

To determine temperature differences between bare ground and adjacent snow covered areas, thermistor probes were held 5 cm above the surface and at intervals of 10 cm, 30 cm, and 50 cm on each side of the snow-bare ground border.

RESULTS

Sociality

Pronghorns displayed a high degree of gregariousness during the winter. Herds numbering up to 1,000 individuals have been reported in this area (Rand 1947:22).

Accurate counts obtained for 11 herds in the study area gave a mean size of 39.8 (SE = 11.5). The reluctance of some indi-

Table 2. Sex and age classes for six pronghorn herds.

| Herd number | Herd size | Males per 100 does | | Female fawns per 100 does |
		Adults	Fawns	
4	22	60	30	30
5	21	75	12	25
7	61	38	9	32
8	17	44	0	44
9	15	50	12	25
10	85	47	10	16
Mean ± SE	36.8 ± 11.9	52.3 ± 5.4	12.2 ± 4.0	28.7 ± 3.8

viduals to cross barriers such as fences, coulees, and deep snow areas caused the splitting off of small groups from herds. As might be expected, pronghorns weakened by malnutrition, exposure, old age, and wounds also became separated from the herd. Various combinations of these factors and human interference may cause a reasonably large herd to shrink to a few individuals in a short period. Herd No. 5 (Table 2) had 21 members on 3 February. By 10 March it was reduced to 2 small groups with 3 antelope in one and 10 in the other.

A sharp reduction in the gregariousness of pronghorns occurred in the spring. The first suggestion of this was seen on 25 March when 2 herds numbering 39 and 31 head were found which had apparently belonged to the former herd No. 10. On the next day herd No. 7 was disbanded (2 groups of 21 and 23 each were located). By 31 March single male adults were seen feeding up to 1.6 km from the nearest herds. An aerial census on 10 April revealed that the largest group had only 10 members. The 35 groups counted had a total of 155 animals. This gave an average group size of 4.4 compared to 39.8 found before 12 March.

Herd Movements

The pronghorns of Canada and Montana are known to migrate considerable distances during winter storms (Rand 1947, Nelson 1960, Martinka 1967). During this study, there was extensive movement of herds in a generally southward direction until the end of January. Of the 7 herds located during that month, only 2 remained in the same locality. The other 5 moved south before the end of the month. January was also the harshest month of the winter (Table 1). From 8 January to 1 February the temperature did not rise above −12 C and 61.7 cm of snow fell at Onefour during January.

Herds found during February and March remained relatively static. The mean locations and standard deviations of latitude and longitude are shown in Fig. 1 for 4 herds which were observed intermittently for periods in excess of 30 days. After migration ceased pronghorns tended to occupy quite small areas. Although there was no overlap of the occupied areas shown in Fig. 1, this may not be of biological significance. Different herds were not seen feeding in the same localities during February and March although herd No. 5 did pass within 2 km of herd No. 4 on one occasion. The failure of herds to intermingle was probably due to the low population density and difficult travel conditions, rather than some form of avoidance.

During their daily movements healthy members of a herd were seldom separated by more than 100 m. The distance covered by a herd in a day was less than the 5 to 7 km estimated by Buechner (1950:305). It

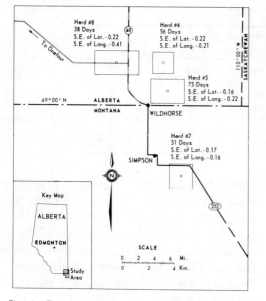

Fig. 1. The mean location of 4 pronghorn herds. The small circles enclosed by rectangles represent the means of herd positions. The rectangles include ± one SD of latitude and longitude.

is doubtful that an individual animal covered more than 3 km from daybreak to dusk during the months of February and March. This was probably due to difficulty of travelling in snow, abundance of forage, and lack of necessity to travel for water (snow was ingested as a substitute).

Factors Affecting Travel

Four-strand barbed wire fences presented a major obstacle. Individual pronghorns spent several minutes moving back and forth along a fence, testing it at many spots before going under it. Only 4 were observed jumping over a fence.

Herd No. 8 was usually located within 0.5 km of Highway 48, but crossed it only once during the study. Avoidance of the road was probably due to traffic (0–6 vehicles per day) and the 90–150 cm deep snow in the ditches. On at least 4 occasions, herds were seen feeding along a fence until

it was intersected by another fence or road. In all cases they reversed their direction of feeding, rather than cross the fence or road.

High graded roads were beneficial to pronghorns for the ditches acted as snow traps and produced adjacent feeding areas with a low snow cover. Herd No. 8 was observed feeding and resting along the bare portions of ground on the lee side of a road for 3 days.

Herd Composition

The sex and age composition of 6 different herds was determined. The male to female adult ratio of 52:100 ($N = 221$) (Table 2) was lower than the ratio of 72:100 found during the previous summer in this zone (Armstrong 1968:4). The fawn to doe ratio was 41:100. This was 16 fawns per 100 does fewer than the minimum of 57:100 found in southern Alberta during the 1968 summer census (Armstrong 1968:4). The male to female fawn ratio during this study was 42:100. Herd composition remained quite stable. Nine fawns and 8 adults were lost. One male fawn and 3 male adults were shot by a poacher. One female fawn was killed by an eagle (Bruns 1970:303).

Pawing for Food

Pawing for food could be observed during any feeding session within the 8 January to 18 March period, when most of the ground was covered by snow. Pawing was last observed on 18 March, when there were sufficient bare spots to allow continuous feeding. Data concerning the pawing are summarized in Table 3. The mean depth of snow in the rangeland feeding areas was 27.4 cm as opposed to 15.0 cm in the cropland area ($P < 0.05$), but forage in the latter was completely covered. Herd No. 7 fed consistently on croplands. It numbered 61 head in contrast to the average herd of 32 head observed on rangeland. Rangeland

Table 3. Pawing activities of pronghorns feeding on rangeland and domestic croplands. All measurements are seconds of pawing per 10 minutes of feeding.

	Rangeland				Sprouted cover crop and crested wheat grass			
	Adult		Fawn		Adult		Fawn	
	Male	Female	Male	Female	Male	Female	Male	Female
Mean	41	31	49	29	98	62	51	65
N	10	10	7	9	5	5	4	5
SE	6.7	6.7	8.4	3.0	13.5	10.3	6.9	10.9

forage was predominantly hoary sage. Dock from creek beds and dry lake beds was also favored but limited distribution reduced its importance as a staple food. Herd No. 7 had a strong preference for a mixed crop of rye, oats, and wheat which had sprouted before being covered by snow.

Comparison of the 2 feeding areas for all classes combined showed that on rangeland 6.2 percent ($N = 36$) of feeding time was spent pawing, while on cropland the value was 11.5 percent ($N = 19$). The difference between areas was significant ($P < 0.01$) for male adults and female fawns (Table 3), but not for female adults and male fawns ($P > 0.05$). The difference in pawing times may result from the structural nature of the vegetation, the vigor of the animals feeding on it, or both.

The time spent eating was quite constant regardless of the forage type. The means for 10-minute feeding sessions were as follows: male adults, 7 minutes 32 seconds ± 10.9 seconds ($N = 37$); female adults, 7 minutes 22 seconds ± 11.2 seconds ($N = 35$); male fawns, 7 minutes 24 seconds ± 13.3 seconds ($N = 28$); and female fawns,

7 minutes 38 seconds ± 10.9 seconds ($N = 32$). These values show that pronghorns spent 70 percent of their winter feeding sessions ingesting food. The remainder of the sessions was usually spent pawing (6–12%), and walking from one bush or crater to another (18–24%). The feeding times did not differ significantly ($P > 0.05$) between rangeland and cropland animals.

Pronghorns did much pawing for hoary sage below snow level, even though portions of the bushes were numerous above the snow. Hoary sage above snow level was almost odorless in sharp contrast to the strong aromatic smell present when sage from below the snow was exposed by kicking the snow aside. On 19 March, samples of hoary sage were collected from above and below the snow (Table 4). These suggested that pawing may be advantageous since forage from above the snow may have lower levels of moisture, protein, Ca, and P, and a higher level of crude fiber.

Intraspecific Interactions

Aggression was the main theme of interactions. Butting and hooking were much more frequent in herd No. 7, which had 61 members, than in any of the other herds. Most of this was associated with feeding craters. The reduction of such behavior in smaller herds could indicate that the dominance order was better established. There was also a distinct difference in the diets of these herds. Members of herds feeding on

Table 4. Chemical analysis of two samples of hoary sage collected at Wild Horse, Alberta, on 19 March 1969.

Sample	Moisture (%)	Protein (%)	Fiber (%)	Ca (%)	P (%)
From above snow	8.4	4.5	51.5	0.32	0.05
From below snow	12.8	8.2	46.5	0.36	0.08

JWM 41(3): 566

Table 5. Frequencies of aggressive interactions between pronghorn classes, using observations of all herds.

Dominant	Subordinate				
	Adult		Fawn		
	Male	Female	Male	Female	Total
Adult					
Male	35	22	11	6	74
Female	0	13	2	11	26
Fawn					
Male	0	14	2	2	18
Female	0	5	0	2	7

hoary sage may be subjected to much less competition and crowding than those feeding on grains. This hypothesis is supported by the absence of aggressive behavior in herd No. 10 (85 head) when it was feeding on hoary sage.

The frequencies of interactions between 4 pronghorn classes are listed in Table 5. These data were gathered from all herds and include all 3 types of dominance behavior. The initiator of the interaction was considered to be the dominant animal even though there were a few occasions when it was repelled or ignored. The data indicate that male fawns directed most of their aggression toward female adults. This may be due to a preponderance of female adults, rather than selection by male fawns. The dominance order of pronghorns during the winter is probably male adult, female adult and fawns.

There were 61 observations of play. This was recognized when movements and postures were exaggerated, and the outcome of such behavior accomplished no apparent objective. Winter play of pronghorns included sparring, herding of one individual by another, bush beating, and exaggerated running (Bruns 1969:30).

Interspecific Interactions

Pronghorns often fed in close association with domestic cattle and horses. They also shared their winter range with mule deer

(*Odocoileus hemionus*) and white-tailed deer. Encounters with these species usually involved mutual curiosity and sometimes alarm; no species appeared to be dominant over another.

Five interactions between coyotes (*Canis latrans*) and pronghorns were observed. Two of these involved hunting of pronghorns by coyotes (Bruns 1970:302). In the other 3 cases the presence of coyotes in the vicinity caused alarm among herd members. On no occasion did the pronghorns attack coyotes or follow them as has been reported to occur at other times of the year (Buechner 1950:312, Van Wormer 1969:64).

Golden eagles are capable predators of pronghorn fawns in the early summer (Buechner 1950:611). One kill of a female fawn by an eagle was witnessed; 6 incidents of eagles harassing herds were observed (Bruns 1970:303). The flight of an eagle over a herd caused pronghorns to run together into a compact group. If the eagle remained in sight, the herd would stay bunched for a considerable time. On 24 February an eagle kept herd No. 7 bunched for 37 minutes before some members resumed feeding and lying down. On one occasion an eagle flying approximately 0.4 km away alerted a herd. Owls, hawks, and low flying aircraft caused similar reactions in herds.

Microhabitat Selection

It is logical to expect that pronghorns occupy microhabitats which minimize the energy drain caused by heat loss and travel through deep snow. In order to detect this, a weather and snow analysis was made. The characteristics measured and the results of t-tests between the area and preferred sets are shown in Table 6. Pronghorns did occupy microhabitats having climatic conditions significantly more favorable ($P < 0.01$) than the surrounding area. The re-

Table 6. Comparison of weather and nival factors in the habitats used by pronghorns (Preferred) and on the whole study area (Area).

	Mean		Standard error		N		P
	Preferred	Area	Preferred	Area	Preferred	Area	
Wind direction							
(° from north)	105	175	4.7	4.2	729	730	<0.01
Wind velocity (kmph)	6	16	0.3	0.5	729	730	<0.01
Temperature (C)	−7.2	−7.8	0.6	1.2	729	730	>0.05
Wind chill (C)	−9.4	−13.9	0.7	1.0	729	730	<0.01
Relative humidity (%)	76	78	1.7	1.3	112	730	>0.05
Snow depth (cm)	19	25	0.5	0.4	685	686	<0.01
Snow hardness (g/cm²)	56	428	10.1	87.1	334	362	<0.01
Snow density	0.2	0.3	0.007	0.007	334	362	<0.01
Thickness of hardest							
snow layer (cm)	4	3	0.4	0.2	335	335	>0.05
Height to top of							
hardest layer (cm)	16	18	0.7	0.6	335	335	>0.05
Hardness of hardest							
layer (g/cm²)	1032	1920	94.3	155.2	335	335	<0.01
Density of hardest layer	0.3	0.4	0.011	0.013	335	335	<0.01

duction in wind velocities was due partially to barriers such as creek and river banks. Road fills and dikes also reduced wind velocities. Pronghorns feeding in tall dense hoary sage and dock, or on the lee side of such stands avoided much wind. Herd No. 5 spent 36 days (6 March to 10 April) living in a dry slough bed. On 29 March 56 wind velocity measurements were taken in the slough and immediately to windward of it on the open prairie. On the open prairie the mean velocity was 12.6 km/h ± 0.43 compared with 7.9 km/h ± 0.26 in the slough area ($P < 0.01$). Thus, the pronghorns living in the slough were subjected to 37 percent lower wind velocity than they would have been on the open prairies a few hundred paces away. Mule and white-tailed deer also made heavy use of this same slough for the entire study period.

The air temperatures and relative humidities in the preferred microhabitats were not significantly different ($P > 0.05$) from those of the general area (Table 6). This is not surprising when one considers the low vegetation, frequent winds, and open terrain. These temperatures, however, were recorded 71 cm above the ground (back region of standing pronghorns). They probably do not reflect behavioral adaptations for the reduction of heat loss while bedded down. Pronghorns bedded exclusively on bare ground when the snow was melting. This may have resulted from the increased freedom of movement or the higher temperatures found on bare ground during the snow melting period, or both. Temperature probes placed on bare patches and adjacent snow cover revealed significantly different temperatures ($P < 0.01$). The mean of 87 measurements taken above the ground surface was 4.4 C ± 0.20; 87 corresponding measurements above the snow surface had a mean of 3.1 C ± 0.18.

Pronghorns frequented areas of reduced snow accumulations (Table 6) such as the edges of ditches, creek beds, washouts, strips of cover crop, and lee sides of thick sage stands.

Snow hardness and density in preferred habitats were significantly less ($P < 0.01$) than in the area locations (Table 6). It is logical to assume that the light, soft snow was favored because it reduced energy expenditure. Differences in the height and thickness of the hardest layer of snow in preferred habitats and average areas were not great ($P > 0.05$). The hardest layer was formed by melting near the surface of the snow or by drifting. Such conditions were common over the entire area. Pronghorns did not seek out snow cover which would support their weight, probably because such areas (hard packed drifts) were relatively scarce. On the other hand, they moved about in areas of extremely deep snow on occasion. Several individuals pushed through soft snow above their chest level (approximately 46 cm) to reach dock plants. On 8 March herd No. 4 moved into a stand of tall dense hoary sage where the snow was 42 cm deep as opposed to the 32 cm average in the area. This was believed to be in response to the 27 km/h winds and drifting snow at the time. Movement in such deep snow was characterized by bounding leaps, indicating that the animals were in some difficulty.

Daily Activity Patterns

Pronghorn daily activities became conservative during the northern winter. Foraging for food and lying down followed each other with monotonous regularity. Play was rare or absent. Travel was limited to short walks from one sagebrush to another while feeding. The only breaks in the pattern appeared to be caused by the approach of vehicles or predators.

Pronghorns remained lying down until well after sunrise. This was also the usual case (season unspecified) with Texas pronghorns (Buechner 1950). The beginning of the first daytime feeding periods seemed to vary with snow cover, vegetation, and temperatures. On 15 March (28 cm of snow, -17 C) herd No. 5 did not begin feeding until 2.5 hours after sunrise. Six days later herd No. 8 began feeding 37 min-

utes after sunrise (bare patches of ground, -10 C). By 29 March herd No. 5 was feeding within 27 minutes after sunrise (bare ground, except for patchy overnight snow cover, -9 C). The shortening of the post-dawn period of inactivity was attributed primarily to the decrease in snow depths and the reduction in energy output which would result.

A total of 11,184 antelope minutes was spent observing the activities of individuals from all 4 sex-age classes. The samples of feeding and resting times were obtained from the same individuals on the same days. The duration of feeding times was quite variable; the mean of 15 samples measured before 20 February was 108 ± 11.2 minutes, while mean of 38 feeding periods after this date was only 68 ± 6.3 minutes. This difference was significant ($P < 0.01$); it supports the findings of Buechner (1950:302), that pronghorns lengthen their feeding times under snow conditions. The resting periods were slightly longer after 20 February, the means being 79 ± 3.3 and 89 ± 1.0 minutes ($P > 0.05$).

Resting periods were spent lying down. It was rare to see an individual spend more than 5 minutes ruminating in a standing position. The resting postures were described by Gregg (1955). A record of the percentage of animals lying with their head curled back alongside the body was kept, the hypothesis being that pronghorns may assume this posture in an effort to minimize heat loss from the body. From Fig. 2, it can be seen that this behavior increased in frequency as the wind chill factor increased.

Some data were collected on the orientation of the body axis of resting animals to the direction of the wind. A large number of samples could not be collected over a wide range of chill factors, but the 12 samples plotted in Fig. 3 show that pronghorns oriented their anterior downwind at wind

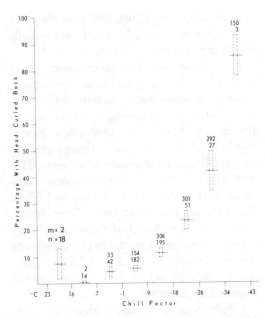

Fig. 2. The relationship of head curling response of resting pronghorns to chill factors. The vertical rectangles represent one SE on either side of the mean for each 8 C interval of chill factor, m = number of animals lying with head curled back, n = number of herd observations in each interval.

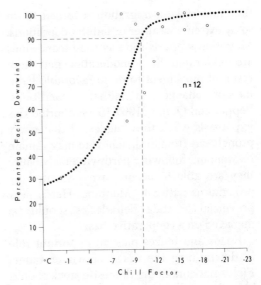

Fig. 3. The relationship of wind chill and the body orientation of resting pronghorns. The 12 samples included 285 animals oriented downwind.

chill temperatures below −11 C. This behavior would, of course, reduce the surface area of the animal which was exposed to the direct blast of the wind. The reduction in heat loss may have been considerable since destruction of coat insulation could well have been reduced. Wind blew for 200 (55%) of the 365 hours spent observing herds. The mean velocity, excluding zero values, was 1.29 km/h ± 0.43. The maximum recorded for any occupied microhabitat was 41.8 km/h. The maximum for an average area was 59.5 km/h. Thus, it would be important for this species to have resting postures which would reduce wind chill effects.

I suspected that pronghorns oriented their bodies at right angles to the sun while resting on windless days, but observation of 10 herds under such conditions failed to show any significant differences. The only obvious response of resting pronghorns to direct sunlight was first observed on 26 March when the daytime temperatures exceeded 10 C. After that date, an occasional animal was seen lying on one side with all 4 legs stretched out from the body. Records of the percentage of animals feeding downwind at various chill factors failed to show any correlation. The winter pelage and other morphological adaptations of the pronghorn's body were probably sufficient to make such behavior unnecessary after suitable wintering areas had been located.

DISCUSSION

The winter behavior of northern pronghorns should be considered in their management. Since several herds had passed through the study area prior to February, it may be they are opportunistic migrants. That is, the same individuals may not migrate to definite wintering areas each year. They appear to be like the saiga (*Saiga tatarica*) (Bannikov et al. 1961:78) in that they undertake a migration if forced to do so by extreme weather or habitat conditions. Migration stops as soon as these conditions are moderated. Such moderation may be a result of movement to more favorable habitat, or changes in climatic conditions. Pepper and Quinn (1965:10) supported this hypothesis when they suggested that many pronghorns from Saskatchewan may remain in Montana following hard winters, because they are able to occupy areas vacated by pronghorns native to Montana. Herds near provincial or state boundaries should be managed on a cooperative basis.

Roads and fences play an important role in determining the usage of winter range. Fields not containing domestic stock should have the gates left open and antelope passes installed near corners. All fences should have a minimum clearance of 46 cm below the bottom wire (barbless). If roads must be built on winter ranges, the snowfree lee sides should be given the most consideration during range improvement efforts. These areas will be utilized more than those on the windward side.

The small number of fawns per doe (41: 100) found in January suggests that there had been a considerable loss of fawns in the area since August when the ratio was at least 57:100 (Armstrong 1968:4). The male to female ratio in January was only 42:100. During his study of newborn pronghorns in Alberta, Mitchell (1965:36) determined the male:female ratio to be 93.9:100. Spring tagging operations in Montana have indicated a ratio of 110 to 120 males per 100 female fawns (Martinka 1967:162). Mortality of males during their first 7 months may be much higher than for females.

The idea that pronghorns do not readily paw through snow in order to obtain feed (Webb et al. 1967:106, Van Wormer 1969: 142) is a misconception. The pawing behavior of this species also leads one to doubt

Pruitt's statement (1960:68) that they are chionophobes (animals which are unable to adjust to snowy conditions).

If the proposed dominance order (male adults, female adults, and fawns) is correct, it would account for a portion of the relatively high winter mortality of fawns reported by Martinka (1967:162). Fawns would have to spend more energy pawing new feeding craters and locating beds. This dominance order is common among ruminants during the winter (Hafez and Shein 1962, Hafez and Scott 1962, Geist 1968). The dominance of mature males could contribute to increased mortality of subordinate classes during the winter. Thus, bucks should be kept near the minimum number required for breeding.

Although coyotes and golden eagles are not likely to be serious predators under normal winter conditions, their activities may become serious during severe winters or when pronghorns reach low densities.

Since pronghorns do respond to snow and wind conditions, any efforts to conserve or improve winter ranges should be aimed at microhabitats which have shallow, soft snow and protection from wind. Winter habitat could be improved by encouraging the growth of sagebrush and dock species. Fertilization to raise Ca and P levels may also be an economical means of increasing winter survival.

LITERATURE CITED

ARMSTRONG, G. 1968. Antelope aerial surveys. Alberta Fish Wildl. Div. Proj. No. W.-1-68 Region 1. Job No. A-1. 7pp.

BANNIKOV, A. G., L. V. ZHIRNOV, L. S. LEBEDEVA, AND A. A. FANDEEV. 1961. Biology of the Saiga. Israel Prog. for Scientific Translations. IPST Cat. No. 1833, Trans. by M. Fleischmann (1967). Ed. by Prof. H. Epstein. 252pp.

BRUNS, E. H. 1969. A preliminary study of behavioral adaptations of wintering pronghorn antelopes. M.S. Thesis. Univ. of Calgary. 60pp.

———. 1970. Winter predation of golden eagles

and coyotes on pronghorn antelopes. Can. Field Nat. 84(3):301–304.

BUECHNER, H. K. 1950. Life history, ecology, and range use of the pronghorn antelope in Trans-Pecos Texas. Am. Midl. Nat. 43(2): 257–354.

CLARKE, S. E., AND E. W. TISDALE. 1945. The chemical composition of native forage plants of southern Alberta and Saskatchewan in relation to grazing practices. Can. Dept. Agric., Publ. 769 Tech. Bull. 54. 60pp.

CORMACK, R. G. H. 1967. Wild flowers of Alberta. The Queen's Printer. Edmonton, Alberta. 415pp.

COUPLAND, R. T. 1961. A reconsideration of grassland classification in the Northern Great Plains of North America. J. Ecol. 49(1):135–167.

DEPARTMENT OF TRANSPORT. 1968a. Climatic normals, temperature. Can. Dept. Transport Meteorol. Branch. Vol. 1, 551.2.524(71). 66pp.

———. 1968b. Climatic normals, precipitation. Can. Dept. Transport Meteorol. Branch. Vol. 2, 551.577.2(71). 110pp.

GEIST, V. 1968. On the interrelation of external appearance, social behavior and social structure of mountain sheep. Z. Tierpsychol. 25: 199–215.

GREGG, P. A. 1955. Summer habits of Wyoming antelope. Ph.D. Thesis. Cornell Univ. Ithaca. 185pp.

HAFEZ, E. S. E., AND J. P. SCOTT. 1962. The behavior of sheep and goats. Pages 297–333 in E. S. E. Hafez, ed. The behavior of domestic animals. Williams & Wilkins Company, Baltimore. 619pp.

———, AND M. W. SHEIN. 1962. The behavior of cattle. Pages 247–296 in E. S. E. Hafez, ed. The behavior of domestic animals. Williams & Wilkins Company, Baltimore. 619pp.

HENSHAW, J. 1968. The activities of the wintering caribou in northwestern Alaska in relation to weather and snow conditions. Int. J. Biometeor. 12(1):21–27.

MARTINKA, C. J. 1967. Mortality of northern Montana pronghorns in a severe winter. J. Wildl. Manage. 31(1):159–164.

MITCHELL, G. J. 1965. Natality, mortality and related phenomena in two populations of pronghorn antelope in Alberta, Canada. Ph.D. Thesis. Washington State Univ. Spokane. 205pp.

MOEN, A. N. 1968. Energy exchange of white-tailed deer, western Minnesota. Ecology 49(4):676–682.

NELSON, J. L. 1960. Antelope bag check data 1957 to 1960. Saskatchewan Dept. Nat. Resour. 9pp.

PEPPER, G. W., AND R. QUINN. 1965. 1965 antelope population trend survey in Saskatchewan. Wildl. Branch Saskatchewan Dept. Nat. Resour. 11pp.

PRUITT, W. O., JR. 1959. Snow as a factor in the winter ecology of the barren ground caribou (*Rangifer arcticus*). Arctic 12(3):159–179.

———. 1960. Animals in the snow. Sci. Am. 202(1):60–68.

RAND, A. L. 1947. The 1945 status of the pronghorn antelope, *Antilocapra americana* (Ord), in Canada. Natl. Mus. of Can. Biol. Ser. 34. Bull. 106. 34pp.

VAN WORMER, J. 1969. The world of the pronghorn. J. B. Lippincott Co., Philadelphia and New York. 191pp.

VERME, L. J. 1968. An index of winter weather severity for northern deer. J. Wildl. Manage. 32(3):566–574.

WEBB, R., A. JOHNSTON, AND J. D. SOPER. 1967. The prairie world. Pages 93–115 in W. G. Hardy, ed. Alberta—a natural history. M. G. Hurtig, Edmonton. 343pp.

WESTGATE, J. A. 1968. Surficial geology of the Foremost-Cypress Hills area, Alberta. Res. Counc. Alberta. Bull. 22. 122pp.

Received 31 December 1970.
Accepted 7 February 1977.

Appendix 1.   Selected Bibliography of American Pronghorn Antelope Literature

This selected bibliography of literature on the American Pronghorn Antelope includes sources cited in the papers appearing in this volume. Literature citations concerning sources not readily available (e.g., mimeographed or multilith reports, unpublished manuscripts, and Pittman-Robertson reports) were excluded. The citations are exactly as they originally appeared in The Journal of Wildlife Management.

Arrington, O. N., A. E. Edwards. 1951. Predator control as a factor in antelope management. Trans. N. Am. Wildl. Conf. 16:179–193.

Barrett, M. W. 1974. Importance, utilization, and quality of *Artemisia cana* on pronghorn winter ranges in Alberta. Antelope States Workshop Proc. 6:26–56.

Bayless, S. R. 1967. Food habits, range use and home ranges of pronghorn antelope in central Montana during winter. M.S. Thesis, Montana State Univ., Bozeman. 65pp.

———. 1968. Food habits, range use and home range of pronghorn antelope in central Montana during winter. Paper presented at Third Biennial Antelope States Workshop, Casper, Wyoming. 11pp.

Beale, D. M., and G. W. Scotter. 1968. Seasonal forage use by pronghorn antelope in western Utah. Utah Sci. 29(1): 3–6, 16.

Bruns, E. H. 1969. A preliminary study of behavioral adaptations of wintering pronghorn antelopes. M.S. Thesis. Univ. of Calgary. 60pp.

———.1969. Winter predation of golden eagles and coyotes on pronghorn antelopes. Can. Field Nat. 84(3):301–304.

Buck, P. D. 1947. The biology of the antelope *(Antilocapra americana)* in Montana. M.S. Thesis, Montana State College. 70pp.

Buechner, H. K. 1947. Range use of pronghorned antelope in western Texas. Trans. N. Am. Wildl. Conf. 12:185–192.

———. 1950. Life history, ecology, and range use of the pronghorned antelope in Trans-Pecos Texas. Am. Midl. Nat. 43(2):257–354.

———. 1961. Regulations for numbers of pronghorn antelope in relation to land use. La Terre et la Vie 2:266–285.

Campbell, R. B. 1970. Pronghorn, sheep and cattle range relationships in Carter County, Montana. M.S. Thesis Montana State Univ., Bozeman. 87pp.

Cole, G. F. and B. T. Wilkins. 1958. The pronghorn antelope: its range use and food habits in central Montana with special reference to wheat. Montana Fish and Game Dept. Tech. Bull. 2. 39pp.

Cole, G. F. 1956. The pronghorn antelope: its range use and food habits in central Montana with special reference to alfalfa. Montana Fish and Game Dept. and Montana State Coll. Agr. Expt. Sta. Tech. Bull. 516. 63pp.

Compton, H. O. 1958. The effects of predation on pronghorn antelope numbers in south central Oregon. M.S. Thesis, Oregon State University, Corvallis. 71pp.

Deming, O. V. 1963. Antelope and sagebrush. Trans. Interstate Antelope Conf.: 55–60.

Dow, S. A., Jr. 1952. An evaluation of some criteria for age determination of the pronghorn *(Antilocapra americana* Ord). M.S. Thesis. Montana State Univ., Missoula. 71pp.

Edwards, W. C. 1958. A study of the reproductive potential and ovarian structures in the pronghorn antelope, *Antilocapra americana* (Ord.) in Wyoming. M.S. Thesis. Univ. of Wyoming. 63pp.

Einarsen, A. S. 1948. The pronghorn antelope and its management. Wildlife Management Institute, Washington, D.C. 238pp.

Ellis, J. E., and M. Travis. 1975. Comparative aspects of foraging behavior of pronghorn antelope and cattle. J. Appl. Ecol. 12(2):411–420.

Ferrel, C. M., and H. R. Leach. 1950. Food habits of the prong-horn antelope of California. California Fish and Game 36(1):21–26.

———., ———. 1952. The prong-horn antelope of California: with special reference to food habits. California Fish and Game 38(3):285–293.

Foree, W. W. 1960. Nevada antelope studies progress report. Trans. Interstate Antelope conf.: 58–82.

––––––. 1959. Antelope questionnaire. Trans. Int. Antelope Conf. 10:65–75.

Gregg, P. A. 1955. Summer habits of Wyoming antelope. Ph.D. Thesis Cornell Univ. Ithaca. 185pp.

Hailey, T. L., D. DeArment, and P. Evans. 1964. Pronghorn decline. Texas Game and Fish 22(11):22–23.

Hepworth, B. 1965. Pp. 1–12 in Investigations of pronghorn antelope in Wyoming. Proc. First Annu. Antelope States Workshop. Santa Fe, New Mexico.

––––––, and F. Blunt. 1966. Research findings on Wyoming antelope. Wyoming Wildl. 30(6):24–29.

Hockley, M. 1968. Pp. 81–84 *in* Ten years of antelope management in the Gillette Area of Wyoming. Proc. Third Bienn. Antelope State Workshop. Casper, Wyoming.

Honess, R. F., and K. B. Winter. 1956. Diseases of wildlife in Wyoming. Wyoming Game and Fish Comm. Bull. 9. 279pp.

Hoover, J. P. 1971. Food habits of pronghorn antelope on Pawnee National Grasslands, 1970. M.S. Thesis. Colorado State Univ., Ft. Collins. 285pp.

Hoover, R. L., C. E. Till, and S. Ogilvie. 1959. The antelope of Colorado: a research and management study. Colorado Dept. of Fish and Game Tech. Bull. 4. 110pp.

––––––. 1966. Antelope food habits and range relationships in Colorado. Proc. Antelope States Workshop 2:75–85.

Larsen, P. 1964. Some basic reproductive characteristics of pronghorn antelope in New Mexico. Proc. Western Assoc. State Fish and Game Commissioners, San Francisco. 44:142–145.

––––––. 1970. A six-year study of antelope productivity and survival in southern New Mexico. Proc. Fourth Antelope States Workshop. Scottsbluff, Neb. 97–103.

McCutchen, H. E. 1966. Aging pronghorn antelope by the incisor cementum. M.S. Thesis. Univ. of Montana. 49pp.

McLean, D. D. 1944. The prong-horned antelope in California. California Fish and Game, 30(4):221–241.

McLucas, J. 1956. Antelope trapping procedure. Spec. Rep. to Game Mgmt. Div., Montana Dept. Fish and Game, Helena.

Martinka, C. J. 1966. A differential hunter harvest of pronghorn antelope in Montana. Proc. Annu. Conf. Western Assoc. State Game and Fish Commissioners. 46: (In press).

––––––. 1966. The international antelope herd. Montana Wildl. July:28–30.

Mason, E. 1947. Oregon antelope. Oregon State Game Commission Bulletin 2(6):1, 4, and 7.

Mitchell, G. J. 1965. Natality, mortality, and related phenomena in two populations of pronghorn antelope in Alberta, Canada. Ph.D. Thesis. Washington State Univ. Spokane. 205pp.

––––––. 1967. Minimum breeding age of female pronghorn antelope. J. Mammal. 48(3):489–490.

Nelson, E. W. 1925. Status of the pronghorned antelope, 1922–1924. U.S. Dept. Agric. Bull. 1346. 64pp.

Nilsson, Nils N. 1949. Let's Talk Antelope. Nevada Fish and Game, 1(3):8–9.

O'Gara, B. W. 1968. A study of the reproductive cycle of the female pronghorn (*Antilocapra americana* Ord.) Ph.D. Thesis. Univ. Montana, Missoula. 161pp. Multilithed.

––––––. 1969. Unique aspects of reproduction in the female pronghorn (*Antilocapra americana* Ord.) Am. J. Anat. 125(2):217–232.

––––––., and K. R. Greer. 1970. Food habits in relation to physical condition in two populations of pronghorn. Proc. Antelope States Workshop 4:131–139.

Olgilvie, S. 1955. Chokecherry toxic to an antelope. J. Mammal. 36(1):146.

Pepper, G. W., and R. Quinn. 1965. 1965 antelope population trend survey in Saskatchewan. Wildl. Branch Saskatchewan Dept. Nat. Resour. 11pp.

Pruitt, W. O., Jr. 1960. Animals in the snow. Sci. Am. 202(1):60–68.

Rand, A. L. 1947. The 1945 status of the pronghorn antelope, *Antilocapra americana* (Ord), in Canada. Natl. Mus. of Can. Biol. Ser. 34 Bull. 106, 34pp.

Rice, R. W., J. G. Nagy, and D. G. Peden. 1971. Functional interaction of large herbivores on grasslands. Pages 241–266. *in* N. R. French, ed. Preliminary analysis of structure and function in grasslands. Colorado State Univ. Range Sci. Dept. Sci. Ser. 10.

Russell, T. P. 1937. Antelope transplanting is success. New Mexico Mag. 15(6):32–33.

––––––. 1964. Antelope of New Mexico. New Mexico Dept. Game and Fish Bull. 12. 103pp.

Scarvie, O. and J. Arney. 1957. Food habits of pronghorn antelope, *Antilocapra americana*, in October in northern Colorado. Colorado State Univ. 9pp.

Schwartz, C. C., and J. G. Nagy. 1973. Pronghorn food habits studies, 1970–1972. US/IBP Grassland Biome Tech. Rep. 231. Colorado State Univ., Ft. Collins. 32pp.

Schwartz, C.C. 1977. Pronghorn grazing strategies on the shortgrass prairie, Colorado. Ph.D. Thesis. Colorado State Univ., Fort Collins. 113pp.

Seton, E. T. 1953. Lives of game animals. Vol. 3. Hoofed animals. Charles T. Branford Co., Boston. xix+780pp.

Severson, K. E., and M. May. 1967. Food preferences of antelope and domestic sheep in Wyoming's Red Desert. J. Range Manage. 20(1):21–25.

———., ———., and W. Hepworth. 1968. Food preferences, carrying capacities, and forage competition between antelope and domestic sheep in Wyoming's Red Desert. Univ. of Wyoming Agr. Expt. Sta. Sci. Monograph 10. 51pp.

Shaw, W. M. 1961. Miscellaneous data on Idaho antelope. Proc. Interstate Antelope Conf.:15–19.

———. 1960. Notes on Idaho antelope management data. Proc. Interstate Antelope Conf.:92–99.

Smith, A. D., D. M. Beale, and D. D. Doell. 1965. Browse preferences of pronghorn antelope in southwestern Utah. Trans. N. Am. Wildl. Nat. Resour. Conf. 30:136–141.

Spillett, J. J. 1965. The effects of livestock fences on pronghorn antelope movements. M.S. Thesis. Utah State Univ. 138pp.

Sundstrom, C. 1968. Water consumption by pronghorn antelope and distribution related to water in Wyoming's Red Desert. Proc. Third Biennial Antelope States Workshop. Casper, Wyoming. pp. 39–46. Processed.

———., W. G. Hepworth, and K. L. Diem. 1973. Abundance, distribution and food habits of the pronghorn. Wyoming Fish Game Comm. Bull. 12. 61pp.

Taylor, E. 1972. Food habits and feeding behavior of pronghorn antelope in the Red Desert of Wyoming. Proc. Antelope States Workshop 5:211–219.

Van Wormer. J. 1969. The world of the pronghorn. J. B. Lippincott., Philadelphia and New York. 191pp.

Wesley, D. E., K. L. Knox, and J. G. Nagy. 1969. Water kinetics in pronghorn antelope. Proc. Western Sec. Am. Soc. Anim. Sci. 20:79–82.

Yoakum, J. D. 1957. Factors affecting mortality of pronghorn antelope in Oregon. M.S. Thesis. Oregon State College, Corvallis. 112pp.

———. 1958. Seasonal food habits of the Oregon pronghorn antelope. Trans. Interstate Antelope Conf.:47–59.

———. 1967. Literature of the American pronghorn antelope. U.S. Dept. Inter. Un-numbered Bull. 82pp.

———. 1968. pp. 4–14 *in* A review of the distribution and abundance of American pronghorn antelope. Proc. Third Bien. Antelope States Workshop. Casper, Wyoming.

———. 1972. Antelope-vegetation relationships. Proc. Antelope States Workshop 5:171–177.

Index